Shadows on the

A New Theory of Evolution

By Keith Skene

ARD MACHA PRESS

ARD MACHA PRESS

Published by Ard Macha Press
Ard Macha Press, 5A The Den, Letham, Angus, DD8 2PY, Scotland, UK

Copyright © K. R. Skene 2009

All rights reserved

The moral right of the author has been asserted

Produced in Dundee Tel: 01382 223004

First printing 2009

This book is sold subject to the condition that it shall not, by way of trade or otherwise, be lent, re-sold, hired out, or otherwise circulated without the publisher's prior consent in any form of binding or cover other than that in which it is published and without a similar condition including this condition being imposed on the subsequent purchaser.

No part of this book may be reproduced or transmitted, in any form or by any means, electronic or mechanical, including photocopying, recording, or by any information storage and retrieval system – except by a reviewer who may quote brief passages in a review to be printed in a magazine, newspaper or on the web – without permission in writing from the publisher. For more information please contact Ard Macha Press, 5A The Den, Letham, Angus, DD8 2PY, Scotland, UK

ISBN 978-0-9562501-0-0

To Matthew, our beautiful little lad

ABOUT THE AUTHOR

Keith Skene was born in the city of Armagh in 1965. For 15 years, he has worked as a scientist in the areas of developmental biology and evolutionary ecology and has published widely on plant, animal and ecosystem evolution, his work being translated into four languages. A former Rhodes Scholar, he has carried out fieldwork in the Americas, Asia, Africa, Europe and Australia. Aside from biology, his burning passions are blues guitar and philosophy, which, he claims, inform each other fundamentally. He currently lectures in Natural History at the University of Dundee. Keith Lives in Angus with his wife and baby boy.

Preface

This book sets out a new and radically different scientific theory of how life on Earth evolved and how it functions. The repercussions of this theory stretch far and wide, providing a challenge to all of society in terms of how we should respond to some of the great questions that currently face us, from conservation to global climate change.

We examine the current neo-Darwinian theory of evolution, uncovering significant problems that stem back to its historical origin. We take a close look at the controversies relating to current evolutionary theory, and identify key weaknesses in these ideas. The thesis of this book rests on the fact that our present understanding of life on Earth is dominated by competition, survival of the fittest and an all-consuming fascination with the gene as the unit of selection. Life is reduced to a genetic game, with everything interpreted within a model of genetic fitness, driven by mutation, ignoring all of the other levels of organization, such as communities and biomes.

Darwinism bases its understanding of how life evolved upon biology. Neo-Darwinism and Gaian theory are both bed fellows in terms of using chemistry to understand evolution. This book takes a completely different approach, using physics. This makes more sense, since physics lies at the base of the other sciences, and so it seems obvious that we should approach evolution from this direction.

By starting with what we observe, and with no initial theory, there is no need for a single unit of selection. Freeing ourselves from this, we look at how life is really organized. Each level, from gene to biome, has properties that rely on their building blocks, but also has properties that are unique to that level. Energy is the agent of organization, and speaks differently to each level of organization. Energy reaches into biomes, communities, individuals, proteins and genes in completely different ways, which allows us to have one agent, but many different units, each displaying its own response to that single agent. We explore the responses and apply our understanding to some of the great debates in evolutionary biology. We show that evolution works in the empty market place, not in the crowded back alleys.

In a powerful series of analogies, we expose the weaknesses in our current understanding, and emerge with a new way of understanding the world. We use this to resolve the big debates relating to multicellularity, altruism, the tempo of evolution, speciation, emergence and exobiology.

Finally we take our theory for a test drive. What use is this new approach to our everyday lives, and to the enormous challenges that currently face the human race? From understanding our planet as being structured and functioning according to the architect of energy, we can more clearly identify the real sources of the problems facing us, and more simply identify the best ways to resolve these problems, from gender issues to conservation biology, and from climate change to our place in the Universe.

Darwinian evolution and subsequent developments in neo-Darwinian thinking represent an over-simplistic and, latterly, derived approach to our world. They are significantly flawed because they only account for a small part of the whole, and are based on a sub-set of the information available. The new theory presented in this book, instead, incorporates all of the knowledge that is available, and subsequently arrives at a better explanation, one that resolves debate and unites apparently polarized views. Most importantly, like any good theory, it not only provides an explanation for how the whole thing works, but also provides solutions to some of the greatest issues facing humankind.

ACKNOWLEDGEMENTS

I have been extremely fortunate to have been taught, both formally and informally, by some wonderful people. From my early days at the Royal School, Armagh, where Mr Taylor opened the amazing world of biology to me and, with infinite patience, allowed me to re-open the chicken and duck enclosure and put zebra finches in the greenhouse, through to my lecturers at the University of Dundee, particularly John Riley (the real crocodile Dundee), John Raven (our resident genius), Geoffrey Codd, Rodney Herbert, Janet Sprent, Hugh Ingram and Roy Oliver. I owe a huge debt of gratitude to Hilary Young, who allowed me to work in her lab one summer as an undergraduate, which is where I first caught the bug (excuse the pun) for microbiology, and for research. I have also been lucky to work with many people around the world and they have all impacted on my thinking in different ways, including Klement Rejek, Valerie Vranova, Brian Gunning, Gina Czernecki, Huang Diem, Hamlyn Jones, Peter John, Helaina Black, Steve Millam, Chin Ong and John Pate. In terms of writing this book, I can only thank two people, Marion my wife, who has always believed in the project, often more than I have, and my son, Matthew. For years, I had wanted to write this book, but couldn't get it started. Then, in the sleep-deprived months following Matthew's birth, I suddenly started to write, and finished it within a year. Perhaps sheer exhaustion prevented writer's block!

My parents have been hugely supportive of this project, as they have of all that I try to do, in my own imperfect, stumbling and noisy way. I am grateful to Caroline Davidson for important comments on earlier drafts of this work, and to Shelagh Phillips (of Vegas Brats fame) for help in overcoming my word processing confusion. On the subject of music, the following provided a soundtrack during the long hours of writing: The Beatles, REM, Led Zeppelin, Violent Femmes, Yeah Yeah Yeahs and, most importantly, Jerry Lee Lewis! Finally to the undergraduates of the University of Dundee, past and present, who continue to provide inspiration, asking all of the best questions.

Shadows on the Cave Wall

CONTENTS

Section I
Introduction

This book represents a journey, a search for answers to some of the most fundamental questions that exist. In this first section, we prepare for this voyage of discovery, which will take us through uncharted terrain and challenge many orthodox beliefs that we hold dear, by doing what every good explorer should do: checking that we are happy with all of the equipment we are going to use, and making sure it is all safely packed. We open with a fire, the Sun and some shadows on a wall. We quickly find ourselves transported to an ancient cave, tied to a pole and held, transfixed, by dancing shapes in front of us: Plato's analogy of the cave. This marks the beginning of a journey that will take us from early human hunter-gatherers, to modern science, a journey made by man in response to the Universe within which he exists. This book sets out to put forward a challenging new scientific theory, a novel interpretation that asks why the living planet is structured in the way that it is, and how it came to be this way. Along the road, we explore some of the great controversies and debates that currently exist, and try to understand how such polarized views can be accommodated. We start by looking at how we perceive our Universe, by examining the relationship between science and philosophy. Next, we face up to three challenges: that we are biased observers, that we face difficulties relating to how we sense our surroundings, and that our surroundings are dependent on the contexts of space and time. In the end, it is a greater context within which everything is defined. So what is that context? We meet energy, and discover the rules that govern it, controlling how the Universe works. We realize that we are within this energetic context. Finally, we look at how man has interpreted energy through his observations of the physical and metaphysical worlds.

Chapter One

An Ancient Philosopher Escapes from the Cave

Calm descends upon our house at the end of a busy weekend, the last of the guests having just left. It's a cold, clear, late afternoon in Eastern Scotland, and we gather around the fire as flames flicker and dance. The Sun is setting and, in a moment, an extraordinary event occurs. Through a north-facing window, the light of our nearest star, far in the west, floods in and illuminates the fireplace. In that instance, energy from the great nuclear fusion reactor, some 91 million miles away, joins forces with the light and heat released from the burning coal. The energy released from the coal was captured from that same Sun some 300 million years ago, while the kindling was converting the Sun's energy to fixed carbon maybe as recently as two months ago. Now, for a brief moment, 300 million years of energy and carbon are brought together in one place. Shadows form across the walls.

The allegory of the cave

On the television, a movie called *The Matrix* is starting, bringing to mind another fire. Recent movies, including *The Truman Show* and *The Matrix,* explore the possibility that what is seen in the mind is not what is real. However this idea goes back to a much earlier tradition. Plato, one of the greatest thinkers ever to have lived, wrote *The Republic* around 360 BC. In this work he records the '*Allegory of the Cave'*. He describes a horrific scene wherein people are held captive in a cave, bound by chains so that they cannot move their heads, which face away from the entrance, towards the back of the cave. Behind them a large fire burns, and between them and the fire, there is a raised walkway. People cross this walkway, carrying statues. In this acrid environment, the dancing, rhythmic shadows of these statues are projected on to the inner wall of the cave, appearing to move and contort as the fire burns relentlessly. Echoes of the voices of the statue bearers bounce off the cave walls and appear to come from the eerie shadows. To this captive audience, these frolicking, cavorting, talking shadows are reality.

Imagine for a moment that you are one of these prisoners, staring at the back of the cave, hypnotized by the jagged, rhythmic forms that rear up and collapse against the cave wall. This is the sum of your reality. Suddenly, you feel the chains that bind you snap and fall to the cave floor. You are free! Initially, you remain fixated by the shadowy world on the wall, but then you turn around and see the huge fire, the walkway in front of you, and the statues being carried back and forth. You realize that, actually, the shapes on the wall are mere shadows, stemming from the statues that are being carried in front of the fire. Beyond the fire you notice a greater light, and as you move towards the cave entrance, it gets brighter. Leaving behind the crackling fire, the statues and the dancing shadows, you walk out of the cave. After blinking in the bright light that is all around, you begin to see animals, identical in outline to the statues, whose shadows you had originally thought represented reality. Yet these animals are so different, three-dimensional and complex. This is a whole new reality, one on which the statues were based, and the indirect inspiration for the shadows. Surely this is the true reality? Finally you look upwards, and realize that the light is coming from the Sun. You reach the summit of understanding, recognizing that all things come from the Sun.

In this wonderful allegory, Plato was responding to what is called the problem of universals. Already we find ourselves in our first great debate, and it won't be the last! Simply put, the problem of universals hinges on the observation that change is happening constantly. Thus, by the time you gain knowledge, it is already out of date. This is the basis of Nominalism, which lies at the heart of Buddhism. Within this way of thinking, there is no such thing as a universal entity, since it is only a title or name that has transitory relevance in an ever-changing world. Plato distinguished between the world of the senses, or "caveworld", and the world of the intellect – the appreciation of the Sun. Thus, timeless ideas and forms, or universals, can exist in this intellectual world, even though the shadows in the sensual world are fleeting.

In this book, we will re-examine the basis of our understanding of the living world. In particular, we will look at how the present theory of neo-Darwinian evolution has come to be the most accepted scientific explanation. Just like Plato almost two and a half thousand years ago, we will question the adequacy of basing our understanding on the very limited 'shadows' of taxonomy and genetic sequence, while ignoring vast amounts of knowledge from other scientific fields. We discover that there is a deeper scientific basis for understanding how life on Earth has evolved and functions and, escaping from the limited, shadowy world of the cave of physical appearance, we will identify what this basis is. Finally, we will look at the implications of this new theory upon one of the greatest challenges facing us, global climate change.

The great expedition

The driving force behind the uniqueness of man has been his search for an understanding of his place in the Universe. From the earliest discoveries of human remains, there have been associated artefacts that relate to this search. The history of the human race can be recorded as a series of expressions of who we are and what controls our destiny, if destiny there be. Our questions have ranged from the infinite to the infinitesimal. How has life on Earth come about? What are the forces in our Universe that lead to things being the way that they are? Why do we dream and hope? What, in the end, has led to the diversity of life on our planet? What, ultimately, is the meaning of life?

The following chapters represent a synthesis of the journey made by man in response to the Universe in which he exists, and put forward a challenging new interpretation, as to why the living planet is structured in the way that it is, and as to what is the basis of the diversity of life. Along the way, we will explore some of the great debates that currently exist, and try to understand how such differing belief structures can each be sustained in parallel. Finally, we discover that our new approach dramatically alters how we should act if we are to survive in a sustainable way.

This book presents a new scientific theory of biological evolution. I am a mainstream scientist, having studied and worked in Biology for twenty years. I am interested in evolution because it tries to understand how everything came to be the way that it is, and therefore it offers a unique insight into why things work in the way that they do. Evolution also provides us with a key context for understanding our place in the whole scheme of things. Furthermore, if we are to understand the impact that humans are having on our planet, then we need to grasp how our planet works. This again relies on our knowledge of how things came to be the way that they are in the first place.

The theory that I want to present is based on physics, and is therefore radically different from the biology-based thinking of Darwinism and the chemistry-based approaches of neo-Darwinism and Gaian theory. In order to explain why my theory supersedes the other explanations of how our planet works, we need to examine why the other theories don't work. It is in the failings of these other approaches that we find clues that point to a different understanding. So we are going to examine exactly what life is, how the living world works and how this all impacts on us as human beings in the Twenty-first century.

In the next three chapters, we will take on board some essential provisions to see us through this journey. First we want to look at some philosophical issues. What we think is very much governed by the way that we think, and so before we can tackle the meaning of life, we need to reflect on how we approach thinking about these things. So let's make a start.

Chapter Two

The Strained Relationship between Philosophy and Science

It is a widely held view that the history of humankind traces a journey of progress. Each generation improves on the last one, and we are steadily moving forwards. New breakthroughs in medicine, agriculture and engineering continually hit the headlines. We are travelling into a bigger, brighter and better future. Such a view also brings with it the idea that the past offers little in terms of useful comment. The past is less perfect than today and so how can it contribute anything? The vertical line of improvement also lies at the heart of much of our understanding of Darwinian thinking. The tree of life branches out and reaches further towards the sky, with humankind at the top. The process of scientific thinking itself is also seen as continually testing ideas, weeding out the less good and replacing them with better ones.

It's like a walk along a path. We pass milestones that tell us how far we have gone, and stride on into new pastures. The scenery keeps changing and it all looks progressive. Yet how do we know that we are on the right path? Just because we have been walking for hours, and we have passed many markers recording the distance travelled, it doesn't mean that we are correct.

Sometimes we need to stop and reflect on the journey. Why did we turn left at the big oak tree instead of going straight ahead? Why didn't we take the small path up that steep hill instead of running down into the leafy glade where we now find ourselves? One of the problems is that we were born on the path, the journey already on its way. The place that we find ourselves in is determined by a whole host of historical issues: the history of our family, the history of our culture and the history of humanity itself. In this book we want to reflect on the journey that science has taken in its efforts to understand our world, and to challenge to its core the neo-Darwinian theory of evolution, presenting a completely alternative and radical approach. To do this we need to understand what science is, and where it has come from. We also need to question the path that we are on. Then, we want to start a new journey completely.

The mass of humanity that has trodden this planet has produced some brilliant minds, many of them long dead. However their thinking is often disregarded due to our belief in progress. I strongly believe that we should learn from their wisdom, and that many of the brilliant thinkers of the past have contributed hugely. Just because they lived thousands of years ago, doesn't mean that we should ignore their insight. To help in this, we need to look at the journey science has taken, and at the nature of science itself. In this chapter, we will examine the relationship between philosophy and science, look at why science is best viewed as a school of philosophy, and explore why philosophy is so important in our efforts to elucidate the meaning of our world.

Science and philosophy are not so much two sides of the one coin. They *are* the one coin. Together, they represent a set of different approaches to one single thing: the human race attempting to find its place within the multidimensional universe. Humans have observed the world and then interpreted what they have observed. Philosophy, including science and religion, attempts to respond to questions about where it all came from, who we are and where we are going. It tries to understand why things exist in the way that they do, and seeks to define existence and reality itself. Philosophy is not a passive subject. It really can impact upon our lives. Take economic philosophy or political philosophy. Governments have, at the root of their policies, a philosophical framework. The Cold War, that dominated the second half of the twentieth century, saw two great political philosophies, Communism and Capitalism, come, almost, to nuclear blows. People built bomb-shelters under their houses. Many of the genocides on our planet have been driven by philosophy. Philosophy can impact directly upon all of us.

Science and religion

In many ways, two particular strands of philosophy have had a greater impact upon us than all of the others, religious philosophy and scientific philosophy. Science provides an experiment-based explanation, testing hypotheses using the *scientific method.* The scientific method involves four key steps:

Observation: a phenomenon is described;

Formulation: a mechanism or hypothesis to account for the phenomenon is suggested;

Prediction: this mechanism is used to predict what might happen in a particular situation;

Testing: an experiment is carried out to test if the predicted outcome actually occurs.

Let's take an example. While walking through the countryside, you pass through two forests. In one, you notice that there are lots of rabbits and lots of bright yellow flowers. In the second forest, which is otherwise identical to the first one, there are only a few rabbits and one or two yellow flowers. This is your observation.

Next, you come up with a possible mechanism, that the number of rabbits controls the number of yellow flowers. You have now formulated a hypothesis. You suggest that if you buy lots of rabbits and put them into the second forest, then more yellow flowers will grow. This is your prediction. Finally, you actually carry out the experiment, releasing 100 rabbits into the second forest, and you wait to see if more yellow flowers appear. You have now tested your hypothesis. This is science.

Religion usually involves a deity or deities who interact with the material world to different degrees. There are many different religious philosophies. Religious writings are often presented as having been inspired by a deity, or dictated directly by that deity to one or more persons. Normally, a sacred text or texts form the basis of a particular religion, although some, such as Candomblé in Brazil, are solely based on ideas passed down orally.

Many scientists hold to the belief that science, and science alone, can provide the best explanation to the fundamental questions relating to the planet and to ourselves. Yet science is not the only subject that has sought to understand how life works. Art, philosophy, religion and the social sciences have all sought to explain why things are the way that they are, and have presented their own representations of reality, defending them against other schools of thought. The human race has participated to a greater or lesser extent in these debates. Yet of all of these great discussions, the clash between science and the rest has been the most aggressive. This has been recently represented by Dawkin's *The God Delusion*, and the replies from philosophers such as Alvin Plantinga in *The Dawkins Confusion* and from theologians such as Alister McGrath in *The Dawkins Delusion* and John Lennox in *God's Undertaker: Has Science Buried God?* Recent commentaries on religion by scientists point towards the observation that religion is often a political chess piece, and is used as a means to an end, often forming the basis of bigotry, war and abuse. That is, doubtless, sometimes true. However all of the great areas of thought and study, from philosophy to art and from economics to literature, have been similarly used to support ideals that are anything but noble. Indeed science has found itself the tool to support many dubious causes. The consequences to the living planet of biological control, pesticides and genetic engineering have been shown to be negative in many situations. Whatever the arguments, we must understand that the debate is philosophical in nature. Both sides represent schools of thinking and as such are no more or less than the clashing of different philosophical approaches.

Having faith in science

True, science is a logical pursuit, based on apparently cold facts. Or is it? In the end, science too can be seen as a faith-based belief structure. The bottom row of bricks in the scientific pantheon is also missing. We need faith to believe that it all actually exists at all. Religion cannot explain where their deities of choice have come from, but science cannot explain where it all came from either. If energy can neither be created nor destroyed, then there is an "everlasting" element to it, as demanded by the first law of thermodynamics. Also, as we shall see later in this book, defining such things as life and species are often problematic.

A closer look at the scientific community shows that it shares a belief structure not unlike that of many religions. There are many churches, such as neo-Darwinism, quantum mechanics and the Gaian theory, with radically different underlying philosophies. Any perceived threat to any particular church spurs strong response. There is an effort to evangelize, both in scientific and popular media. There is a drive to influence government in a church-state relationship. There is an attempt to create a catechism, for example the Central Dogma. There are apostles to the faith that are lauded, such as Galileo, Newton, Darwin and Einstein. More recently, a self appointed group, naming themselves BRIGHTS, has emerged and their web page sets out their catechism:

A. Promote the civic understanding and acknowledgment of the naturalistic worldview, which is free of supernatural and mystical elements.
B. Gain public recognition that persons holding such a worldview can bring principled actions to bear on matters of civic importance.
C. Educate society toward accepting the full and equitable civic participation of all such individuals. (http://www.the-brights.net/)

Symbols represent the belief, such as the selfish gene and the four bases of deoxyribonucleic acid. There is an infinite being, energy. There is an unknown, immeasurable question: where did it all come from? Finally, science serves a similar service to humans as religion, in attempting to provide a framework within which life makes sense, and within which explanations, the comfort blankets of the subspecies *Homo sapiens sapiens*, can be held. Yet the impacts of politics, philosophy and human nature inform science as a belief structure. In the end, science and religion and all the other belief structures are types of philosophy.

A brief history of science and philosophy

To understand the relationship between science and philosophy, and the important implications of this relationship for our present journey, we need to look at history. As so often is the case, the history of ideas goes a long way to understanding the idea itself. Philosophy and science can be likened to an ill-fated marriage. Of course, marriage can only normally occur between members of the same species, and, as we have established, science and philosophy *are* the one species. Both started out wanting the same thing, and one found itself betrothed to the other. For a long time one partner was dominant over the other, until enough was enough. There was a big argument and a splitting of ways. Over the years, they didn't really speak to each other, and would write searing diatribes against one another. There seemed to be no way forward. Yet, recently, there has been the beginnings of a tentative peace some of the time, although angry outbursts still continue.

It all began a very long time ago, with humans describing their world and recording these observations in cave paintings. However deeper thinking led to us questioning what was reality. The great forces of nature, such as huge tsunamis, volcanic disasters, dramatic changes in rainfall patterns, thunder and lightening, the occasional supernova and close encounters with comets no doubt all provided shocks to the system. The Earliest philosophies were animistic in nature. Animism holds that everything, from mountains to humans, is alive and spiritual. These great events were recognized as having personalities.

Socrates: the father of philosophy

Around 2500 years ago, a significant group of thinkers had formed in Ancient Greece, led by the great father of philosophy, Socrates (469BC – 399BC). Socrates himself never recorded any of his thoughts, and we rely on his students and fellow thinkers of that time for any knowledge about him or his philosophy. In fact it was Plato, the most famous of his students, who recorded much of what we now know. Socrates was executed by being forced to drink hemlock, on a charge of corrupting the minds of the Athenian youths. If we accept that Plato's records were literally that, and not his own musings, then the importance of Socrates cannot be overstated. He introduced a new way of thinking, which consisted of breaking down an issue by asking a chain of questions, whose answers would then produce further questions, leading ever closer to an answer. This has become known as the *Socratic Method.*

Plato was significantly affected by both the teaching and the death of his mentor. He went on to set up the Academy in Athens, one of the earliest centres of study in the Western World, which would continue for almost 900 years. Here, he trained future political leaders in philosophy, his vision being that only philosophy could inform proper decision making. Most of Plato's writings are presented as conversations between Socrates and his students. It is still not known whether these were Plato's own thoughts or whether he was acting as Socrates' recorder. What is clear is that between Socrates and Plato, the foundations of Western Philosophy were laid. As we have seen in his *Allegory of the Cave*, Plato questioned the reliability of the senses to record reality. He proposed that the sensual world was a mere shadow, and only through philosophy could the real meaning of existence be reached. Observations of shadows were seen not to be as informative as reasoning. As a result, for more than a thousand years after this, science was married to philosophy, and became an exercise in logic, rather than observation.

Francis Bacon

It was Francis Bacon (1561-1626) who challenged this marriage. Bacon, whose life was dominated by financial woes, was an English philosopher. In his *Instauratio Magna Part II: Novum Organum,* first published in 1620, he said "*Men have sought to make a world from their own conception and to draw from their own minds all the material which they employed, but if, instead of doing so, they had consulted experience and observation, they would have the facts and not opinions to reason about, and might have ultimately arrived at the knowledge of the laws which govern the material world.*" He is often credited with starting the scientific revolution, and from this point onwards two opposing philosophical groups emerged: the rationalists and the empiricists.

Reason versus experience: The Rationalists and the Empiricists

The rationalists held to the view that reason was the source of knowledge. This group of philosophies basically continued in the thinking of Plato. The empiricists instead argued that knowledge comes from experience, as Bacon had emphasised, and formed the foundations for the scientific method of hypothesis testing. It is ironic, though appropriate, that Socrates had sown the seed for both the empirical, scientific approach and the rational, reason-based approach that now stood in opposition. The appropriateness of the irony stems from the fact that Socrates was famous for the use of irony in his teaching!

The marriage between science and ancient philosophy was irreparably damaged, and the breakup intensified over the coming centuries, with rationalism being developed in more extreme schools of thought such as existentialism (where individuals create the essence and meaning of their lives), nihilism (where existence has no objective meaning) and scepticism (where it is impossible to obtain any sort of knowledge). The natural sciences also broke free of theology. Science embraced the philosophies of pragmatism (where truth is judged by its effect on our actions) and structuralism (where analysis comes from an objective, external position).

With Newtonian physics and Darwinism, there was a cause and effect. There was the ability to predict what would happen, and the objective reality that became known as scientific determinism. Scientific determinism holds that every event is caused by a previous event, and so on, forming a chain of events. Cause leads to effect through time, in a vertical line. It not only allows us to trace causes back in time, but to determine future consequences. Of course, this approach eventually runs into difficulties, as we shall see throughout this book. Basically, the problems are of two types. First, if each event is caused by something before it, then how can there be a start? It is like asking, if God created the world, then who created God? Secondly, if there is no start, then there has been an infinite series of events without a start, and therefore, with no original cause. If you are not lying flat on the floor already, you better do it now before you fall over contemplating this!

Science is not a single, unified school of philosophical thought. In fact, one branch of science has developed in the last one hundred years that has led to a major challenge to scientific determinism: quantum physics, or, as it is also known, the New Physics.

The New Physics

Science is philosophy, or rather a divergent group of philosophies. On one side we have the Newtonian approach of cause and determinism, which also lies at the heart of neo-Darwinism. Here, the material reality, and the laws that control it are predictable, and we need look no further than this to understand the Universe. However quantum physics, or the New Physics, takes a very different philosophical approach.

Classical physics emphasizes cause and effect. Newton's laws allow us to accurately predict what will happen in our universe. The apple will always fall from the tree. The New Physics that works at the sub-atomic level introduced the *Uncertainty Principle*. This states that the speed and position of a small sub-atomic particle cannot both be known simultaneously. It was first stated by Werner Heisenberg (1901-1976), the German theoretical physicist, in 1927. Furthermore, any attempt to measure these things will alter the object that we are observing. Why was this so revolutionary? Simply put, observation disturbs reality. Since we can't be sure of the present reality, we can be less sure of the future reality. This uncertainty therefore breaks the sacred bond between observation and the material world. Albert Einstein, quoted in Floyd Matson's book, *The Broken Image* (1964), stated that "*Even space and time are forms of intuition, which can no more be divorced from consciousness than can our concept of color or shape or size.*

Space has no objective reality except as an order or arrangement of objects we perceive in it, and time has no independent existence apart from the order of events by which we measure it." Amazingly, this resonates with the thinking of those early Greek philosophers.

The journey ahead

In the journey that I want to take you on, we will travel to some unexpected places. We will challenge things that are taken for granted, and question concepts that are not normally questioned. So much of our scientific understanding is framed within accepted boundaries. In order to fully understand our planet, it is this book's strong belief that there should be no initial boundaries, and that we should question everything in order to emerge with a really meaningful explanation. All that I ask is that you approach it with an open mind.

We are looking for an explanation as to how the living world came to be in the form that it is, and why it functions in the way that it does. One of this book's key theses is that our present understanding, as represented by neo-Darwinism, is in fact based on shadows. These shadows are the products of observation of the sensual world. It is not the case that these shadows do not exist, but rather that their existence is the product of a much more profound drive. They represent only the playing out of a much deeper organizational agent than that of the sensual world. Fortunately, there is plenty of observable evidence to point towards this agent, and we will discover that this new approach, outside of the cave, not only provides a more satisfactory answer to many of the big questions, but also finds itself in resonance with our broader sense of being. This is no ordinary walk around the park, but a massive expedition through many charted and uncharted territories. However, by the end of it, I hope you will have gained a new perspective on things, and whether you agree or disagree, that you enjoy the trip!

Chapter Three

Some Problems with Reality

The veracity of the observer: how reliable are we?

At the outset we must recognize that our journey is a human one. In other words, all of the theories and beliefs that have been, are, and will be held by us, are the outcome of human thought. The writer and readers of this book are all human. While we may subjectively argue what it is to be human, we cannot determine what it is not to be human. If an ant or a butterfly were able to write this book, how different would it be? We can hypothesise that, in many respects, it may not be that different, given that the Universe is a common setting for all life, and that many of the key drivers of our behaviour are similar. Yet there are aspects of the human race that appear to be extremely different from those of other members of the living world. This is an important point. Our ability (or our inability) to imbue our observed world with meaning will always be influenced by the experiences that we have participated in prior to the point in time at which the interpretation takes place, both in our own lives, and within the context of accumulated knowledge through our species' existence. Thus the veracity, or purity, of the interpretation will be a product of these experiences, which in turn define the observer. Karl Popper, the late and great twentieth century philosopher, wrote in 1979: '*We all hold theories unconsciously, or take them for granted, although most of them are almost certain to be false...there is no point in discussing or criticising a theory unless we try all the time to put it in its strongest form, and to argue against it only in that form.*'

Of course, being human is, in many respects, not that different from being a tree, a cat, a fungus or any other member of the diverse assemblage of life on this planet, or any other planet. The drives and urges that flow through the living planet are common to all of its members. Resource acquisition dominates, be it the acquisition of energy, space or, in sexually reproducing organisms, a mate. Almost all of life's activities are arranged around resources. As humans, we may be seen to have separated ourselves from the madding crowd that is the rest of life, yet this denial does not alter the fact that we are, essentially, resourcers akin to everything else. We must therefore recognize that our thinking will also reflect these drives. Our attempts to understand the meaning of life can be seen as part of this striving. By understanding our Universe, we can then attempt to manipulate it in order to feed this ancient, fundamental element within us.

Take a group of early humans, who live in grassland where rainfall is sporadic. They look to the sky and realize that the grey thunderclouds, that bring life giving water, are the key to their survival. Having made this observation, it will not be long before they will attempt to manipulate this life-giving force, possibly by building a temple, or sacrificing other life forms, or themselves, in order to satiate the great cloud. This direction will prove popular with the tribe, as it has the potential to deliver a key resource, water, with its concomitant benefits. Before long, a whole belief system, including the river prince, the mud god and the ubiquitous rain dance, develops. The appointed leaders of the tribe are likely to be dominant males and females, and thus their motivation will stem not only from their own survival, one of the fundamental drives that exist in all of us, but also by the need to dominate. Thus, the structure of the tribe will doubtless be influenced by hierarchical maintenance and political manipulation.

Our attempts at understanding our Universe are coloured by human nature, by drives that are much older than we are, and by motives that may distort the initial observation, such as seeking to manipulate others and promote self interests. Argument and counterargument may even be seen to be driven, not only by the search for truth, but by the drive to achieve or maintain position within the tribe. A recent school of thought, *social constructionism*, reflects on the impact of human nature upon our thinking, and, in particular, the possibility of artefacts arising from cultural contexts.

Shadows on the Cave Wall

The validity of our observations

Having questioned the veracity of the observer, we must ask an even more fundamental and intractable question. What is reality? If we are able to use all five senses of sight, scent, hearing, taste and touch to perceive our Universe, how do we know that what we see actually exists in the way that we think it does? At the centre of this lies the process by which stimuli are gathered, transported and interpreted by our bodies. All of our senses are translated into a single type of message, a nerve signal. Our entire sensory world is reduced to electrical signals or action potentials, generated by sodium and potassium transport across the nerve cell membrane. Thus our perception of the Universe is reduced to a set of identical electrical signals. It is only in the brain that these identical signals are interpreted differently, depending on their origin, and where in the brain they arrive, to create what we perceive as our reality.

All statements about reality depend on a huge leap of faith – that what we sense is actually there. This theme has been explored many times and the issue of reality has taxed the minds of humans through history. Scientific thinking relies on our perception of reality being taken as a fundamental truth: that what our minds interpret from the multitude of identical nerve impulses corresponds to the outside world. Without this premise, scientific method is meaningless. Synaesthesia is a condition where the senses can interact such that, for example, numbers can be seen as having colours. Many amputees experience phantom limb sensations in their missing limbs. This is thought to be due to reorganization in the somatosensory cortex, where areas now without input receive input from neighbouring areas. This virtual reality is extremely real for these individuals, and can lead to itches or pain in non-existent body parts.

A much more common example of virtual reality, experienced by anyone visiting a dental surgery, occurs when a local anaesthetic is administered. We have all had the sensation of thinking our lips are much bigger than they actually are. This is a result of the brain noticing that it is not receiving any data from the lip region, and so it attempts to construct a virtual lip based on the information it has. The virtual lip is a pretty good attempt at reconstruction, but is never quite a perfect fit to our real lips. How many of us have attempted to eat soup or drink coffee with our virtual lips? Our brains can also create alarming reconstructions while we sleep, causing us to wake, covered in sweat, or struggling with some virtual opponent. Obviously, discussion on reality is an essential foundation upon which we build our perception of the world.

The vicissitude of the observed

I. The present context

The world, as we observe it, is a snapshot of a journey, a brief moment in time. One of the challenges in studying anything is that time is as important as space. Time can impact upon interpretation in a number of ways. Firstly, as already mentioned, the observer is part of a culture or society, and, as no man is an island, the surrounding culture will impact upon the observer, depending on the moment in time within which they exist. The contexts of their upbringing, education and belief structure may well impact upon how they interpret what they observe.

II. Change through time

Secondly, things also change over time. Geological processes occur over very long periods, and their impact can reach across time to influence the world of today. We now know that the planet's surface is made of huge tectonic plates that have moved across the surface over time. Not only have land masses found themselves in very different positions on the planet over time, but have, at certain periods, joined together to form super-continents. The ancient plant family, Proteaceae (after whom the South African cricket team, the Proteas, are named), is found in South America, South Africa and Australia, and owes its distribution to the fact that when it first evolved, these land masses, along with Antarctica (where fossils of the Proteaceae have also been found), were joined together in a super-continent called Gondwana. The famous marsupials of Australia, such as the koala bears, kangaroos and Tasmanian devils, actually originated in North America, where the only surviving member of this original group, the Virginia opossum, still exists. Again, they spread across land masses that were connected.

Yet more fascinating is the distribution of some of the trilobite fossils. Trilobites are ancient arthropods, long extinct, that existed for some 300 million years. These were extremely successful creatures, surviving many cataclysmic events including a number of mass extinctions. It became obvious that trilobites found in Wales were the same as a small number found in Eastern Newfoundland. These "Welsh-American" trilobites were totally different from those in the rest of North America. Meanwhile, a small number of trilobites that were typical of the rest of North America were also discovered in Scotland. How could this be? An explanation came, in 1966, from John Tuzo Wilson, a geophysicist from Canada, who was a major figure in developing plate tectonic theory. The trilobites died and were fossilized at a time when the world looked extremely different to that of today. 450 million years ago, Scotland and Wales were separated by a sea called the Lapetus Ocean. At this time Scotland was part of a continent called Laurentia, while Wales was part of a different continent, on the other side of the ocean, called Baltica. Trilobites that died 450 million years ago in Wales and Scotland lived on completely different continents. The Welsh trilobites were on the same land mass as East Newfoundland, south of the Lapetus Ocean, while the Scottish trilobites were on the same continent as the West Newfoundland members, north of the Lapetus Ocean. They lived, died and were fossilized on either side of this ocean.

After fossilization of the trilobites, these two continents moved together, and, finally, the Lapetus Ocean disappeared. At this stage, Wales and England were now joined with Scotland, and, indeed, all the land masses of the world came together to form the super-continent, Pangea. Pangea was one giant island, floating in an even greater sea, and our fossilized friends were also now united on the one land mass. Then, about 150 million years ago, the Atlantic Ocean began to form, as Pangea broke up. It split the land, but not quite along the same line as the former Lapetus Ocean. As a result, Scotland and Wales were left on the east of this new divide, while both parts of Newfoundland were west of the new ocean. Our trilobites hitched a ride, and this is why the same species are now found in rocks in Scotland and West Newfoundland, while

Wales and East Newfoundland share different species. Even when you are dead and buried, you can still undertake huge journeys on board your tectonic plate! So we see that time is an important factor in understanding where particular species are found, whether alive or fossilized.

Tectonic plates actually move at roughly the same rate as our fingernails grow. One result of plate movement is that a given location can undergo huge changes in climate, as the plate moves north or south on the planet. For example, the fossil beds of the River Thames, called the London Clay, representing life some fifty million years ago, show that at that time, the climate of the Thames was tropical, with numerous palms growing in the area, some of them resembling those found in Malaysia today. Plate movement can have indirect effects on climate as well. The breaking up of land masses at the South Pole led to the formation of Antarctica, and the development of new currents that brought about a change in climate, leading, eventually, to the formation of a frozen continent.

Estimation of the impact of rising sea levels, due to the melting of glaciers and the thermal expansion of warming oceans, has been complicated by the phenomenon of *rebound.* During a glaciation event, where Scotland, for example, was covered in up to 2 km of ice, the bedrock was pressed upon by a huge weight. Following glacial melt at the end of an ice age, the rock begins to rise, or rebound, when relieved of its icy burden. While this rise occurs, over many thousands of years, it leads to a drop in the sea level at the coast. It is not that the sea itself is dropping, but rather that the land is rising. A result of this is that even when sea levels rise, as they are presently doing due to global warming, not all parts of the world will experience this equally. In fact it might appear that the sea levels are falling in some parts of the world, while rising in other parts. If the land has had glaciers on it, even thousands of years ago, it may still be rising in response to having this huge burden removed. It's a bit like standing on a rising escalator in the London Underground. Imagine that the underground system is flooding with water. As the water moves up, you may still move away from the water, if the escalator moves you upwards faster than the water rises.

As we mentioned at the start of this chapter, energy can travel through time too. Fossil fuel deposits, representing the Sun's energy of many millions of years ago, can release this energy today.

III. The historical context

A third important aspect of the temporal context of the observer is that the system which is being observed, be it a protein, an organism or a community of species, will be within an evolutionary setting, and its historical context will be at least as important as its present context in terms of what is happening. Biological processes change over time, but often lag behind the present, in that they are responding to change around them. There is a significant difference between examining how a technological innovation, such as a microwave oven works, and how a woodland community works. The microwave oven uses the latest technology in a rapid response to the present-day market. The woodland community will be responding to its present-day market forces, such as climate change and acid rain, but will most likely lag behind. Mutation and change in biological systems take a very long time to occur, while environmental change can operate within a much shorter time frame. It is a bit like two conveyor belts moving at dramatically different speeds. If change in the environment occurs too quickly, extinction of species can occur, or mass extinction, in an extreme event. In the last two and a half million years, there have been a series of ice ages, interrupted by interglacial periods, one of which we find ourselves in at present. These have brought with them changes in temperature and CO_2. However the present change in temperature in the last two centuries has been at a rate ten times that of the great "warm up" at the end of the last ice age. Thus the environmental conveyer belt has accelerated, and the fear is that the living planet may struggle to keep up. The rate of change can be as important as the absolute change.

Lagging behind

So the moment in time at which we observe something can be important, and we can see that time defines space in many ways. Also, some things change with time, while other things are not able to change. Biology can take an intermediate position, changing with time, but lagging behind the environmental changes that surrounds it. Two examples will serve to illustrate this point.

Predators past and present

Species often behave very differently when subjected to predation than when living in a predator-free area. The red colobus monkey occurs in equatorial Africa, and may co-exist with the chimpanzee, which is a predator of the colobus. If we compare the populations of red colobus in habitats with and without chimpanzees, we see differences in the colobus population structure and behaviour. There are a higher proportion of male colobus when chimpanzees are also present. The time between births is reduced and the annual birthrate is, concomitantly, increased when chimpanzees cohabit. This is likely to be a response to increased losses of young red colobus, the preferred prey of chimpanzees. Thus, a shorter gestation period reduces the maternal investment in each offspring and the reduced time between two conceptions allows for replacement of lost offspring. Red colobus groups exposed to predators also have higher male:female sex ratios than non-predated populations, most likely because males help in defense. Finally, birth clumping (that is, synchronized births across the population, often with all births occurring in a narrow window of one to two weeks), only occurs when chimpanzees are absent. In the presence of the chimpanzees, births are spread throughout the year. This is likely to be in response to the chimpanzees being predators that can kill more than one prey item at a time. Thus, swamping the predator with lots of potential prey items by birth clumping is not likely to work. Birth clumping works as a form of defense against a predator if the predator only takes one prey item at a time.

Given all of this, it would seem straightforward to compare populations and determine if predators were impacting on social organization and demography. However if a prey population has recently lost its predator species, there may still remain characteristics of a predated population. Such populations are termed *shadow prey* and can be extremely misleading. Are the characteristics latent or are they real, in terms of the causative effects? In other words, if we observe behaviour that seems to represent predator response, is this related to a co-existent predator, or one that is no longer present?

Species numbers on islands

Another example will highlight the difficulty in interpreting what we see due to temporal lag. Islands can form in lots of ways. Sometimes, this can come about due to a rise in water level around them. An area of land, formerly part of a much larger whole, can become separated. This process of separation drastically reduces the area and type of land available for species living on the island. We know that the number of species on an island is related to the area of the island. Small islands have less species on them than do large islands, mostly because they have fewer habitats available. Over time, the species numbers will reduce, or relax, to a lower level, appropriate for a reduced area. If we assess an island for species richness during this period of relaxation, we may get a false idea of the species that are actually supported by this island. Trinidad, an island in the Caribbean, is an example. Trinidad has recently separated from Venezuela, and although relatively rich in species, particularly of birds, it is anticipated that following relaxation, species numbers will be much lower than now. This is a natural re-adjustment. Serious decline in species numbers may not be due to present new threats, but rather may be merely a re-adjustment to a smaller area following fragmentation. The Barro Colorado Island in Panama was formed artificially, in 1914, when a lake was formed as part of the Panama Canal. The island had originally been a hill and had an estimated 208 bird species in the 1920s, but by 1970, forty-five species had been lost. Of these, thirteen species were thought to be lost due to relaxation.

A final word on context

We return now to Karl Popper, who stated that '*If perception is wholly dependent on context, then stripping away context is a strategy of doubtful value.*' So what are the contexts that influence perception? Temporal contexts, as we have seen, are important. Temporal change in conditions, both biotic (such as phantom prey) and physical (such as island areas), often occur within a different timescale compared to change in response by a given species. Response may also be limited by an inability to change. There are many such constraints on change as we shall see later.

We have seen that the past informs the present, and may limit the future. Artifacts, due to time lag or irreversible change, impact upon our interpretation of reality, and, in particular, our attempts at elucidating how things work. Temporal aspects of culture are also important. The observer can be heavily influenced by the moment in time of the surrounding culture, both at a human level and in the minutia of an individual life history. To gain an understanding of why life is organized in the way that it is requires us to be aware of such spatial and temporal contexts.

The games that nature plays

At the end of this brief introduction, we come to a keystone question. What is the context of biology? The thesis of this book rests on the following statement: the games of biology are played to the rules of chemistry, and the games of chemistry are played to the rules of physics. A game is an outcome of a set of rules. To understand the game, we must first understand the rules. The game is like a shadow, which is defined by the object that lies between it and the light source. The shadow only exists because of the object and merely represents the outline of the object, rather than the object itself. Just as in Plato's analogy of the cave, the biology of our planet is a consequence of the chemistry, just as the shadows are a consequence of the objects being carried across the platform. Yet these objects themselves are the consequence of the real, living creatures outside of the cave. So too, chemistry is a consequence of physics, playing out its existence but dependent on the rules of physics. This book seeks to understand the biology of our planet by looking for the ultimate explanation, rather than the consequences. Since shadows can only inform us about a small part of the nature of the objects being carried in front of the cave fire, and these objects are a weak representation of the creatures outside the cave, any theory that tries to explain how life evolved and how the diversity of the planet works must look far beyond the biology and chemistry.

Shadows on a cave wall are, ultimately, merely that. Present explanations of why the living planet is organized in the way that it is, how it came to be that way and how we are impacting upon it as a species, are at best incomplete, and, at worst, based on illusions. The shadows may dance, flicker and prowl across the wall, but they are not, in themselves, a sufficient basis upon which to interpret the reason for what we see. It is this book's premise that the questions relating to life ultimately find their answers not from a study of life itself, but from an understanding of energy. It is the energetic context that ultimately offers the best explanation for how the planet works. But what is energy anyway and why is it so central to our approach?

Chapter Four

Energy: the light beyond the shadows

We all think that we know what energy is, and we all use the word in our conversations. "*He's full of energy*". "*I don't think I have the energy to do that*". We buy energy drinks, and energy cereal bars. And its scientific definition, the ability to do work, certainly relates to these uses. Energy is like a substance, in that you either have it or you don't. It is measurable and has units, just like distance is measured in metres, and time is measured in seconds. These units are called joules after James Joule (1818-1889), the English physicist. You can gain energy and you can lose it. However there are a number of interesting aspects to energy. It comes in different forms. Light energy is the most obvious one. It can also appear as heat energy, chemical energy, gravitational energy, electrical energy, nuclear energy, wind energy and sound energy. Also, energy of one kind can be converted into another kind. For example light energy can be converted to chemical energy in the process of photosynthesis. Chemical energy can be converted into heat energy. In the end, our sensual perception of our surroundings is completely based on electrical energy. Light is visible only because our retina convert the light radiation into electrical energy, and our brains reconstruct these signals into visual images.

Colour is another energetic phenomenon. It depends on the wavelengths of radiation that are absorbed. An object looks red because it absorbs every wavelength of light energy except red, which then reflects off it, giving it its colour. Sound is wave energy too, but with a much longer wavelength. Our ears intercept this energy, and again, convert it into an electrical signal which our brains then reconstruct into what we know as sound. Taste and smell intercept chemical energy while touch responds to pressure. So our sensual world is energetic, and reflects an energetic reality.

However we only sample a part of this world. Many animals can hear a wider range of sounds than we can. Other organisms can "see" ultraviolet light, which is invisible to us. Many flowers look completely different in UV than in visible light. An insect will therefore see a "different" flower than we do. As, a result our sensual reality is only part of a greater reality, and different parts of the living planet experience more or less of this reality.

Potential and kinetic energy

Energy can be separated into two different types. We can envisage this if we think of a sprinter in a 100 metre race. At the start of the race, the sprinter is poised, ready to go. He has the potential to explode off the line and is full of energy waiting to be expressed. At the finish line, the sprinter is in full stride, using the energy in order to move quickly. The start line energy is all about potential. This potential to do something is like a savings account, which is there ready to be spent. It is invisible, but exists because it has been built up over time. It is measured in terms of how different it is from zero. One classic example is a diver, who climbs up a cliff before diving into the water far below. As he climbs he uses energy, because he is fighting against gravity. However, not all of this energy is lost. Instead, he gains energy because he has, temporarily, put himself somewhere that gravity doesn't want him to be. The higher he goes, the more potential energy he gains, and when he jumps, gravity acts to accelerate him towards the water. The higher he climbs, the harder he will eventually hit the water. This is because he has built up potential energy by fighting against gravity. The finish line represents kinetic, or movement energy. Here, the potential has been converted into actually doing something.

The First Law

All this energy swapping is well and good, but are there any rules that regulate energy? In fact there are. The first rule, states that energy can neither be created nor destroyed. Its proper title is *The First Law of Thermodynamics*. Thermodynamics (literally, the power of heat) is the study of energy, and the word hints at the fact that this whole field of study really began with steam, or, more specifically, steam engines. This is an extremely important rule. Since you can't make energy, you need to get it from somewhere else. Because you can't destroy it, you can only pass it on to something else. I often look at old coins in my pocket and wonder where they have been during their existence. Were they ever the property of somebody famous, or involved in a crime? Did they ever get lost down the back of a sofa, only to emerge after years of hiding? The same can be said of energy. Imagine some solar energy arriving on Earth 200 million years ago, and being converted into chemical energy by a plant. The plant dies and the energy eventually becomes part of a coal seam beneath the ground, where it hides until a mining company digs it up. Then, last week, you bought it, in the form of a bag of coal, and burnt it, releasing it as heat and light energy.

One of the challenges of the first law is that it demands that there was never a beginning. Energy cannot be created, and so it has always been there. This is where physics meets metaphysics. However it is an important point to make. We need to be aware of the full repercussions of our rules. However, a bit like our old coin, the energy that flows through us is on an infinite journey of its own.

We often talk about using up energy or consuming energy. In fact this couldn't be further from the truth. The first Law of Thermodynamics clearly tells us that energy cannot be used or consumed. It merely passes through. It may change its form, but the amount of energy stays constant.

The Second Law

So we see that we cannot create energy. But why does it keep flowing through us? Why do we continuously need to acquire it? Why do we have to work just to stand still? Potential energy is there because of where the diver is compared to where he would be if hadn't bothered to climb. It depends how far you are from where you would end up without doing anything, and this place is called equilibrium. Everything in the Universe is destined to end up at equilibrium. Equilibrium is the place of complete chaos, where things can't be any more disorganized. The ultimate situation of equilibrium is when every particle is evenly spread. This tendency towards complete disorder is called *entropy* and is summarized in the Second Law of Thermodynamics, which says that any system plus its surroundings tends spontaneously towards chaos. Entropy, meaning, literally, *in transformation* or *content transforming*, was given its name by Rudolf Clausius (1822-1888), the German physicist, and father of thermodynamics, in 1865. You can observe it in action if you take a glass of water, and put a single drop of ink into the water. Over time the drop of ink will gradually disperse, eventually dispersing evenly. The same thing works with perfume. Someone wearing the latest fragrance, walking through a room, will leave a trail of delightful scent, and this scent will spread throughout the room, eventually spreading completely evenly. This is the second law in action. Order is temporary whereas chaos is the ultimate destination. The result of this law is that in order to construct something, like a living organism for example, you need to oppose this natural route that leads to destruction. You need a continuous flow of energy through you to stave off chaos. This is why you need to eat. Once you die, your body starts its journey, inexorably, towards equilibrium. We are all like balls on a sloping hillside, which will all roll downhill, unless energy is used to keep us in one place, or move us up the hill. Everything in the Universe is on this slope.

The repercussions of the second law are huge. Any decrease in available energy, and there will be a change in what is possible. Any object that has structure (and so is far from equilibrium) will start to struggle, and the more energy needed, the more the struggle will be. Humans have gradually become more dependent on energy as their lifestyles have become more complicated. As a result, our sub-species would suffer more than most if energy levels fell. How could this happen? During a mass extinction, energy from the Sun often decreases because the sky becomes full of dust. This dust can come from the impact of a huge asteroid striking the Earth, or from volcanic material thrown into the atmosphere. As a result, sunlight is blocked before it can reach the surface of the planet, and the amount of energy available to create order decreases.

Even more importantly, there is a direction to energy processes. Some processes happen spontaneously, others don't. There is an inevitability, a direction, about so much of our Universe. It is this aspect of energy that answers the "*why*" rather than the "*what*" of our questioning. It comes down to one thing. Anytime anything is built up, a concomitant amount of chaos is made, plus a bit more. Another way to put this is that you can't even break even. There must always be an increase in disorder. So by fighting against the process of entropy, more energy is needed, and even more disorder will be produced. This is why it is often argued that the Second Law, entropy, dictates that an evolving planet will become more complex with time, as this increasing complexity will demand increasing chaos, which agrees with the law of entropy. Certainly, the second law directs processes and gives energy an organizational role. We shall see the importance of this later.

So the Universe as a whole is becoming more disordered as it slips towards complete chaos. Yet our planet seems to be bucking the trend. How come this is happening? The reason is that we are benefiting from a source of energy coming from our neighbouring star. This allows us to exist far from equilibrium, for a while anyway. Photosynthesis grabs some of this solar energy and the whole show of *pass-the-parcel* begins, generating entropy as it proceeds, but allowing us to operate in an ordered way. It could even be argued that we are slaves of entropy, destined to use more and more energy, and develop more and more complex solutions that will push us even further from equilibrium. The chemical and biological games that are played out on planet Earth are all to do with entropy.

Energy on Earth: The green machines

Of all of the processes on our planet that are energetic in their nature, the key one is photosynthesis. Photosynthesis basically converts light to chemical energy. It is so crucially important because it is the doorkeeper that controls how much energy flows through our living planet, and, therefore, provides the energy that allows us to stay far from energetic equilibrium, performing our merry dance in the face of impending chaos. Without this energy, nothing but the most basic life forms could exist. Photosynthesis, basically, is a very simple concept. It uses a small part of the Sun's energy to glue carbons together in what is called *carbon fixation*, making sugar. This sugar is then burned to release energy, which in turn is used to make lots of other things. The whole process allows energy from the Sun to be passed throughout the planet, without which this world would be a very different place, a theme we will return to throughout this book.

Just as in Plato's story of the cave, our energetic journey begins with the Sun. Our Sun is a giant nuclear fusion reactor, that is, it fuses two hydrogen atoms together to make helium and a neutron (a small particle that is part of every atom), with a concomitant release of energy. This energy results from the fact that two hydrogen atoms are heavier than the helium plus the neutron, and so the mass that is lost is released as energy. The amount of energy can be calculated from Albert Einstein's famous equation, $E = mc^2$ (energy equals mass times the speed of light squared). Although the mass loss is miniscule for each helium atom formed (6×10^{-30}kg!), with many such fusion reactions occurring simultaneously, a huge amount of energy is released from the surface of the Sun. A small amount of this energy is intercepted by our planet, as it revolves around our nearest star.

The key trick for any living organism on Earth is to gain energy and to pass this energy through itself in order to stay alive. Energy is continuously dissipated, and so new energy must be accessed. Energy is passed between things by the movement of tiny, charged particles called electrons. Molecules with energy lose electrons when they are burnt, and these electrons are passed on to other molecules in a process called reduction. Thus, sugar is broken down to form carbon dioxide and water, releasing energy and electrons, while carbon dioxide is converted to sugar, gaining energy and electrons. It's like passing a parcel along a line of people. As electrons get passed along, so does energy. Of course, the whole process cannot begin without a parcel!

So where do organisms get their first electrons from? Early in the history of life on Earth, before the advent of photosynthesis, these electrons came from sulphur or iron. There are still creatures on our planet, such as sulphur-reducing bacteria, that do this. The process is called chemosynthesis, and in the early history of life on Earth, several billion years ago, it ruled the waves, or, rather, ruled beneath the waves. Life at that time was forced to remain under water, as there was no oxygen in the atmosphere. This meant that there was no ozone (the molecule which acts as a barrier to harmful ultraviolet radiation, and is made of three oxygen atoms joined together), and thus a large dose of ultraviolet radiation impacted on the surface. The UV would damage deoxyribonucleic acids (DNA), the molecules responsible for making the all-important proteins. Water also acts as a barrier to radiation, and so by living deep in the ocean, organisms used the water as a shield. The great breakthrough for life on Earth was to use water, which was all around, in plentiful supply, as the source of electrons. What an advance this was, and one that would change the story of life on Earth. No more searching around for iron and sulphur, true, but that wasn't the greatest outcome. By splitting water, three things happened. Electrons were freed, hydrogen ions were produced, and, most dramatically, oxygen was released. Oxygen began to build up on planet Earth! The electrons could then be used to make material that could, in turn, be oxidised. It is a bit like a relay race, where the baton of electrons is passed along a chain of runners, ending up with carbon.

There are many amazing molecules involved in photosynthesis, but two of these stand out from the crowd, one called Photosystem II and one called RUBISCO. These are not simple structures. Each is made up of a number of parts, and they act together as giant protein cities. They both occur in the chloroplasts, these ancient structures that formerly were free-living bacteria before their "capture" by the eukaryotes.

Photosystem II is made up of lots of different proteins and pigments. It absorbs photons of light from the Sun and uses this energy to excite electrons. When an electron is excited, it leaves where it was, and is replaced by another electron. The source of these electrons is water. In this instance, water is split, producing electrons, hydrogen ions (protons) and oxygen. The production of oxygen, a waste product of photosynthesis, has led to oxygen levels building up in the atmosphere, and to the production of the protective ozone layer. This, in turn, has allowed life to emerge from its watery origin onto land, no longer at the mercy of the powerful ultraviolet radiation.

As oxygen levels increased, this allowed aerobic life forms to evolve, and, at higher levels still, allowed them to attain a multicellular state. The more cell layers an aerobic organism has, the higher the oxygen levels outside that organism have to be, in order for oxygen to be able to diffuse into the centre of the organism at sufficient levels. Of course circulatory systems allow even more complex organisms to exist by transporting oxygen to all parts of the body.

The water splitting reaction was revolutionary and became known as the green revolution. However this oxygen was not good news to all of life. Anaerobic organisms were poisoned by oxygen, and so from their point of view, this poisonous gas marked a significant event in their evolution, forcing them to live in low-oxygen corners of the world. It is a remarkable and humbling observation that the oxygen revolution was brought about by a mere side product of the water-splitting reaction, given the huge impact it has had on the planet, from UV-protecting ozone, through to aerobic respiration and multicellularity.

This also relates to our discussion, in the last chapter, on the impact of time upon what we observe. There are two consequences. Plants today suffer from a problem called photoinhibition. This problem arises due to too much light energy being absorbed by their pigments, leading to the destruction of part of the Photosystem II complex, the D1 protein. Plants have to replace the damaged protein, and this repair has costs, both in terms of actual work, and loss of operational time. This seems hard to understand. Photosynthesis has been around for billions of years and yet there is a significant problem at the heart of it. Surely evolution would lead to a solution? The problem results from the ancient origin of the system, which evolved under the water. Water not only absorbs harmful radiation, it also absorbs light. As ozone formed, this led to a drop in UV radiation reaching the planet. Organisms headed towards the surface of the ocean, freed from concerns relating to high UV, and became exposed to greater levels of light. The complexity of Photosystem II was such that it hasn't been possible to be re-engineered in order to fix the problem. This shows the limitations that can arise in evolution. There are design constraints that sometimes only appear later. It is like building a skyscraper. Once the foundations are laid, and the two hundred floors are built on top of this, there is no possibility of altering the original foundations without risking the entire building.

The second problem relating to changing environments occurs with the machine that glues the carbons together to form sugar, or, strictly speaking, bits of sugar. This machine is known as RUBISCO, or, the more cumbersome, ribulose bisphosphate carboxylase oxygenase. If we took all the proteins on the planet and arranged them into piles, RUBISCO would be the biggest pile. This hugely important protein is extremely interesting in a number of ways. In plants, it is assembled within the chloroplasts, but part of it is coded for by genes in the nucleus and part of it from genes in the chloroplast, representing a division of labour between the plant and its captive organelles. The enzyme, as its name suggests, attaches different things to ribulose (a five carbon sugar). Not only can it attach carbon (the carboxylase function) but it can also attach oxygen (the oxygenase function). It becomes a sort of competition as to which one of these two elements binds to the ribulose, and this competition is what lies at the heart of the matter here, as we shall see.

The binding of oxygen creates a real problem for present day plants. When oxygen attaches to the sugar, this creates a toxic product that must be destroyed, involving an expensive set of reactions. Thus, energetically, it is two steps forward and one step back. If you try walking down a street doing this, you will quickly realize that, while it is fun, and certainly will draw attention from anyone you pass (if you manage to pass anyone!), it takes a lot longer to complete your journey, and may lead to you missing the bus or train that you had aimed to catch! Why do plants do this? Why is this important enzyme, which lies at the heart of almost every food chain, so badly designed? The answer lies, again, in its origin, on a planet that had virtually no oxygen around at that time. When RUBISCO was designed, the world was a very different place, and the chances of oxygen competing with carbon for attachment were minimal. Ironically, the very process of which it is a part, photosynthesis, led to the increase in oxygen levels, and thus led to the problem of competition, and increased cost, a cost known as photorespiration (respiration involved in getting rid of the problematic product of photosynthesis).

This ancient enzyme has not been able to be redesigned, in spite of selection pressure to do so. In fact some plants have gone to extraordinary lengths to cope with the troublesome RUBISCO. Species including sorghum, corn and sugarcane, along with fourteen of the world's worst eighteen weeds, use a clever trick, creating a sort of time machine, to fool the enzyme into thinking that it is 3 billion years ago! These plants put the enzyme into a cell and squirt in extra carbon dioxide so that the enzyme experiences an artificial atmosphere, mimicking that on Earth billions of years ago. By doing this, they reduce the chances of oxygen outcompeting carbon, and thus reduce the costs of dealing with the troublesome product of this costly union.

Energy: the visible and invisible reality

The physical world is a relative thing. By this I mean that depending on our sensual equipment, we will experience it in a particular way. There are, as a result, parts of the physical world which any particular organism cannot perceive. The whole subject of what reality actually is, given that it can differ between organisms, is a difficult issue. Our Universe is energetic in its essence. It is made of energy and behaves as we would expect energy to behave. It is governed by rules and usually operates in a way that is imperceptible to us. We most often see the effects of energy on our world rather than the energy itself. Yet energy, although mostly invisible, is as real as the effects that it creates. It isn't a matter of our perception of reality not being absolute, but, rather, being incomplete. The study of things that lie beyond the physical world is called *metaphysics*. The term, literally meaning beyond or after physics, originated from Aristotle (384 – 322 BC), one of the great Ancient Greek philosophers. Aristotle was a student of Plato, and studied at the Academy in Athens for many years. He eventually became the tutor of Alexander the Great. He wrote a book on Physics, and followed this with one on metaphysics, which he defined as "*the knowledge of immaterial being*". As discussed in Chapter Two, there has been a great division between physics and metaphysics, the physical world being the domain of science and the metaphysical world being occupied by the likes of philosophy and religion (although the New Physics broaches this divide).

Energy accounts for the visible and the invisible, the heard and the unheard, the smelt and the unsmelt, the felt and the unfelt, the tasted and the untasted. It operates at sub-atomic levels and at cosmic scales. If our thesis is correct, that energy is both the substance and the architect of the living world, and the true basis of evolution and structure of the living world, then, surely, we would expect to see some account of energy as central to metaphysical explanations. Let us take a look at some of the major metaphysical belief structures and see if we can find evidence of this.

Energy and its place in religious thinking

In the many Hindu faiths, *Aum* represents, among other things, the sound that was first produce at the creation of the Universe. In the holy writings of the Vedas, Aum represents the sound of light. Taoism focuses around *Tau*, the way of the Universe, and a force that runs through all things. The great way of Tao is made up of energy (*Jing*), the flow of energy (*Qi*) and the spirit (*Shen*). Another important concept is that change is a constant, driven by this flow of energy. This is very much in agreement with the laws of thermodynamics.

Thought to have heavily influenced later belief structures such as Judaism, Christianity and Islam, Zoroastrianism, one of the world's oldest religions, holds light as symbolic of God and goodness. Fire temples are significant places of worship for Zoroastrians. They refer to the cosmic energy that sustains and originates life as *asha–chithra*, or, the seed of Asha. The symbolism of fire as representing deities is also found in the Holy Bible and the Qu'ran.

Cosmic order is called *Rta* in Ancient Aryan belief. Rta, the basis of dharma in the Hindu faith, literally means "the course or order of things". In its earliest nuance, it was a force used to account for the natural world, explaining how the heavens and weather systems worked, growing out of man's attempts at understanding what lay behind the observed Universe. Not a deity itself, unusually for the Aryans, it represented the cosmic order of the Universe. Rta controls the process by which the world unfolds at different levels (sound familiar?). It is the law of becoming, a blueprint, according to the philosopher Jeanine Miller, that sets out how the world becomes manifest in the phenomenal sense, but stemming from a transcendental level. Rta, the one voice, is expressed at all levels.

Hindu faith also embraces a cyclic creation and destruction of the Universe, akin to the theory of cyclic big bang events in modern physics. *Tapas* is another aspect of Vedic thought, portraying the force that drives the Universe from the beginning to the end of the cycle, and is literally translated as "heat". This is an uncanny coincidence, given that the early work on entropy defined it in terms of heat loss. From the *Chandogya Upanishad*, one of the oldest Vedic holy books, we read "*Everything we touch, see, is a differentiated manifestation of all pervading Akasha (space). Prana (the vital force) acting on Akasha is creating the whole of this Universe*."

At the heart of Jainism lies a formulation that is very similar to the first law of thermodynamics: the belief that nothing in the Universe is destroyed, but, rather, things change from one form to another. Jainism also holds that energy processes are what control the Universe, being created, regulated and administered by cosmic laws. The Universe is divided into two forms of energy, *Jada* or *Ajiva* (matter) and *Chetana* or *jiva* (life). Jada has three forces: gravitation, magnetism and electricity. Of all of the belief structures, Jainism is the closest to modern scientific theories.

The largest religion in the world is Christianity. Its sacred text, the Holy Bible, is littered with references to energy. The first act of creation was the creation of light. Light, as a theme, runs through the entire collection of writings. Lucifer, the great angel, whose name means light bearer or son of dawn, fell and became Satan. The fall of Lucifer introduced chaos into the Universe, a fascinating parallel to the Second law of

Thermodynamics. The themes of evil, disorder and entropy are deeply entwined in Christian theology. The visitation of chaos upon creation, symbolized by the departure of Adam and Eve from the Garden of Eden, led to a curse including "*From dust thou art, and unto dust shalt thou return*". Death is envisaged as a consequence of the chaotic events of the Garden of Eden.

The relation between the fall of energy and evil is a continuing theme, as referenced to by the symbolic statement "*Wide is the gate and broad is the way that leadeth to destruction*". Again this very much echoes the message of the second law of thermodynamics. What is clear is that order, chaos, good, evil and energy are all associated with each other. The uses of energetic symbols such as light and the concept of its "fall" again reflect the reality of the entropic context and the drivers of processes in the Universe. The concept of order and the need to work towards it, combined with the natural tendency towards chaos, are also of note.

Interestingly, more eastern forms of Christianity, as found in the orthodox belief structure, place an even greater emphasis on energy in their theology than do Latin or Reformation theologies. Orthodoxy believes that the creator figure is energetic, and that the creative force continues through time, an idea resonating with Rta, although in orthodoxy, the energy is thought of as grace, a very different interpretation than Latin or reformationist theologies. Thomas Aquinas (1225-1274), the great Jesuit thinker, recognized prime matter as the universal substance, and this was acted upon by energy and action separately. Energy has always been viewed as a function of essence in the east, while Latin scholars looked upon energy as being essence. The Reformationists viewed energy rather differently, expressing it as "will".

A typical metaphysical question would ask '*Why is there something rather than nothing?*' While science addresses the nature of the necessarily existent, metaphysical questions are important and cannot be dismissed. Just because a scientific framework cannot answer these questions, it does not mean that they should not be asked. This is no more apparent than in Cosmology, and in particular, Cosmogeny (theories relating to the origin of the Universe).

We find *Homo sapiens sapiens*, with great thinkers throughout the ages, who express themselves in different fields. The scientist, the philosopher and the artist each use their minds to understand and represent how they feel that the world works. We have seen that the minds that have worked on attempting to understand the Universe through a metaphysical approach have often developed their thoughts in ways that are much more resonant with scientific thinking than some would expect. In the end, these are thoughts that have come from much work, and find in themselves a resonance with human experience. They seek to explain how the Universe works, set within a wide range of metaphysical contexts, but it would seem extremely shallow to dismiss them from our consideration. While this book is based on the physical world in terms of setting out a different way of understanding the biological planet, the all-pervasive, multifaceted explanation presented here has many common themes with some of the great belief structures on our planet. This shouldn't surprise us. The many members of the species to which we belong, both dead and living, have been observing the same Universe with the same basic hardware, our senses, and imbuing this raw data with meaning using the same basic organ, the brain. Surely, then, if the explanation offered in this book is correct, other interpretations will find some common ground with it. Indeed, given that our explanation is based on energy, which is observable mostly through its effects, then metaphysical belief structures will almost certainly reference it. This book does not rest itself upon such writings, or use them as any kind of apology for the energetic theory, for there is plenty of material in the physical world to defend its position as we shall see. However, the fact that there is a resonance is not so much surprising, as expected.

At the heart of our journey in this book is the recognition that since energy is central to just about everything, and the laws of thermodynamics are central to how energy behaves, then surely any theory on the evolution and functioning of life must be based on energetic considerations. The dominant explanation for how life came to be organized and functions in the way that it does, the neo-Darwinian theory of evolution, takes a completely different approach, ignoring energy as an essential and central player. That, in itself, is surely a serious omission.

In this section we have been preparing for a journey towards a new understanding of how and why our living world looks like it does, and where we fit into it. Yet our perception of the physical world, that has been the focus of scientific attempts at explaining how life evolved and how it functions, does not represent the foundations that can provide this explanation. The games of biology are merely that. To understand the origin and meaning of life, we need to look far beyond it. However, before we can begin the search for this meaning, we need to ask a more basic question. What is life anyway?

Section II

What is Life?

This section asks the deceptively simple question: what is life? Many textbooks of biology start with a list of seven characteristics of life: reproduction, growth and development, biological evolution, regulation, response, metabolism and a cellular basis. We discover that there are significant problems with each of these traits, totally undermining the whole as a meaningful definition. So what is life? Is it a stream that runs through time, a seamless transition from one generation to the next, a genetic lineage or a pulsating set of vehicles? If it is a lineage, how did this lineage start? We need to consider the question in a different way. What is the purpose of defining what life is? Our desire to set criteria that allow us to distinguish life from non-life is driven by a need to separate the living from everything else. We examine the history of our attempts at defining life, discussing Vitalism, spontaneous generation and the difficulties in theories relating to the origin of life. We encounter a mesmerizing medic, a sterile mule and the weight of a soul, and come to a startling conclusion, that life, itself, is a shadow. We finally examine another way of looking at life on Earth: the Biosphere.

Chapter Five

The Seven Troublesome Characteristics of Life

Many textbooks of biology start with a simple list of seven characteristics of life: reproduction, a cellular basis, growth and development, biological evolution, regulation, response and metabolism. To be deemed as truly living, any potential member of this elite club must demonstrate all seven special properties. Each is fairly mundane, but as a united whole, the special club of seven, they form the password to life itself. However, problems immediately arise. All seven characteristics are indeed signs of life, but many only occur for a brief period in a given lifetime. If an entity does not show one of these characteristics at a given time, is it still alive? What if two of these characteristics, or three, are not found? How many of the characteristics are needed for something to be categorically alive?

Reproduction

Many organisms cannot, or choose not to, reproduce. Some organisms are sterile as a result of being hybrids (the consequence of having parents from two different species). The mule is a classical example. It is the product of a union between a donkey and a horse. It cannot participate in reproduction because of this, but does this mean it is not alive? Many plant species can only reproduce in certain conditions, but are sterile in other conditions. For example the Corsican pine cannot seed in Scotland because it is too cold. Is it any less alive in Scotland than in Corsica, where it seeds readily? If a human is sterile and you kill him, have you actually killed him, or is it that he was never alive and so he cannot die? In some normally single-celled organisms such as slime moulds, individuals group together at certain times, usually when they are short of food. They form multicellular structures that look like little towers. At the top of the towers, round, spore-producing structures are produced. Only individuals that are at the top of the tower get to make spores and to reproduce. The others form the tower structure, but don't reproduce. So are individuals that act as support cells non-living because of this?

Cellular basis and the problem of the virus

What about non-cellular organisms? Viruses are non-cellular, and require a host to reproduce. They are classed as non-living because of this. Yet they are capable of evolving, spreading, reproducing and surviving as well as, if not better than, any officially living organism. The need to class them as non-living would appear to stem from a weakness in the definition of life. Viruses are not alone in requiring a host within which to replicate. A whole range of parasitic organisms, from the malaria-causing *Plasmodium* through to pentastomid arthropods (parasites in, for example, rattlesnakes), require some elements of a host. Many other organisms utilize other organisms as an essential part of their survival and reproduction. If a coral reef is purged of its green partners, the Zooxanthellae, then the outlook is grim. Does this mean that the coral is not living because it relies on another life form for its survival?

Obligate symbionts cannot survive without their partners. One interesting example is the orchid. In order to maximize distribution of offspring, orchids produce extremely small seeds. The seeds of many orchids are so small that they do not contain enough resources to allow for proper germination. Seedlings need to grow sufficiently to allow photosynthesis to occur. It's a bit like packing a rucksack for a long hike. The heavier it is, the harder it is to carry it, but the lighter it is, the less useful things you can carry. Orchids get round the problem of an almost empty rucksack by immediately forming a relationship with a fungus right after germination. The fungus supplies needed resources, allowing the orchid to reach a critical size. The relationship is ended tragically, when the orchid seedling eats its fungal partner as a final Scooby snack! So the orchid could not survive without the fungus, but surely these spectacular plants are alive?

Witchweed, a parasitic plant, is even more dependent on a host. Its seeds germinate when the roots of its host are detected. The parasite then attaches to the host root, and taps into the sugar and water supply systems, allowing it to grow. Plants usually have to control how much water they lose by tightly regulating little pores in their leaves. These pores let in carbon dioxide, which, as we have already seen, is used in the production of sugar. However, while they are open, they let out water. Witchweed doesn't care about this, and doesn't waste energy controlling its leaf pores. Thus it drains water in a profligate way from its host, putting a huge strain on its host's water supply. It's a bit like your neighbour plugging his elaborate Christmas decorations into your mains supply. No matter how careful you are to switch off the lights and turn down the heaters, the thousands of brightly-lit, revolving Santas and singing snowmen next door will lead to a crippling electricity bill! Witchweed could not exist by itself as it would neither germinate, nor be able to regulate its water loss. Is it alive?

All green plants live only because of captive prokaryotes, the chloroplasts, enslaved at an early point in Eukaryotic evolution. We can get even closer to home with this. All eukaryotes would not survive without the use of critical machinery sourced from other organisms. Mitochondria were free living prokaryotes but are now entrapped within eukaryotic cells, carrying out crucial parts of our metabolism. If we were to purge ourselves of these prokaryotic partners, we most certainly would not find ourselves classified as life forms any longer!

Growth and development

Growth and development in determinate body plans (that is, bodies that grow and develop for a period until reaching a determined end point) only occur for a limited time in many organisms. When the organism stops growing, is it alive?

Biological evolution

Biological evolution does not normally occur within the lifetime of an organism, unless Lamarckian evolution is more prevalent than we think! Jean Baptiste Lamarck, the renowned French biologist, viewed evolution as proceeding by acquisition of traits during a lifetime, which could then be passed on to the next generation. Thus if biological evolution is a characteristic of life, then life must refer to a length of time greater than the lifespan of an organism. How long do we allow, and how much evolution is necessary? Would one base change do, or would we need a speciation event to say that evolution has occurred? We would then have to rule out organisms that were clonally or vegetatively spread as being alive.

Regulation, response and metabolism

Regulation is an important keystone in any definition of life. However, resting spores of many species will show metabolic stasis, yet must be considered alive. Again response raises important issues. A comatose organism will show no response, and yet may recover consciousness. Was that organism alive during the period of coma? Is there a difference between a coma that ends in consciousness and one that doesn't end? Metabolism is, once more, problematic, as catabolic reactions can occur after death, and form part of the entropic *danse macabre* demanded by the second law of thermodynamics.

Genetic material

What about genetic material? Does the presence of genes distinguish the living from the non-living? If the gene is key to our understanding of why the living planet exists in the way it does, then surely the phenotypic vehicle need not be a cell, thus allowing viruses to become alive. Yet viruses aren't classed as being alive.

Temporal and spatial issues

So we see that the seven characteristics used to define life have within them some significant problems. However, questions relating to the definition of life go deeper than this. Two areas cause particular concern: spatial and temporal considerations. By spatial considerations, we refer to the building blocks of life. If we keep adding atoms to a consortium of other atoms, at what stage is that consortium deemed to be living? It's a bit like asking when does a hamlet become a village, and when does a village become a town? When does a stream become a river, and when does a series of images become a film? Yet it is much more significant than these demarcations. We are asking: when does chemistry become alive?

Temporal considerations ask "*when did life begin*?" At what stage did Earth have its first living entity? Both of these considerations are related, and responses to these questions are often formulated together. Isolated DNA cannot be considered as living; neither can any of the molecules that make up a living being. However some relatively simple molecules can be considered to show signs of life. For example, prions, the agents thought to be responsible for Creutzfeldt-Jakob disease, are proteins that can replicate.

So what is life? Is it a stream that runs through time, a seamless transition from one generation to the next, a genetic lineage or a pulsating set of vehicles? In any of these cases, if it is a lineage, how did this lineage begin? We need to consider the question in a different way. What is the purpose of defining what life is? Our desire to set criteria that allow us to distinguish life from non-life is driven by a need to separate the living from everything else. The need to distinguish living from non-living has a deep significance on many levels. A life form takes on a new meaning, a higher consideration, especially if couched in terms of a lineage. From a human perspective, the sanctity of life accompanies any definition of life itself. As it became apparent that we were made of the same chemical elements as everything else, both living and non-living, the need to separate living organisms from the rest took on a greater importance, driven by teleological thought, that is, that there is a difference between a flame and a living being, the former being a product of oxidation, the latter being a part of a continuous line of existence with an evolutionary history, adapting, responding and metabolizing. Where would we be if we were just a bunch of atoms, like the rocks and water around?

Man's attempts to determine what makes something alive go back through the history of the human race. Early focus was on the breath of life, wherein life was a force that was breathed into otherwise non-living entities, and, upon death, the organism breathed its last breath, and lost its life. The living force has its most detailed analysis in Vitalism. Vitalism represents a key insight into the human mind, and the search for the meaning of life. This search has permeated chemistry, physics, biology and religion, and underlines the drive to separate the living from the dirt upon which we tread. By tracing the history of Vitalism, we will come closer to understanding why science has struggled with understanding the meaning of life itself.

Chapter Six
The Rise and Fall of Vitalism

The idea that there is a force that separates the living from the non-living is an ancient one. As early as 440 BC, Empedocles asserted that life derived from ether. He set out four key elements that make up life: earth, fire, water and air. A vitalistic element runs through almost every belief structure, from Qi in Chinese belief to Ka in ancient Egypt, and from the North American Algonquian *Gitche Manitou*, literally meaning great connecting spirit, through to the *mbec*, or energy, of the Ghedee energy workers of West Africa. Animism attributes spiritual forces to animals, plants and mountains, to name but a few things, and rituals from early times were utilized as a means of influencing existence by attempting to please the forces that control existence, as brilliantly portrayed in the movie, *The Wicker Man*. The possession of a life force as being inseparable from matter also finds a home in the thinking of Holozoism and Zoroastrianism.

The concept of a life force, that permeated the living, was not only in the religious domain. Science, too, aligned itself to this principle. Chemists were rapidly coming to terms with the fact that elements were common to living and non-living things. Were we merely made of the same stuff as dirt and dust? Surely this couldn't be true. From its early days, chemistry incorporated within it a solution to this sticky problem. The idea that a vital force existed had an important role in distinguishing between chemistry of animate and inanimate objects. Substances were categorized as 'organic' if they changed irreversibly upon heating and 'inorganic' if they reverted to their original form upon cooling. Not only did organic matter possess this weightless, invisible substance or vital force, but also organic matter could not be made from inorganic matter. It was special and different.

Surely the synthesis of an organic compound from inorganic material would put an end to vitalistic chemistry? In 1828, Frederich Wohler did just this, synthesizing urea from cyanic acid and ammonium. He later wrote of the '*slaying of a beautiful hypothesis by an ugly fact*'! Jacob Berzelius agreed, stating, in 1836, that there was no special force. Yet this by no means put an end to Vitalism. Justus von Liebig, the German chemist, who, bizarrely, was once imprisoned for three days for knocking the hat off a policeman, disagreed. He felt that the concept of a vital force was essential in understanding metabolic control, and could be seen as part of a mechanistic philosophy, arguing that it was of an equal significance to other physical forces.

Spontaneous generation, Vitalism and alcohol

The first half of the nineteenth century was a hotbed of debate in the natural sciences, and two extremely unlikely bedfellows came together with explosive results: spontaneous generation and Vitalism. Spontaneous generation, the theory that life arises spontaneously without reproduction, actually comprised of two schools of thought. Firstly, abiogenesis states that life arises from inorganic material, while the second school, heterogenesis, states that life arises from organic, but dissimilar parental material. Aristotle, in his seminal work, *De Generatione Animalium*, recorded the earliest detailed account, where he explained that bloodless animals came from decaying earth and excrement. Other Greek philosophers, such as Anaximander, believed that all life had arisen from slime in the primordial sea. As late as 1867, this belief received a brief resurrection, when a mysterious amorphous jelly called *Bathybius*, recovered from the sea floor of the Atlantic Ocean, was heralded as the stuff from which life arose, and the missing link between inorganic and organic life. It was later found to be a precipitate of calcium sulphate!

Pliny the Elder (23-79AD), the Roman naturalist and philosopher, who was to die in the destruction of Pompey, cited many examples of spontaneous generation in his *Natural History*, and the Roman poet, Lucretius, referred to a tiring mother Earth, exhausted by her initial creative efforts, now only giving birth to some lower life forms spontaneously. Spontaneous generation survived the spread of early Christianity in good shape, helped by Saint Augustine who used it to explain how many small creatures survived the flood without being on board the ark, and how they spread to islands afterwards, an awkward problem at the time, and possibly the earliest contribution to the field of island biogeography.

With religious backing and no competitor, it wasn't until the seventeenth century that a new, more rigorous application of science to biology, borne out of the new physics, challenged spontaneous generation. Francesco Redi, the Italian founder of helminthology, in 1668, wrapped meat in some gauze, allowed it to rot, and observed no spontaneous generation of flies. He concluded that maggots did not arise spontaneously from meat, but rather arose from eggs, which the gauze prevented from coming into contact with the meat. Redi still felt that gall insects (that hatch from specially constructed swellings on plants) and parasites arose via heterogenesis, i.e. from spontaneous, dissimilar origins.

Jan Swammerdam, the first man to describe red blood cells, ruled out heterogenesis in gall-forming insects. He went further, also dismissing gradual development and instead pursuing the idea of preformation, that is, that any organism is merely unfolding from a pre-existent, complete form carried in the reproductive tissues of the parent. Preformation, in a modified version, would emerge as a mainstay of genetics in the early twentieth century. Meanwhile, the father of microscopy, Anton van Leeuwenhoek, muddied the waters by concluding that while most organisms arose from sexual reproduction, little microbes (or, as he called them, *animalcules*) had such a high rate of population growth, that they were different from other organisms, and most probably formed from organic matter in a process of microcosmic heterogenesis.

By the eighteenth and nineteenth centuries, people were boiling broths all over the place, trying to prove or disprove that microbes spontaneously regenerated. The theory was that heat would kill any potential parent figure, and so if life returned after boiling, it must have arisen from scratch. Some, like John Needham and Félix-Archimède Pouchet, found that there was life after boiling, while others, such as Lazzaro Spallanzani and Louis Pasteur, found that nothing grew after boiling. Eventually the whole messy, broth-boiling business was settled by an Irish physicist, John Tyndall, who showed that repeated boiling ensured that no life could grow. He recognized that after one cycle of boiling, heat-resistant spores could survive and germinate, whereas a second boiling killed these off. Spontaneous generation was surely well and truly dead and buried. However a resurrection was about to occur, and spontaneous generation would become an integral part of the neo-Darwinian concept of life, as we shall see a little later.

Fermentation

Fermentation is the process where sugar is converted into alcohol. It occurs when there is not enough oxygen to burn the sugar. Anyone who has gone to a fitness gym or ran a race will have experienced the pain of fermentation, when the muscles are burning sugar at a faster rate than oxygen can be supplied. At this point, lactic acid is produced, leading to a sharp agonizing cramp due to acid levels building up. Fermentation is central to the brewing industry, where alcohol is produced.

Berzelius and Liebig both agreed that fermentation was a matter of simple chemistry. However Theodore Schwann, later famous for his part in formulating cell theory, observed that yeast was involved in fermentation. Louis Pasteur became a champion of Vitalism too. He demonstrated that by killing cells, no fermentation took place, and he categorized fermentation as one of the special reactions found only in living organisms, thus labeling it as a vital action. His work, which was to challenge spontaneous generation to its foundations, strengthened his belief in Vitalism.

Vitalism and developmental biology

It was not only in the realm of biochemistry that support continued for a vital force. Developmental biologists such as Nicolas Malebranche (1638-1715) felt that complex body plans necessitated a preformation to have occurred. He presented the theory that germ cells had included in them the organism itself. With the discovery of parthenogenesis, where an egg cell can develop into an adult form without a sperm cell, these arguments appeared to be supported. Hans Driesch, the eminent embryologist, proposed the presence of a substance that controlled developmental processes. He applied the word *entelechy* to this substance, a term originating from Aristotle, who coined the word with a meaning of something working to be itself. Driesch carried out experiments to show that blocking this substance would result in physical and psychological disorders. Around this time, the philosopher Henri Bergson wrote his influential book, *L'evolution Créatrice*, where he argued that an *elan vital* was common to all living things, observing that whether your view was that there was a determined end point (teleology) or an unfolding from a given starting point (mechanism), there was a need for a vital force. In other words, something had to guide the process.

Mesmerizing Vitalism

The verb *to mesmerize* comes from Franz Anton Mesmer (1734-1815), the German physiologist who coined the term *magnétisme animal*. He contributed an interesting and controversial chapter to the history of Vitalism. He defined animal magnetism as a type of magnetic force only found in animals and humans. Initially he gave his patients a drink containing iron filings, and used magnets to create a kind of tidal influence within the body. This stemmed from his interest in the role of the Moon and the planets on disease. He then claimed that it was magnetism in his own body that was the secret to healing, and dispensed with the inanimate magnets. His most famous early patient was a young composer called Maria Theresa von Paradis, who he treated for blindness. Rumours of a scandal brought an end to the treatment and led to a move to Paris for Mesmer. Here, he gradually re-established his reputation and developed his theory of animal magnetism, wherein disease could be healed by removing blockages in the body that inhibited the flow of the life force. As a physician, he viewed himself as a conductor of magnetism. His fame grew and the last king of France before the Revolution, Louis XVI, set up a commission to investigate his work. This commission in turn appointed a number of top scientists including Anton Lavoisier, Benjamin Franklin and Joseph-Ignace Guillotin. They could find no evidence of a vital fluid and this brought to an end Mesmer's work in Paris. His theories did, however, lead to the development of hypnosis as a treatment, championed by the Scottish neurosurgeon, James Braid.

Two interesting asides arose from the story of Mesmerism. Five years after his work on the commission, Joseph Ignace Guillotin became a deputy in Paris, where he suggested the guillotine as an improved method of execution. Four years after this, King Louis XVI, who had appointed the original commission into Mesmerism, was himself executed by the machine that derived its name from its protagonist. The second connection between those involved in Mesmerism is a musical one. Mesmer used to finish his sessions with patients by playing music on an unusual instrument called a glass amonica. Composed of a series of glass bowls stacked within each other, and of increasing diameter, the instrument is played by rubbing the edge of the glass as it rotates, producing an eerie, high-pitched sound. The glass contained lead, and possibly resulted in lead poisoning of the player, leading to madness rather than mesmerism! Rumours that the music itself could lead to madness greatly reduced sales. Not only was Benjamin Franklin another famous glass amonica player of the time, but he actually invented it. Whether or not they discussed their common interest during the investigative commission is not known.

Six humans, fifteen dogs, six ewes and a ram: the weight of a soul

Another unusual episode in the story of Vitalism occurred in 1906, with the publication of an infamous piece of work. In Haverhill, Massachusetts, Duncan MacDougall measured weight loss at the time of death in six humans, and found a sudden decrease in weight at the moment of death. He concluded that there was some soul substance that left the body upon death, but found no such loss in fifteen dogs, thus deducing that dogs have no souls! This caused a lot of excitement at the time, and would later inspire the name of the movie, *21 grams*. In fact, MacDougall's measurements varied between eleven and twenty-one grams. However, the work has since been deemed as fallible due to small sample size and experimental difficulties in determining the precise moment of death. Later work by Louis Hollander in Oregon actually reported a transient gain in weight in six ewes and a ram!

So what happened to Vitalism?

What then of Vitalism? The advent of neo-Darwinism, combined with more advanced understanding of chemistry and embryology, has led to the demise of Vitalism as a force in biology. Its modern day equivalent is the theory of *Emergence*. Here, a level of organization may have characteristics that cannot be explained by its component parts. The term was first coined by the English philosopher, George Lewes, in his important book, *Problems of Life and Mind*, published in 1875. A car can be seen as a product of the bits that make it a car. Each process is a result of parts of the car working to produce that outcome. There is no mystery in this. However some things can be viewed as emergent properties, and, most relevant to this chapter, life itself may be one of these. Emergent properties are radically new, maintained over a period of time and at a global level, capable of evolution and open to perception. The greater the number of components, the greater the likelihood of emergent properties, although in complex systems, the emergent property may be masked by the vast number of interactions, some of whose outcomes may work against it. One of the most commonly cited examples of emergence is in the social Hymenoptera, such as ants and bees, where individual insects, without direct leadership, work to produce extremely complex outcomes, such as the sophisticated termite mounds. Intelligence can be viewed as an emergent property of neuron connections. However emergent properties may occur at a much more basic level. It has been suggested that even the laws of physics that we recognize today may be emergent from one fundamental law. Mass, time and space may be emergent properties of Higgs bosons, wherein particles called bosons are given mass by their interaction with the Higgs field. The Higgs field is viewed as an all-pervasive lattice, which causes boson particles to slow down, thus giving them mass. Indeed the very perception of a determinate reality has been suggested to be an emergent property itself.

If we believe in a mechanistic model, that is, one where all phenomena can be explained as a product of their components, then emergent properties must, in the end, be explainable. There must be causes. In a way, the emphasis on emergence is a deliberate juxtaposition to reductionism (where everything stems from the components, and thus any process can be *reduced* to these components), and, as such, serves a useful purpose. The reductionist viewpoint fails to explain emergence. However, unless emergence is given some additional attribute, such as a vital force, then we are left with an explanation reflecting on the simple reality that when a system attains a certain level of complexity, emergent properties will be observed. What can be useful is that any theory explaining something must allow for the emergence of that thing, otherwise we rely on an unnatural origin or an explanation that demands that the object has existed forever. Later in this book we will offer a new and radically different explanation for emergence, stemming from our new theory on evolution, but we have a journey to complete before then.

When we consider what life actually is, we are faced with a basic question: does it exist at all? Our need to define it has led to more questions than answers. While we have dismissed a vital force, we are then faced with a vacuum. If life really is an emergent process, then why do we exclude viruses? Our seven characteristics of life that we mentioned at the beginning of this chapter are attempts at describing an entity, a living being. Yet if there is such a thing as life on our planet today, it did not always exist. Even if we rely on Panspermia, the theory that the Earth was seeded by a pre-existent life form, we must still face the reality that at some point, somewhere, life started. If life came from non-life, then we must be adherents of the theory of spontaneous generation. Even cell theory, another great step forward of the nineteenth century, and famously summarized by French chemist, François-Vincent Raspail in his maxim "*Omnis cellula e cellula*" (every cell originates from another cell like it), runs into a roadblock, in that the original, *ur-organism* (meaning the first 'living' organism) must have come from a non-cellular origin. Indeed, if life came from non-life once before, and if cells came from non-cells once before, then why couldn't it happen again? All of the characteristics of life happened for a first time somewhere and at some point in our Universe. It is clear, then, that a definition of life is tested to the extreme by explaining where this emergent property came from. We can build wonderful and ornate temples of explanation as to how life has evolved and diversified, but if the first row of bricks is missing, our entire edifice cannot be sustained. At the bottom line, if it exists at all, how did life start?

Chapter Seven

The Origin of Life

In this chapter we will examine all of the theories that currently exist to explain how life on Earth began. Any workable definition of life must also account for its origin, and as we shall see, there are significant problems here.

Panspermia: seeding planet earth with life

There have been a large number of explanations offered over many thousands of years as to how life actually started. A wide range of them involve some god or gods. Mechanistic explanations vary widely. The least useful is Panspermia. Here, life arrived on the planet, pre-packaged, from somewhere else. This explanation offers no understanding of how life actually arose in the first place, but merely passes the buck to another planetary system. In this respect, it is attractive, as it avoids the really difficult question. The most extreme version of Panspermia actually negates the question of origin, by stating that life has always existed. Cosmic ancestry argues that neo-Darwinism cannot account for the production of life by spontaneous generation (i.e. from non-living material) nor can it explain how genetic programmes have developed that can sustain the generation of new evolutionary features. Cosmic ancestry suggests that life forms have survived and spread forever. Fred Hoyle (1915-2001), the English astronomer, was a strong advocate, and coupled this concept with his theory of a steady state universe, which was continually recycled. He felt that an eternal universe was more believable than a universe from nothing, and thus advocated that life was also eternal. Thus, he opposed the concept of the Big Bang. Interestingly it was Hoyle who first used this term, as a criticism of the concept. The Big Bang theory has held sway recently, but new thinking includes a succession of big bangs and big crunches, bringing it more in line with a quasi-steady state, wherein the beginning of the process may merely follow the end of a previous state.

Panspermia is less contentious, in that it does not state that life is eternal, but still fails to provide any clear evidence. It also fails to provide an answer as to the universal beginning of life. This is interesting, because it plays to an audience that holds to the "specialness of life" and to opponents of spontaneous generation. By not addressing the question of how life began in the first place, it avoids the issue of origin completely. So although Panspermia is included as a set of theories relating to the origin of life on Earth, it actually fails to account for the origin of life itself. The possibility that comets could transport living material throughout the Universe, while providing adequate protection from radiation and cosmic rays, has been suggested, but no evidence exists to this day. Exogenesis is a more limited definition, not claiming that life exists throughout the Universe, but rather that life on Earth came from somewhere beyond the planet.

A final subset of beliefs is what is known as directed Panspermia, whose adherents included Francis Crick, co-discoverer of the structure of DNA. This idea suggests that an extraterrestrial life form deliberately seeded our planet with DNA.

Designed and spontaneous generation

If life didn't come from outside of the planet, then there is only one other option – that it arose on Earth independently. This does not preclude the possibility that it arose independently on other planets too. All other theories relating to the origin of life pertain to this model, and fall into two broad categories: designed generation and spontaneous generation.

Designed generation looks to an external influence acting on this planet. There are many cultures with intelligent design running through their belief systems. From the earliest written records on humankind, there have been many versions of a creation event, usually involving some deity. These range from the Jewish, Islamic and Christian traditions, to a whole array of small island beliefs. Present day interest in intelligent design has been rekindled. The number of different accounts is so varied that we will not try to discuss them, but rather summarise them as providing a 'step back' approach to the mystery of how life originated, much like Panspermia. Central to most of these beliefs is a vitalist element, a spirit, or breath, of life. While they cannot be proven, neither can they, generally, be disproven. Their continued prevalence points as much to the vacuum of our knowledge as anything, in that there are, clearly, some questions that we are not close to answering in terms of the origin of life, and indeed of our Universe.

It is ironic that one of the great debates in nineteenth century science focused on spontaneous generation. Pasteur's work, among others, led to a firm rejection of spontaneous generation. Yet science relies on some initial generation of life from non-life to explain where life came from. At the outset, however, it must be firmly stated that no life form has ever been observed to arise from non-living matter.

Adherents to spontaneous generation fall into a number of different schools of thought. The main challenge has been to explain how the building blocks of life such as amino acids and nucleic acids were formed, and how they subsequently became organized into replicating life forms capable of evolution. Alexander Oparin (1894-1980), the renowned Russian biochemist, suggested that the early Earth had a strongly reducing environment, with methane, water, ammonium and hydrogen in ready supply in a primordial soup. From this, he suggested that organic molecules would form. Stanley Millar and Harold Urey (the latter already a Nobel Prize winner for his discovery of Deuterium and heavy water) placed water, hydrogen, methane and ammonia in a flask, and subjected this mixture to constant electric current, mimicking a perpetual lightening storm. After a week of this treatment, they discovered that amino acids, including alanine and glycine, had formed. In 1961, Juan Oro, the Catalan biochemist, demonstrated the synthesis of adenine from hydrogen cyanide and ammonia. This was even more exciting, as adenine was one of the four bases in DNA and a key component of the energy currency of life, adenosine triphosphate. The remaining three bases were later synthesised in a similar manner.

These and many other experiments appeared to show that early Earth could provide an environment in which the building blocks of life could be assembled. The brave new world beckoned; with the building blocks in place, it surely wouldn't be long before we understood how these blocks were put together to produce living beings.

The next problem facing spontaneous generation is how a system, wherein DNA replication and transcription require proteins, and proteins require coding by DNA, can come to exist in the first place. However, even before attempting to address this potentially intractable problem, we are faced with another reality, that our building blocks are not as solid as may have been suggested. DNA is basically a ladder that has been twisted to form a helix, composed of phosphate, sugar and four other chemicals called bases (adenine, guanine, cytosine and thymine). The problems begin immediately. Conditions that are good for making bases such as adenine are not good for making sugars. Thus we would need to have material moved from where it could be made to a different location, in order for sugars and bases to come together. Furthermore, the short bases (pyrimidines) do not react with ribose. Pyrimidines also do not stack well. The next problem is that available phosphate is rare, yet became a key part of the backbone of DNA, RNA and ATP (adenosine triphosphate, the key energy currency of life).

Left- and right-handed problems with spontaneous generation

Another issue that impacts upon any theory espousing spontaneous generation of life on Earth relates to the fact that many molecules have left- and right-handedness. Your hands are not identical, but rather form mirror images of each other. A molecule with various bits sticking out can be like this too. It will have the same number of fingers and thumbs in all cases, but they can be in a different arrangement. These similar but spatially different molecules are called *enantiomers*, and can be either left- or right-handed. Different enantiomers can have completely different properties. The most infamous example is thalidomide. One form is an effective sedative, counteracting, among other things, morning sickness, while the other form is a teratogen, causing severe developmental alteration to the foetus. Unfortunately, the human body can convert one form to another, so even giving only the sedative form could still produce the devastating symptoms, as the teratogenic form would be produced too.

Penicillin only breaks bonds between bits of proteins called D-alanine peptides (right-handed molecules), which are found in bacteria, but not in humans (who have left handed alanines), and therefore we can use penicillin safely. As a result bacterial proteins are broken up, but not human ones. In DNA and RNA, the sugars must all be of the same enantiomer (the right-handed type) for the chain to form. The problem is not that the left-handed sugars cannot be used, thus reducing the sugar available. It is much more serious than this. If a left-handed sugar is attached, the chain cannot lengthen anymore. However there are roughly equal amounts of left- and right-handed sugars made in the first place. This has provided a huge barrier to spontaneous generation. In order to get round it, the extreme suggestion has been made that biomolecules were delivered to Earth on interstellar grains, upon which partial asymmetrical photolysis led to the segregative destruction of the wrong handed races. This would involve the production of a special type of polarized radiation, from a neutron star remnant of a supernova. Once again, when the going gets tough, the explanation heads to outer space. If in doubt, blame it on the Martians! A further problem with ribose, in addition to the evil twin, is the fact that it is not easily made, and when it is made, it is usually a minor bi-product. Additionally, the other sugar products formed with it will combine with bases to inhibit RNA replication and synthesis. Although recent work has suggested that the amino acid serine may recruit other amino acids of the same handedness, this does not explain away the inhibitory effects of other enantiomers which would still be present in the case of, for example, ribose.

RNA world: Did RNA come before DNA?

In spite of these significant problems with producing the basic building blocks, humankind has pursued the problem of assembling these blocks. Today, the key processes of genetics are summed up in the Central Dogma, first introduced by Francis Crick, the co-discoverer of the structure of DNA, in 1958. It states that DNA makes RNA and RNA makes proteins, and always in that order. The use of the word dogma has created controversy, and Crick admitted, as quoted in Horace Judson's book *The Eighth*

Day of Creation: Makers of the Revolution in Biology (1996) that "*I just didn't know what dogma meant. Dogma was just a catch phrase.*" Whether meant or unmeant, it carries with it the tone of molecular evolution at its core: that there is only one way to understand things, and the Central Dogma became the neo-Darwinian mantra. This dogma has limited the search for the original replicating unit. The elevation of this description of a small piece of biochemistry to the status of a dogma points to the neo-Darwinians' favourite child, the gene. To emphasise its importance, its place is celebrated in the most holy of masses, the ultimate celebration of reductionism, that DNA begets RNA begets protein. It was a slight inconvenience that RNA can beget DNA, for example in the HIV virus, or in retrotransposons in eukaryotes, and that prions may be able to replicate, even though they are proteins. Viruses could be ignored as they are not deemed to be living.

Ultimately, the great deity, DNA, had to be questioned in terms of its role as progenitor of all, the original naked gene. In 1963, Alexander Rich posited that original life forms may have used RNA instead of DNA. While DNA is more stable than RNA, it is limited in its function. RNA on the other hand, not only can replicate and code for proteins, but can also act as an enzyme. In RNA world, it is envisaged that RNA carried out the roles of DNA and proteins initially, acting as an independent life form. Then, DNA evolved, initially copied from the RNA, and took over the role of carrying the information between generations. Proteins evolved, also coded by RNA, and took over the role as enzymes. The RNA world has attractions because it explains how proteins and DNA could emerge. RNA became the middle man between the DNA and proteins, but may have originally been the one and only lead violinist.

As we have seen, however, multiple problems surround the basic components of RNA, let alone their assembly. RNA contains uracil instead of thymine, but this is a design flaw since cytosine can be converted to uracil relatively easily, thus changing the coded message. RNA is also inherently less stable than DNA. Both of these issues create problems for RNA as the first replicative molecule, especially one relying on sequence for ribozyme function. Also, conditions on early Earth would have been more likely, rather than less likely, to select for DNA over RNA, given the greater instability of the environment at that time.

In what became known as RNA world, it was thought that RNA would act as a catalyst and be able to self-replicate. Ribonucleotides (phosphate-sugar-base building blocks) were easier to make than deoxyribonucleotides, and RNA could form ribozymes, a type of enzyme. Thus RNA had the potential to self-catalyse its replication. Of DNA, RNA and proteins, RNA seemed the most likely early vehicle.

So where does this leave spontaneous generation? RNA world as a hypothesis at least did get one thing right, that DNA was probably not the key to the origin of life, nor was it likely to be the original replicating system. However, we may need to go beyond its junior (or maybe more senior) sidekick, RNA, to find a meaningful answer. Günter Wächtershäuser, a German chemist whose career intriguingly went in the opposite direction of Albert Einstein, by moving into patent law *from* science, suggested that sulphides could provide the energy needed for metabolism, and that metabolism pre-dated genetics. His ideas were taken further by the discovery of black smokers (submarine hydrothermal vents). It is envisaged that small hollows in the vents may have acted as primitive cells, with metal sulphide walls. This move away from any part of the central dogma is of interest. By stepping away from the central dogma, and looking at the problem of the assembly of replicating systems, perhaps more progress can be made. At this point our story takes an interesting side step.

An inorganic beginning?

One of the more intriguing suggestions as to the origin of life on Earth was that of Alexander Graham Cairns-Smith, an organic (ironically) chemist from Glasgow, which he set out in his famous book, *Seven Clues to the Origin of Life: a Scientific Detective Story,* but first developed in a paper in 1966. He suggested that the original replicating machines were inorganic. Laced with quotes from Sherlock Holmes, the legendary fictional detective created by Arthur Conan Doyle, Cairns-Smith presents his seven clues. Firstly, he relates that because genetic material is the base of evolution, then there must have been naked genes in the beginning. Secondly, DNA and RNA are what he terms "suburban molecules", far removed from central pathways and, as we have already seen, hard to make at the outset, due both to problems of building blocks and assembly. Therefore, he concludes, these molecules were latecomers to the replication party. He then, thirdly, concludes that there must have been some scaffolding, some missing framework that predated DNA and RNA. His fourth point is that transformation is possible between one type of genetic material and another through time, in what is termed genetic takeover. Next he states that primitive machinery is usually different in design compared to later versions. His sixth point is that crystal growth processes may possess the qualities needed for the replication of complex information. Cairns-Smith's crystal gene is identified in his seventh clue, as clay crystals.

A series of negatively and positively charged layers, where substitutions can alter the charge, forming a framework, combined with inherent defects in crystals, led to variation, and a basis for selection. The crystal gene can replicate and adapt over generations. Thus Cairns-Smith visualizes an inorganic replicator that provided the framework for organic molecules to form around. It breaks the hold of organic chemistry, the last vestige of Vitalism, and instead turns to inorganic chemistry. His ideas seem so foreign because we have become hotwired into thinking in organic, DNA terms, but if we accept that things may not always have been this way, then he presents an interesting, if untested, set of ideas. Given the significant problems related to an organic beginning of life, his theory is at least as valid as any other on the table. The concept goes one step beyond RNA world, but uses the same principle, that existent structures originated from earlier blueprints. The emphasis on DNA as the key to life on Earth has led to his theory being ignored by many, but it is as attractive a proposition as anything currently available. As we have seen already, there are significant problems with a DNA or RNA origin of life.

Of course, if the clay crystal gene was the original replicating "life" form, then the whole organic world is merely a shadow of a clay origin, and the world as we know it is merely the outcome of geology. Now that is quite radical! In addition to this silicate origin, it can be argued, somewhat tongue in cheek, that we are moving to a new silicate reality in the form of a silicon chip-driven world, where artificial life forms may eventually dominate the planet. Maybe this is the natural end point of our clay beginnings!

Cairns Smith raises some important issues. Firstly, why should we limit ourselves to an organic origin of life? Our distaste for these ideas may relate to a harbouring of Vitalism. Secondly, why should we limit ourselves to a DNA/RNA model? Again this may stem from the gene being seen as the explanation for how and why life on Earth is organized in the way that it is. We shall come back to this in the next section.

Life as a shadow on the cave wall

So we return to our search for the origin of life. If life doesn't have to involve organic chemistry, then our search can be broader. Do we accept that life can be inorganic? We are faced with a separate challenge anyhow, whatever we think about this. When does a bunch of molecules become alive, whether they are organic or inorganic? Perhaps another question will help. Is an atom in a living organism different than one in an inanimate object?

What is clear is that there is no easy answer to the origin of life. There are difficulties with all the present theories and we end up having to choose from an identity parade, where the individual subjects really all look highly unlikely. Maybe, then, we are trying to define something that isn't really there, a shadow on the cave wall. Perhaps it is life itself that is the problem.

Vitalism, in the end, is something we like to hold on to, and even our non-vitalist science of today searches for a way to explain where life came from, turning to non-cellular spontaneous generation as an unavoidable foundation. Biochemistry has replaced organic chemistry as the vitalist principle. Yet we cannot think of the moment when life came to be. With a need for a beginning, but no beginning possible, life can only be seen as an invalid concept. The question is not so much what is life? It is, rather, why do we need to define life? The answer to this most likely rests more with our need to define ourselves, and, begrudgingly, some other things, as living organisms. We draw the line at allowing obviously simple biomolecular machines such as viruses to get on board the bus. Deep within us may rest a fear of reducing all of this multi-dimensional, walking, talking, singing and dancing show of life to mere chemistry and physics. We may be made of the stuff of rocks and dirt, but we are more than this, surely? We couch our new understanding in terms like *generation-to-generation*, *genetic lineage* and *survival of the fittest*, and these terms bring comfort and allow us to feel part of a vital heritage. The genetic code is the language of life, and if life has a language, then that is all the better. Our attempts to communicate science meld with our desire to be alive. The Central Dogma, natural selection, those finches, wrinkled pea seeds and the selfish gene all provide reassurance, and these dancing shadows, so compelling, must surely represent the real answers to our questions. On a mild sunny day in April 1999, I remember standing beneath the bell tower in Cold Spring Harbor, former centre of the Eugenics movement in America in the early twentieth century, and looking up to see the four letters representing the four bases of DNA, one on each side of the bell tower. The religious symbolism felt more than just tongue in cheek, lying at the heart of one of the world's leading genetic research centres, whose chancellor, until recently, was none other than James Watson, co-discoverer of the structure of DNA.

Given all of this, isn't it easier to think that the most likely explanation of the origin of life is that it never originated in the first place? It is merely a term that is historical baggage. Instead, this book suggests that life is part of the continuum of matter responding to forces that determine all structure. The need to define life as special, and to imbue it with special meaning remains in science, as it has done for the human race through time. DNA is often cited as the code of life. Organic chemistry is still a commonly used term. Yet if we can't explain how life emerged, how to characterize it and how it differs from any other game of chemistry, then we are really dealing with a shadow. The flickering dance on the wall is not a product of a living, vital force but, rather, is a result of energy flowing through matter and producing something that can be misleading. By this, I mean that if we focus on the dancing shadows, then we may fail to understand the dance. If life itself is a shadow, then we can have a fresh look at how the living planet is organized, freed from a constraint that has limited our interpretation. The basis of evolution does not have to be limited by life forms, but rather can be seen as part of a much greater story. At this point we need to introduce the idea of the Biosphere as a more manageable way to discuss life on Earth. As we shall see in the next chapter, this allows us to break free from individual life forms, and instead provides a greater context within which to examine evolution. What exactly is the Biosphere, and how is it structured?

Chapter Eight

The Biosphere and Its Hierarchy

The birth of the Biosphere

The birth of the term *Biosphere* occurred in 1875, in a book by Eduard Suess (1831-1914). Suess was a geologist, born in London, who made a huge contribution to many fields. While studying fossils of the ancient gymnosperm, *Glossopteris* (usually, wrongly, referred to as a fern), he recognized that samples found in India, Africa and South America, were very similar. This led him to suggest that these land masses were formerly all joined together. This idea came well before the concept of continental drift and plate tectonics, and marked an important point in the development of geology. He was also an expert in the European Alps, and suggested that they were once underwater, again, a revolutionary idea. Compared to these huge achievements, truly visionary at their time, his introduction of the term *Biosphere* was almost a throw-away comment!

Seuss recognized that the land, the water and the air were all key compartments of the planet (the lithosphere, hydrosphere and atmosphere, respectively). However he felt that another compartment was needed, where life existed. In his classic book *The Origin of the Alps*, in 1875, he wrote "*The plant, whose deep roots plunge into the soil to feed, and which, at the same time, rises into the air to breathe, is a good illustration of organic life in the region of interaction between the upper sphere and the lithosphere, and on the surface of continents it is possible to single out an independent biosphere*".

Biofera: the greatest book of the twentieth century?

Since its inauguration, the Biosphere has undergone changes in its meaning. The first of these came from an interesting character, Vladimir Vernadsky (1863-1945), the Russian geologist. His life took many dramatic twists. His first PhD supervisor, the famous Italian geologist, Arcangelo Scacchi (1810-1893), had become senile by the time Vernadsky started working with him, and so the young student had to start a new research project. Back in Russia, the Revolution forced him to flee, and he was lucky to survive this period. His great work *Biofera*, was published in 1926, though the first full English translation didn't appear for another 70 years. It is a truly visionary book, and, in my personal opinion, one of the greatest of the twentieth century, marking the beginnings of the fields of geochemistry and biogeochemistry, areas of study that are, even now, only coming to the forefront of modern thinking.

Vernadsky viewed the Biosphere within the context of the cosmos. He saw it as a "thick layer of new molecular systems", and felt that it owed its existence as much to the Sun as the Earth, a view strangely in resonance with Plato. In this way he changed the emphasis, from Seuss's compartment where life exists, to the living matter itself. He was the first to recognize that oxygen, carbon dioxide and nitrogen were all products of the Biosphere, and emphasised the role of the Biosphere in shaping the planet. He went further, and set out three spheres: the Geosphere, the Biosphere and the Noosphere. The Noosphere was the sphere of human thought, which interacted with the Biosphere, while the Biosphere interacted with the Geosphere. These ideas were developed by the famous French Jesuit priest and philosopher, Pierre Teilhard de Chardin (1881-1955), in his book, *The Phenomenon of Man,* published in 1955. He put forward the idea that evolution is a process leading to reflection, and eventually reaches an end point, the *omega point*, which represents a form of universal conscience. The recent dominance of the internet has been recognized as some form of planet-wide conscience, and Teilhard de Chardin has been given the accolade of patron saint of the internet!

So the Biosphere has come a long way in a short period of time. Gaian thinking has recognized it as a single organism, very much along the lines of Vernadsky, which operates by interacting with the chemical world, in some form of harmony, reacting to perturbations and maintaining some kind of feedback-based constancy. To modern geochemists, the Biosphere is the sum of all living things.

Popularizing the Biosphere

The term became more popular in the 1950s, as ecologists such as Evelyn Hutchinson and Eugene Odum began to use it more and more. It started to enter popular thinking. In 1968, the United Nations Educational, Scientific and Cultural Organization (UNESCO for short) held an inter-governmental meeting entitled *Use and Conservation of the Biosphere*. This led to the establishment of the *Man and the Biosphere* programme, and the establishment of 531 Biosphere Reserves across the globe. In 1970, a landmark publication by Scientific American, *The Biosphere*, brought together a series of papers written by leading scientists of the time, highlighting the importance of the Biosphere to human activities.

The Biosphere in modern science

The Biosphere is now recognized as being constructed of a series of levels of organization. The individual species occur as populations. Populations of different species are gathered together in communities, and these communities interact with their environment. The communities and their environments together form ecosystems. Similar ecosystems around the world are called biomes. Finally, all the biomes together form the Biosphere.

Thus, the term Biosphere refers to all organic life forms on the planet, and to this pyramid of organization. The organisms are distributed between the lithosphere, the hydrosphere and the atmosphere. Many organisms will use all three of these compartments during their lives. For example puffins nest on land, feed at sea and fly in the air. Plant seeds will often disperse in air or water, but the adult plant will grow on land. Many pathogenic bacteria spread through the air but attack land-based organisms. Amphibians often return to the water to lay their eggs, while many sea turtles come on land to lay their eggs. Through evolutionary time, the use of each compartment can also change. For example, whales came from land-based animals, but these terrestrial forefathers themselves trace their origins back to the sea. Land plants have evolved from aquatic ancestors too. In fact all terrestrial life forms originally came from the water. While all of this is agreed, the *importance* of each of these levels of organization, and the significance of these levels in understanding the evolution and function of the

Biosphere as a whole, are topics of extreme disagreement among biologists. So what are these different approaches, and how do they impact on our understanding?

The different approaches to the Biosphere

There are two very different approaches to the Biosphere, so different that they lead to completely different understandings of our planet, and which are mutually exclusive. In fact, the Biosphere acts as a defining point in terms of this great debate. These two world-views, that divide scientists, are the Neo-Darwinian and the Gaian schools of thought. In looking at how these two scientific philosophies approach the subject of the Biosphere, we can learn much about them.

The Neo-Darwinian School and the Biosphere

Firstly, we can view the Biosphere as being all about Darwinian and neo-Darwinian evolution. Everything is related to everything else, and so we classify it in terms of similarities. Very similar organisms are called *sub-species*. Similar subspecies are grouped together as *species*. Similar species are called *genera*. Similar genera form *families*. Families form *orders*, orders form *classes*, classes form *phyla* and phyla form *kingdoms*. Take us, for example. We are subspecies *sapiens*, species *sapiens*, genus *Homo*, Family Hominidae, Order Primate, Class Mammalia, Phylum Chordata, Kingdom Animalia. Phew! Darwinism is consumed with labels and relatedness. The species is the unit of the Biosphere and the living planet is understood in terms of taxonomy. Evolution is measured in terms of speciation. The genes are trapped within species, and the Biosphere is merely the product of the gene, a natural outcome that can be reduced to a genetic world. The organism is seen as a product of selfish genes, intent on survival and judged by reproductive success. As a result, Neo-Darwinism uses only one of the levels of organization to understand the Biosphere. All the levels of taxonomy relate, in the end, to the species, and the species, represented by populations, is only a small part of the overall Biosphere, a single level. All other levels are ignored.

Gaian Thinking and the Biosphere

Gaian thinking, as we have noted already, looks at the whole show as one super-organism that is self-controlled and regulated, just like any other organism. This organism is called the Biosphere. It is the opposite approach from the labelling of Darwinian thinking, which reduces the Biosphere down to the genetic level. Here, the living planet interacts with itself as a single unit. The individual species are part of a bigger whole. It is a top down approach, rather than the neo-Darwinian bottom up approach. The whole Biosphere produces feedback that impacts on individual species, and it is the interaction between this Biosphere and the chemistry of the atmosphere, hydrosphere and lithosphere that leads to a strong feedback, producing a stable environment. Perturbation of this environment will lead to the Biosphere responding to re-adjust itself. This re-adjustment alters its effect on the chemistry of the planet. In this way, this great super-organism will act to restore the balance. The Gaian view of the Biosphere is the opposite of Neo-Darwinian thinking. Organisms are merely products of the Biosphere. However it is the same as Neo-Darwinism in that it takes only one level of organization and attempts to understand everything from this.

Advocates of both camps strongly believe in their approach, and whole scientific fields have developed around each school of thought. Darwinian and neo-Darwinian thinking is embraced by population biologists, geneticists and molecular ecologists, while the Gaian approach is central to geophysicists, biogeochemists, atmospheric physicists and many ecologists.

A new way to view the Biosphere

Gaia provides an explanation for the function of the Biosphere, but not how it evolved. Neo-Darwinism provides an explanation of evolution, but not how the Biosphere functions. Neither approach provides an explanation as to why life has developed in the way that it has. This book sets out a completely new theory that answers all of the questions relating evolution, function and structure, both mechanistically and in terms of the direction that has been taken. It is a third way, different from both of the other two interpretations, and this is no more clearly visible than in how it interprets the Biosphere. Not top down, nor bottom up, instead we look into the heart of the Biosphere, and recognize an intricate and beautiful thing, made up of different levels of organization. Rather than becoming consumed with the species, we focus on how the Biosphere is organized. We can't hope to understand how it came to be unless we actually understand how it is put together. So we see the Biosphere as being divided into biomes, the biomes being composed of ecosystems, the ecosystems being made of communities, the communities formed from populations, and the populations being composed of individuals. Hardly radical, you might say. But what is radical is that we don't recognize any one of these levels of organization as being more important than any other, and we view each of them as being a response to exactly the same organizing agent. By doing this, we can then try to discover what the organizing agent is for the Biosphere. That *is* a radical thought. We can try to determine the answer to why it all exists in the way that it does, and where we fit into this picture.

Each level is organized in its own way, and has a personality of its own. The Biosphere is not a super-organism, nor is it the product of selfish genes, but rather it is made up of a number of levels, that have their own rules and regulations. Each level, from gene to Biome, is organized differently. The different levels are organized by one single agent that speaks in a different way to each level. The answer to the questions of how the Biosphere came about lies not in any one level, neither in the whole, but, rather, it lies within each level. By approaching the Biosphere in this way, we will discover that we can understand both how it evolved and how it functions. No other theory has done this. If we are to understand what drives the Biosphere and has led to its production, we need to listen to all of the conversations that this driver has. By ignoring most of the levels of organization, both Neo-Darwinism and Gaia have failed to provide a meaningful explanation of this complex structure.

Shadows on the Cave Wall

By taking all of our knowledge on the living world together, and recognizing the significance of all parts of the Biosphere, we will come to a completely new explanation of our world, one that not only provides the mechanism of change and structure, but also one that provides important insights into how we can respond to some of the great challenges facing us in the twenty-first century.

Before we set out this new approach, we need to deal with the old one: neo-Darwinism. How did we end up with a taxonomy-based, gene-centric understanding of the Biosphere, and what are the problems with it? Why do we need a new theory to explain how our living world evolved, functions and is structured? In Sections III and IV, we will explore these questions.

Section III

What is the unit of Diversity?

There are millions of species on the planet, and if we are to understand how the Biosphere has evolved and what controls its diversity and function, we first need to understand how it is structured. This brings us to an important issue that lies at the heart of this section. How we define diversity greatly impacts upon how we understand it. If we focus on any one level of Biosphere organization as the single most important one, this can have significant repercussions in terms of what theories we come up with to explain the evolution and function of the living world. In this section we examine the ways in which man has attempted to describe the living planet, and discover some significant problems with these concepts. We take a look at this through an historical approach initially, moving from hunter-gatherer to Linnaeus. We then look at the importance of the work of Gregor Mendel in how Darwinian evolution actually works. We examine the marriage between evolutionary theory and diversity, otherwise known as the tree of life. The tree of life is central to Darwinian thinking, depicting the Biosphere as having evolved from a common ancestor in the dim and distant past, with genes being passed down the generations within species, like a baton in a relay race. We encounter a different type of race, where baton-swapping between lanes is *de rigeur*. This undermines the tree of life as a valid analogy. Next we look at what a species represents. We discover that species are actually very difficult to define. The other groupings that we use to describe life on our planet are equally problematic, such as individuals, populations and communities. We meet a brown recluse spider, a jellyfish named after Frank Zappa and some nightclub bouncers who only let you in if you are wearing green shoes. We conclude that many of the key definitions of diversity, on which classical evolutionary theory relies, do not provide the firm foundations that we may have taken for granted.

Chapter Nine

What is a Species?

What's in a name?

Our planet is teaming with a myriad of organisms. Estimates of the number of species vary between two and one hundred million. This incredible diversity poses many challenges, some of which we will tackle in this chapter. How is this biodiversity organized? How did we get to this situation? Why are these organisms designed in the way that they are? These questions lie at the heart of understanding our world and ourselves.

For as long as humankind has existed as a species, we have had a very strong drive to describe and communicate how the Biosphere is organized. This drive is called survival. As early as 32,000 years ago, paintings in the Chauvet Cave system in France show images of rhino, hyenas, owls, bears and panthers. Humans were already describing the diversity around them. Ancient Egypt had advanced records of the uses of plants in medicine, cooking, mummification and perfume. While words like taxonomy, classification, cladistics and phylogeny may not carry with them any sense of urgency or vital importance, early man needed to work out what plants and fungi could be eaten safely, and which ones were toxic. Medicinal use of plants is noted early in human records, and by the time of Ancient Egypt, this was highly advanced. Indeed, up to the fifteenth century, all herbal books were copies of Egyptian, Greek and Middle Eastern writings from up to two thousand years earlier. It was this early interest in plant identification that led to the modern taxonomic system. By the end of the sixteenth century, all medical practitioners were fundamentally botanists. Much of their training involved identifying and using plants.

By this stage, plants and animals had been given polynomial names, that is, their Latin names were composed of a series of words and phrases. For example, the humble catnip was celebrated with the resplendent title "*Nepeta floribus interrupte spicatus pendunculatis*" (namely, *Nepeta* with flowers in an interrupted pedunculated spike).

Carolus Linnaeus, having trained as a doctor, specialising in the treatment of syphilis, decided to simplify the system, by using two names, a binomial, the first being the genus, and the second being the species. Actually, the binomial system had first been used much earlier, but was not popularized until Linnaeus. One interesting aside was the basis that Linnaeus built his taxonomy upon, the sexual system. He used the number of stamens (the male reproductive parts) and pistils (the female reproductive parts). This was viewed as profane and offensive by many at the time, especially because of the way he phrased his findings, such as "nine men in the same bride's chamber, with one woman"! The German Botanist, Johann Siegesbeck, referred to Linnaeus' work as "*lothesome harlotry*". Linnaeus, believing that revenge is a dish best served cold, retorted with taxonomic vengeance, by naming a small, insignificant weed, *Siegesbeckia*!

As Darwinian theory developed in the nineteenth century, a new approach was taken in an attempt to reflect the relationships of different organisms to each other. Now it was not just a matter of grouping organisms together that looked like each other, but rather, grouping them together in a sort of family tree. The marriage of taxonomy and phylogeny (the evolutionary relatedness of organisms to each other), where the origins and names of species became linked, was driven by Charles Darwin's image of the tree of life, which traced all life from a starting point through to the many branches of existent life, each branch originating from an earlier point, and the branches elongating by the process of natural selection. New branches were formed by speciation. Fossil species could be fitted into parts of the tree, who's highest, most central branch was always the wise one, the greatest and ultimate end point, *Homo sapiens sapiens*. This made evolutionary theory a lot more palatable, much like mapping the world with Europe on the top, the right way up. Although we may not be God's special creation, we were, at least, the most advanced organisms on the planet. It also gave a sense of destiny to evolution. Natural selection led to survival of only the fittest, and through time, the branching tree of life was growing upwards and was heading for the Sun. The human was the final celebration of all that was good. Poor design had been left behind, withered branchlets long forgotten, while the continuing arborescent structure improved with time, becoming fitter and fitter, until it ended with us. Here we are at the top of the tree, the product of lessons learnt and struggles won, the natural outcome of natural selection.

When Darwin put forward his theory of evolution, he did not know how the process of natural selection actually worked in terms of a mechanism. It was the work of Gregor Mendel that provided this explanation.

The work of a monk from Brno

Johann Mendel was born into a poor farming community in Austria in 1822. On finishing high school, his father was seriously injured by a falling tree, and only the financial help of his sister, who loaned him her dowry (money that was given to a husband upon marriage, and therefore extremely important to the prospects of any unmarried woman at the time), allowed him to continue his studies. This money eventually ran done, and so, in 1843, he entered an Augustinian friary to continue studying without further cost. At this time he changed his Christian name to Gregor. The image of a meddling monk messing about with a few pea plants, and stumbling on a great scientific truth has come into common folklore, but couldn't be further from the truth. St Thomas' Friary was no ordinary friary. It was a centre of research, with renowned philosophers, mineralogists, mathematicians and botanists, and had a huge library, herbarium and experimental gardens.

Mendel initially set out to prove Jean Baptiste Lamarck's theory of inheritance of acquired characteristics. This theory stood in juxtaposition to Darwinism. It suggested that organisms could develop responses to their environment, which would then be passed on to the next generation. Darwinism, on the other hand, suggests that variation is created by sexual reproduction, and the new characteristics are randomly generated and tested in the next generation. Mendel found no impact of environment, but rather concluded that offspring inherited their characteristics from their parents. He then started to work on breeding experiments with mice, but was dissuaded from this by the local bishop, who found the whole idea offensive. So Mendel turned to the more acceptable approach of working on pea plants. Over seven years (1856-1863) he grew 28,000 plants and, in 1865, presented his breakthrough findings to the Brunn (now Brno) Natural Science Society. His *Treatises on Plant Hybrids* was published a year later. He had identified the mechanism by which evolution appeared to work, and is now recognized as the father of genetics.

He died in 1884, unrecognized for the revolutionary work that he had completed. Another common misconception is that the reason for his theories being undiscovered for a further 35 years was because no-one knew what this obscure monk in Moravia had done. This, again, was untrue. He sent copies of his paper to 44 of the most famous plant biologists in Europe at the time, but they all failed to recognize its significance. In 1900, three scientists working independently, Carl Corens in Germany, Hugo de Vries in Holland and Erich von Tschermak-Seysenegg in Austria, were attempting to publish their work, when they were forced to recognize that it had been done before.

The work of Gregor Mendel in the beautiful Czech city of Brno, led to a mechanistic explanation for Darwinian evolution (i.e. that transmissible, particulate matter from parents carried the genetic information that produced the characteristics in offspring), and, in the twentieth century, the neo-Darwinian approach reached its apogee with population genetics, the gene and, finally, the selfish gene. Mendel's transmissible characteristics came to domination and would replace Darwin's contribution in all but name.

From two kingdoms to three domains: the ever changing world of taxonomy

At the heart of Darwinian theory sits the idea of a tree of life, where, over time, species evolved and diversity increased. Darwin believed that all species originated from one beginning, and that we can trace all species back through time to this common origin. Gradually, changes accumulated, from generation to generation, and these changes led to new species being produced. Recently, the idea of a rooted tree of life has come under close scrutiny. To understand this, we need a brief history of the ways that we have divided up the living world into groups.

As early as 350BC, Aristotle had developed the first system of classification of life. He divided organisms into two kingdoms, Plantae and Animalia. This remained unchanged for over 2000 years. Then, in 1866, Ernst Hackel, the German evolutionary biologist, added a third Kingdom, the Protista, defining it as organisms with little or no tissue differentiation. In 1938, Herbert Copeland (1902-1968), an American biologist, came up with a new set of 4 kingdoms, the Monera (commonly known as the Bacteria), the Protista, the Metaphyta (plants) and the Metazoa (animals).

By 1969, Robert Whittaker (1920-1980), an American ecologist, had expanded this to 5 kingdoms, Monera, Protista, Fungi, Plantae and Animalia. Hamilton Traub (1890-1983), at the ripe old age of 85 years, put forward a new approach, grouping all living organisms in two super-kingdoms, the Prokaryota (organisms with no nucleus) and the Eukaryota (organisms whose cells have nuclei). In 1977, Karl Woese was working on bacteria, and realized that there were significant differences within this group of organisms. The cell walls and membranes were different in their structure, and the DNA was also arranged in very different ways. What emerged was that the Bacteria were not a unified group, but, rather, some of them, which he called the Archaea, were sufficiently different from the Bacteria to merit a separate stage on which to dance. Thus, he introduced a six kingdom system, Eubacteria, Archaea, Protista, Plantae, Fungi and Animalia.

These Archaea are an interesting group of creatures. Some use hydrogen gas to make methane. These creatures live in swamps and are also found in the guts of mammals, producing 2 billion tons of methane gas each year (a significant contribution to the greenhouse gas budget). Other Archaea, called extremophiles, live in some of the harshest environments on Earth, tolerating temperatures of 80°C, glacial ice and extremes of acidity. Given the characteristics and habitats of this group of organisms, it is thought that they may be the most ancient forms of life, and may be the kind of creature to be found on other planets.

Further analysis by Woese led him to put together the most recent, and radical system for classifying the living world. The Archaea were very different than any other organism, and thus were raised to a status above that of Kingdom. He realized that the molecular diversity of living creatures really only called for three groupings, the Bacteria, the Archaea and the eukaryotes. Indeed, the Archaea are now recognized as being more closely related to the Eukaryota than to the Bacteria.

A prokaryotic world

The new system meant that two thirds of the Biosphere was dominated by prokaryotes. While most evolutionary theory relates to eukaryotes, the prokaryotes actually form the main part of life on Earth, in terms of biogeochemical cycles, genetic, metabolic and ecosystem niche diversity. Biogeochemical cycles are crucial in determining how our planet works. Material moves through the planet and this movement determines availability of raw materials to living organisms. Microbes facilitate this movement. Take nitrogen for example. Some bacteria produce nitrogen gas (called di-nitrogen, because it is made of two nitrogen atoms tightly joined together) from more complicated nitrogen-containing compounds. This gas is released into the atmosphere. Without microbes, there would be no nitrogen in the atmosphere. Today, the air around us is composed of around 78% of nitrogen. The nitrogen in the air dilutes the oxygen, preventing it from reaching levels where it could spontaneously combust. Thus, our microbial friends are also providing a chemical fire blanket!

At the same time there are microbes that absorb nitrogen from the atmosphere. These convert it into a form that plants can absorb, and are called nitrogen-fixing bacteria (since they "fix" nitrogen into a useable form). A third group of bacteria act to decompose dead organisms. It's the main reason why we are not up to our elbows in dead bits! When a living organism dies, its nitrogen is tied up in complicated compounds. These can't be recycled, and so bacteria break these complicated compounds down, and release the nitrogen for other life forms to grab. Without the microbes, nutrients like nitrogen would become unavailable, and so life would grind to a halt.

But bacteria don't just control the availability of nitrogen. Carbon also becomes trapped in dead organisms. If bacteria did not release it as carbon dioxide, then plants would have no carbon with which to make sugar. All the carbon dioxide would be gone in a few thousand years if the microbes went on strike. Although we are all concerned about carbon dioxide increasing in the atmosphere, possibly leading to a greenhouse effect, if carbon dioxide was not in the atmosphere, we would suffer from global cooling. This could be more disastrous, as we need the greenhouse effect to keep the planet warm enough for life. So bacteria are crucial, both in maintaining the cycling of carbon on the planet, and in maintaining the right temperature for life. It was the Bacteria who created the oxygen atmosphere that allowed ozone to form, and thus permitted life to move to the surface of the ocean and on to land. It was the bacteria that raised oxygen levels high enough to allow multicellularity. Oxygen, mostly produced by Cyanobacteria in the oceans, would disappear in a few million years if the microbial world didn't release it.

Bacteria are now thought to be the key factors in precipitation in clouds, acting as nucleating centres around which water molecules cluster. Interestingly, in 2008, Brent Christner, a scientist at Louisiana State University in the USA, discovered that the most important bacteria in creating precipitation are plant pathogens. This must sound out a warning. As we increasingly use more powerful methods to kill plant pathogens, in response to the need to feed an ever increasing population of humans, we could be seriously damaging a key step in rainfall production, particularly in warm regions of the world, where these bacteria are particularly important in producing rainfall. So we may have the healthiest plants around, but they will die of drought! It is thought that the bacteria hitch a ride on the cloud to get to new plants. Christner even isolated these bacteria from Antarctic snow, many thousands of miles from a plant host source, showing that long distance transport is possible.

At a more local level, bacteria allow many plant-eating animals (herbivores) to access energy, by living in their guts and breaking down extremely complicated plant compounds. These compounds are like Rubik's cubes, in that they are very hard to break down, and the animal cannot digest them on its own. The bacteria contribute around 50% of the total energy obtained by a herbivore from its food. This is essential in many food chains, as it improves the movement of energy through the Biosphere.

So bacteria are crucial to the continued function of the Biosphere. This is a very hard thing to accept, given that we usually can't see them with the naked eye, and that we can't appreciate their roles easily, as they act at the molecular level.

At the heart of every eukaryote lies a prokaryote

Yet not only do prokaryotes dominate the functioning of our ecosystem, but they are at the heart of every eukaryote. The prokaryotic organisms, the Bacteria and Archaea, existed long before the eukaryotes did. Today, the eukaryotes have a number of key characteristics that were stolen from the prokaryotic organisms many millions of years ago. The prokaryotes invented them in the first place. For example, mitochondria and chloroplasts used to be free living prokaryotes, but infected (rather than were swallowed by!) an early eukaryote. Since then they have been passed down from generation to generation. Cilia are tail-like projections, which humans have in their windpipes, where they beat to move mucus and foreign debris out of the lung. Female mammals have cilia in the fallopian tubes, where they sweep the egg from the ovary to the uterus. These structures also originated in the prokaryotes.

Eukaryotes as a sideshow: two fundamental questions

The eukaryote can be viewed as a special case, an experiment that, in a way, is just an interesting side show, whereas the main action in the Biosphere occurs in the prokaryotic world of the Archaea and Bacteria. All of the core metabolic processes that eukaryotes use were invented by the prokaryotes long before eukaryotes ever existed.

The eukaryotes represent bags in which these things are collected. Yet evolutionary theory has been based, largely, on the eukaryotes. When *The Origin of Species* was published, there were still only two Kingdoms recognized, Plantae and Animalia. Two key questions must be asked at this stage. These questions are important as they highlight significant problems with the Darwinian approach to evolution

Firstly, if the eukaryotes did not exist, how different would the planet be? It is clear that it is the Archaea and Bacteria that provide the life support system within which the eukaryotes live, and so the eukaryotes are dependent, for their function and their structure, on these microbes. From mitochondria to nutrient cycles, the microbial world controls things. Because prokaryotes are usually invisible to the naked eye since they are so small, they were overlooked by Charles Darwin. At the time of his writing, little was known about them. However today, we recognize that they are central to all the processes of the Biosphere. It is unlikely that the planet would be that much different without the eukaryotes.

The second question is more challenging, but essential to face up to. If eukaryotes did not exist, then how different would our understanding of evolution be? Two-thirds of the Biosphere is microbial, and for the first two-thirds of the history of life on Earth, they were the only representatives of the Biosphere. Thus all the key evolutionary developments occurred within them, not in the Eukaryotic late-comers. Since early life on Earth was microbial, then we need to check that microbes behave in the same way as eukaryotes, in terms of their evolution, reproduction and function. If they are different, then the whole foundation of evolutionary theory will be based on a minority of organisms that are not representative of those that existed at the most crucial period of evolutionary history. That would be a very serious problem for any such a theory, existing in the bliss and ignorance of Eukaryotic isolation.

The big news is that prokaryotes *don't* behave like eukaryotes. Significantly, some of the fundamental processes involved in evolution, such as the passage of genetic material from generation to generation, are not as universal as we might think. It's like trying to understand Shakespeare by studying the stage set and lighting of a modern production. The stage props represent a consequence of the play, but studying them gives us no clue as to how the play was written. Many hundreds of years have passed between the production in your local theatre and the writing of the work. So it is with the eukaryotes. They dominate our thinking in terms of evolution, but yet they weren't there when the big events were happening. Unless they behave in the same way as the Prokaryotic innovators of that time, they will lead us astray in terms of our understanding of evolution. So how different are the prokaryotes from their eukaryotic offspring? To consider this, let's go to the races.

The baton- juggling relay race: problems with the tree of life

There are two races in town. In the first, six teams line up in a relay race. Each team member runs around the track, and hands the baton to the next runner of his team. Provided that they don't drop the baton, the last member of each team will cross the line at the end. This is what we know as vertical gene transfer, where the genetic legacy can be traced from one generation to another through time. It forms the basis of what is known as the tree of life, Darwin's hidden bond, where present-day organisms are the surviving representatives of a lineage that eventually goes back to the most recent common ancestor.

But hang on; there is another race across the road going on. Here, six teams line up as before, and it looks like a regular relay race is about to start. However, as the runners are sprinting around the first bend, they do something completely unexpected. They make several copies of their batons, and pass them across the lanes to runners from other teams. Soon, several of the runners are clutching a whole armful of different batons, and one of them is actually juggling them in the air as they run! At the finish line, the last team member of each team crosses the line, and not only raises the team baton aloft, but holds several other ones in the air too. In fact, it's difficult to know which baton each team started with, as several teams have the same batons.

Horizontal gene transfer: the net of life

This race is called horizontal gene transfer (HGT), and ends up with a net of life, not a tree of life. This is indeed an odd race, but recently, we have come to realize that it better describes what is going on. Present-day organisms have a whole range of genes from a whole range of sources, some vertically passed on, but others more recently acquired from different species. So what is horizontal gene transfer? Also known as lateral gene transfer, it is the movement of genetic material between different species. First recognized in 1959, by a team of scientists from Japan led by Tomoichiro Akiba and Kunitaro Ochia, western scientists took much longer to recognize its importance. It allows genes and sometimes whole groups of genes to be copied into a completely unrelated set of organisms. The actual transfer can be carried out by a host of vectors, from viruses to mites.

This movement of genetic material is seen most clearly in the field of antibiotic resistance, where bacterial species can gain resistance to specific antibiotics from other bacterial species or strains, allowing a faster response than would be possible due to random mutation. Often, these resistance genes come from a special group of bacteria, called Actinomycetes, which actually make antibiotics. The only problem with making something that can kill bacteria arises if you are a bacterium yourself! To avoid committing accidental suicide with your new lethal weapon, it is a good idea to have some sort of bullet-proof vest. Thus, many of the antibiotic resistance genes come originally from the species that made the antibiotic in the first place. These secret solutions are then obtained by other bacteria via horizontal gene transfer.

Larger chunks of DNA, containing enough genetic material to make entire biosynthetic pathways, can also be moved, allowing instant access to complicated metabolic machinery such as how to make vitamin B12 in *Salmonella*. Smaller amounts of DNA, less than the size of a gene, can be transferred, giving the resultant protein a slightly altered shape. These modifications can prevent penicillin, for example, from recognizing the new "hybrid" protein as its target. *Streptococcus pneumoniae* has such modified proteins, which still function properly, but are not recognized by penicillin, thus giving resistance. These "false moustache and spectacles" proteins are useful products of small scale gene transfer.

However the batons are not just swapped between bacteria. Twenty five percent of the genes of *Thermatoga maritime*, a hypothermophilic member of the Bacteria, have come from the Archaea, a completely different domain. Bdelloid rotifers are tiny freshwater animals that are exclusively asexual, yet there are 360 species. They can acquire genes from plants, fungi and bacteria, and it is thought that this transfer of genetic material has led to the development of different species. One of the most remarkable discoveries involves the brown recluse spider. This notoriously toxic spider from southern areas of the United States of America, which can kill small children, shares its toxic gene with a pathogenic bacterial species of *Corynebacterium*, a group that includes the diptherial agent in humans. Analysis shows that this was a single event, but it is not known who gave the toxin to whom. In either case, we see that a piece of weaponry has changed hands, not just between species, but between kingdoms and domains.

Evidence now exists for many such exchanges. The eukaryotic protists display many examples of genetic exchange with prokaryotes. One interesting aside is the observation that of the protist eukaryotes that show significant HGT, most are unicellular grazers. Genes move from the food items to the protists. Thus, in a genetic sense, it can be said that they are what they eat! Imagine if this happened in humans. The perusal of a restaurant menu would become a much more serious business indeed! Genes can move in the opposite direction too. *Legionella pneumophilia* can capture genes from its eukaryotic protist hosts.

The most important HGT events happened at the birth of the eukaryotes, and lie at the very centre of multicellular diversity: mitochondria and chloroplasts. In both cases, these originally free-living prokaryotes were initially taken into a cell by phagocytosis, and then, over time, through a kind of genetic lobotomy, large chunks of their DNA were removed and incorporated within the nucleus of the host. This meant that the captured prey could no longer "think" for itself, and so the host could control it. Of course, the use of the word *captured* is highly questionable in itself. It is the view of the author that we could equally argue that mitochondrial and chloroplast organisms forced themselves upon the early eukaryotes, and that the genetic takeover was one where the prokaryote infected the eukaryote. Let's call it the *infection theory*. The process of transfer of genetic material from the prokaryote into the eukaryote was also most likely driven by the prokaryote, as these organisms have the machinery to do this, using horizontal gene transfer.

So the eukaryotes can be viewed as the outcomes of infection, and are merely vehicles used by prokaryotes. It's a bit like a country being invaded by an army from another country. We would not look at this situation as being one where the invaded country had captured the army, but rather that the army had captured the country. Thus, the idea that eukaryotes swallowed their organelles is less likely than that they were infected by them. We still suffer from bacterial and viral infection today. The need for the eukaryotes to do the capturing smells of the drive within us to assert that we, as eukaryotes, arose by our own cunning, rather than being the hapless victims of infection!

In corals, there is a more relaxed relationship. The trapped photosynthetic cells are still intact and, if pollution brings extra nutrients, they can multiply and lead to the death of the coral. Genes have also moved between plant species via parasitic plants, and from plants to viruses and endophytic fungi.

The evolutionary significance of horizontal gene transfer

So what is the significance of HGT for our understanding of diversity? Certainly in the Archaea and Bacteria, we are not dealing with a species, but a cloud of non-species, a sort of interconnected gene-swapping syndicate. Bacteria can be seen as an evolutionary patchwork quilt, made up of genetic material from lots of different sources, and the now dubious tree of life on Earth would have its root blurred, so as to be unrecognizable, like a television documentary where the key witness is not in focus and distorted. The thought that the genealogy of an organism rests on historical commonality of inheritance of most of its genetic material is out of the window. The majority of genes in most genomes are patchily distributed and the hidden bond of commonality of descent, as Darwin referred to it, is significantly weakened. Sure, most of the Animal Kingdom may have reduced levels of HGT, but the whole origin of the eukaryotes is masked in a mist of gene swapping. Tal Dagan, from the University of Dusseldorf, has put it in its strongest sense by renaming the tree of life as the tree of 1%. By this she means that 99% of proteins in eukaryotes have not originated from vertical inheritance, but rather have been collected by horizontal gene transfer.

So the traditional tree of life, based on inheritance, is a poor explanation of things. Certainly the concept of a bifurcating tree is not a valid one, given HGT and endosymbiotic gene transfer. Professor Lynn Margulis (b. 1938), the celebrated American microbiologist, and a strong advocate of endosymbiotic gene transfer as a significant process in evolution, goes as far as to dismiss the neo-Darwinist approach as "*a minor twentieth-century religious sect within the sprawling religious persuasion of Anglo-Saxon biology*".

HGT is now recognized as a powerful and significant evolutionary force. While vertical transfer remains a key process, it is not the only game in town. In order to understand how diversity arose and how the present Biosphere is structured and connected, horizontal transfer must be taken into consideration. Furthermore, the search for the most recent common ancestor is likely to end in a fog so thick that we wouldn't be able to discern the end of our nose let alone our next door neighbour. Rampant HGT among gene collectives at the earliest stages of organismal existence on Earth would not only blur any search for such an ancestor, but also would promote spread of innovative genetic material. HGT has also been fingered as a possible answer to problems relating to rapid bursts of evolution and the widespread occurrence of parallelism, where a number of unrelated species share some similar characteristics. Instead of having to evolve separately in each group, the characteristics may have moved from a single species into other species.

The species concept and speciation

Whatever taxonomic approach is taken, the Darwinian building blocks are species, even though Darwin himself struggled with the species concept, finally concluding, in *Variation in Animals and Plants under Domestication* (1968), that species were defined from other species by an "*absence of fusion*". So what is a species anyway? We are very familiar with the Linnaean binomials given to species, such as *Grevillea robusta* Cunn ex R. Br., a member of the Proteaceae family of plants from the Southern Hemisphere. *Grevillea*, the genus name, celebrates C.F. Greville, a patron of botany and onetime president of the Royal Society of London, and *robusta* refers to the fact that this member of the genus *Grevillea* is the largest (most robust) one. Cunn. reflects the first European to describe the species, Alan Cunningham, while R.Br remembers Robert Brown, who published the first botanical description (this is, incidentally, the same Robert Brown who described Brownian motion, and gave the cell nucleus its name). So a species name can be quite informative, not only in terms of the species itself, but of the people involved with its discovery. There have been many interesting, unusual and even infamous people connected with species' names. William Shakespeare finds himself attached to a eulophid wasp (*Geothaeana shakespearei*), an encyrtid wasp genus (*Shakespearia*) and a species of rather unpleasant bacteria (*Legionella shakespearei*). Frank Zappa, the late, great musician and song writer, is associated with a goby genus (*Zappa*), a fossil gastropod (*Amaurotoma zappa*), an orb-weaving spider (*Pachygnatha zappa*) and a jellyfish (*Phialella zappai*), while George Bush Jnr, Richard Cheney and Donald Rumsfeld, the American politicians, find their names linked to three species of slime mould beetles (*Agathidium bushi*, *A. cheneyi* and *A. rumsfeldi*, respectively). Gary Larson, the cartoonist behind the wonderful *Far Side* cartoons, is noted in an owl louse (*Strigiphilus garylarsoni*), a butterfly (*Serratoterga larsoni*) and a genus of beetle (*Garylarsonus*). Being named after someone infamous can be disastrous for the innocent members of that species. The blind cave beetle, *Anophthalmus hitleri,* is now endangered, due to obsessive collectors of all things linked to the disgraced former leader.

Problems with defining what a species is

Whatever the names and their origins, each describes a species. Defining what the word *species* actually means, however, can be much less straightforward than you might initially think. So what is the problem here? Surely a species is easy to define? According to Edward Poulton (1856-1943), the British evolutionary zoologist, a species is a group of organisms that can interbreed in the wild and produce fertile offspring. However, this definition runs into a number of sticky problems. Firstly, not all members of a supposed species may encounter each other, particularly if they are globally distributed. Hence we may never know if *all* members of a species are actually sexually compatible. Only overlapping populations have the realized opportunity to prove themselves against our definition. Secondly, many supposed species are asexual.

A third and more serious problem arises when we realize that, in the real world, many species can successfully breed with other species. The world of ornithology has been rocked, not only by the revelation that species, previously thought to be monogamous, actually have 30% of their offspring sired by males who were not their partners, but also that 10% of all the bird species have bred with birds of other species. So while birds of a feather certainly do flock together, plumage of a different variety may actually be of more interest in terms of sexual relationships. In that great inner sanctum of evolutionary biology, the Galapagos Islands, three species of Darwin's finches are among the participants in this union between species. The medium ground finch mates with the cactus finch and the small ground finch, and these illicit unions are actually thought to have saved the rare cactus finch from extinction, bringing in much needed genetic variation. Other examples include little terns and fairy terns.

A quite bizarre blurring, literally, of the species barrier arises in cichlid fish. These fish form one of the three most speciose vertebrate families on the planet at present, with as many as 2000 species, including the delicious *Tilapia* genus from Africa. What is all the more remarkable is that they have been produced by a rapid radiation in the last 2 million years. Although looking different from each other, the family has low levels of genetic difference across its members. Due to deforestation and soil erosion, the water of lakes where these species live, such as Lake Malawi and Lake Victoria, has become really murky. Cichlids rely on being able to see colour differences in order to identify members of their own species for the purpose of mating. Unfortunately, the murky water inhibits their ability to make this judgement call, and so they often end up mating with the wrong species, producing fertile hybrid offspring. It is definitely a case of love being blind!

This creates a challenge for our definition of speciation, where one species divides into two or more populations that can, eventually, no longer interbreed. If they can still interbreed, then speciation hasn't actually occurred. It had been believed that animal hybridization was a rare event, but recent research has revealed that in fact hybrids are produced in large numbers across the world and that many products of such conjugations are fertile.

Of more immediate relevance has been a debate over whether modern humans could have hybridized with Neanderthals. A 29,000 year old Romanian skull has been suggested as such a hybrid, although this is contested. In Abrigo do Lagar Velho in Portugal, a 24,000 year old skeleton of a 4 year old child also was put forward as evidence of a hybrid. Leif Ekblad, a computer programmer from Sweden, has presented a theory that a group of neurological disorders, including attention deficit hyperactive disorder (ADHD), Asperger's syndrome, autism and dyslexia, is a remnant of Neanderthal-human hybridization. However this is without scientific evidence and is highly contentious.

Another problem comes with fossils. It is impossible to know if two similar skeletons are from the same species, as we cannot determine if they could mate together, for obvious reasons. Thus, giving the same species name to any two sets of bones is, at best, questionable. Another issue with our definition of a species is that sterile individuals would be deemed to be non-species. Like the undead, they would then become ostracised from any of the activities that species undergo. This would be totally unacceptable.

The final death knell for the reproductive species concept is horizontal gene transfer. As we discussed earlier, if DNA can move between species and even between domains, then this acts as a short circuit to any reproductive isolation. It is a form of molecular hybridization, and leads to a mosaic rather than a unified species.

Other ways to define a species

In the last few decades, there have actually been many alternative definitions of what a species is. The phylogenetic species concept suggests that all members of a species should have a single common ancestor. This would embrace asexual and sterile organisms, but runs into problems at a population level. Here, any particular population may well have a single common ancestor, and thus would become a species. Thus, if a male and a female squirrel rafted across a lake on a piece of wood to an island, mated and formed a population, then if no other squirrels immigrated from the mainland, this population would need to be considered as a species. Of course, speciation can occur in this way, but if every population stemming from two founder individuals became a species, then we would quickly find ourselves in a taxonomic wonderland, with myriads of pseudo-species (although that is perhaps what we have already).

The ecological species concept defines a species based on its members sharing a distinctive niche. The problem with this is that a niche is a multidimensional space, and separate populations may be fine-tuned to slightly different conditions, or may show plasticity and therefore have options between numbers of micro-niches. Thus we would need to define the limits of a distinctive niche. How distinctive is distinctive?

When does a species become a species?

The next difficult question is: when does a species actually become a species? If sexual compatibility is insufficient to delineate one species from another, then when did

Homo sapiens actually become a species? We share 99% of our genes with bonobos, the chimpanzee-like primates from central Africa. Our behavioural drives are readily recognizable in many other life forms. Early man couldn't write or speak. So was the first human born one sunny day? If this was the case, were his parents not human? If we decide that the parents were in fact human, then what about their parents? How far back in each of our family histories do we go before the previous generation was not human? This is a difficult issue indeed.

As we found in our search for the first living being on the planet, so we find for the first member of a species. We must conclude that at some point, one species gives birth to a totally new species. If we were able to line up our ancestors in a row, with our father at the front, then his father, then his father and so on, and our mother began to walk back in time along this row, how far back would she need to go to find an individual that she was not sexually compatible with? Would the distance of the walk coincide with a similar walk where she stopped when she recognized an individual as being of a different species?

We have seen that using the species as the unit of diversity is problematic, both in terms of actually defining where a species starts and finishes, and in terms of its lineage. The vertical line through time is confused by horizontal transfer of genetic material. Indeed, when we go back to the time before eukaryotes were around, the prokaryotic world would have been a scene of rampant gene swapping, where the idea of a species would most certainly not have been appropriate. In other words, we are faced with a reality, that the concept of the species is dubious at best, both in terms of describing diversity and of offering a basis for understanding evolution. Yet we need to be able to describe what we have before we can understand how it evolved and functions. Indeed, if, at the outset, we wrongly describe it, then what chance is there of working out how it operates? How else can we understand the structure of the Biosphere? In the next two chapters, we will consider the other levels of organization, and examine whether or not they offer a more satisfactory way to describe this great array of life.

Shadows on the Cave Wall

Chapter Ten

Individuals and Populations: Chasing Tails in Search of Diversity

The individual as the unit of diversity

If the species concept is not a meaningful way of describing diversity, then how else can this be done? At a more basic level, we could look towards the individual. It is variation among individual organisms that provides the raw material upon which natural selection acts. If we were all the same, then there would be no selection possible. Like a big box of chocolates that were all identical Savoy truffles, there would be no basis for choosing which chocolate to eat, as there is no choice.

Obviously describing diversity in terms of individuals would be a near impossible task given the huge numbers involved. A second problem comes from the fact that many organisms, such as plants, are often clones, and so the definition of an individual becomes blurred. These clones are produced by vegetative reproduction. For example strawberry plants produce copies of themselves that grow and develop like independent plants, but are exactly the same as the original plant. The individual may actually be made up of many thousands of identical beings, akin to the Borg in Star Trek, acting as a collective unit. Even if an individual is a single, unique organism, its survival may well depend on other organisms. Sexually reproducing organisms generally require a second individual in order to reproduce. There may well be the option to choose a mate from a number of possible individuals, but the quality of choice will depend on the population size and history. It is the individual that mutates and survives, but it is the population that provides the genetic variation available for sexual reproduction.

Species are divided into populations, and so populations are the meaningful units of species. For example, an oak tree growing in America is unlikely to breed with an oak tree of the same species that is growing in Scotland. Natural (and artificial) selection acts on the individual. It is the individual who lives or dies, and who passes part or all of their genetic material on to the next generation. Individuals contribute to what we call the gene pool, that is, the genetic variation held in a population. The gene pool also represents the potential variety available to the next generations. If we think of a species existing as a series of pools, the larger pools will be more likely to survive than will the smaller pools. This is because the environment changes over time, and a population will be more likely to survive this change if it has a greater number of options within it. The more diverse the individuals are collectively, the larger is the pool that they are a part of. The more individuals in a population, the more likely it is that the population will have a high genetic diversity.

In the small subset of diversity that is the Eukaryota, individuals often arise from sexual reproduction. Thus they are usually dependent on the population in which they live for a mate. The present size and structure of a population will have a determining effect on the future size and structure of the population, and also on the individuals that make up that future population. Since the individual arises from the population, and the population is made up of individuals, then selection acts upon both the individuals and the population. Both can be selected for or against. The failure of one reflects upon the other. In sexually reproducing organisms, the individual cannot really be separated from the population. Of course neither can act alone, but their fates are inextricably linked. It doesn't matter how great your genes are, since your offspring will be 50% something else, and that something else is dependent upon the population within which you exist.

The population as the unit of diversity

Can we then consider populations as a unit of diversity? To a certain extent, the answer is yes, at least in terms of sexually reproducing organisms. However, as we have seen, among the Archaea and Bacteria particularly, horizontal gene transfer and asexual reproduction combine to reduce the importance of populations. Thus populations are only clearly definable among a relatively unimportant and limited number of organisms which have only been around for the last quarter of the history of life on Earth, arriving long after the evolutionary party had begun. Like any latecomers, they have missed out on important conversations that happened before they arrived. Also, many eukaryotes reproduce asexually, or may be able to disperse across great distances, again reducing the importance of local populations. For example pine pollen has been found on Greenland, some 1000 km from the nearest pine tree. Pollen from Antarctic beeches (*Nothofagus*) in South America has been found on the Tristan de Cunha Islands, an incredible 4500 km from their origin. Moss spores can travel 2000 km. This blurs the edges of any population concept. The way that a population behaves depends upon the reproductive strategies employed by the species to which it belongs. By this I mean that a species that disperses widely, such as a plant whose pollen is light and wind-dispersed, will have populations that cover very large areas, with a large number of possible mates, whereas a species such as the savannah elephant will likely have only a very limited area and a small number of potential partners. So we see the species impacting upon populations and individuals by dictating the way that they operate. There is no such thing as a global population theory or a global population model. Populations will behave completely differently depending on what species they are.

Random mixing and the dating game

One of the key elements of population modelling is the premise that there is random mixing among the individuals, in other words, there is an equal chance that any one female will mate with any one male. While pollen dispersed over thousands of kilometres by wind is likely to come close to random mate selection, this is not often the case among other, non-wind dispersed eukaryotes. The structure of the population can have a significant impact here. The sex ratio of the population is crucial. How many members of the opposite sex are there? It is no good having a genetically varied, fit and healthy population if they are all of the same sex. A second important aspect is the age structure. Is the population too young or too old to provide a compatible mate? Given a suitable sex ratio and a suitable age structure, the next important thing is the actual size of the population.

Sexual selection: how long should your tail feathers be?

Even if all of these boxes are ticked, mating is seldom random. Indeed, an organism may have extremely expensive and elaborate ways of attracting a mate, or may become involved in fights to the death with same-sex rivals. Charles Darwin recognized that flamboyant structures such as peacock tails may not be easily explained by natural selection, and in his book, *The Descent of Man and Selection in Relation to Sex* (1871), put forward the idea that females choose mates purely on aesthetic grounds. He used the term *sexual selection* to refer to the drive that female desire created, leading to the male becoming elaborately ornamented.

Where natural selection represented the struggle to survive, sexual selection could be viewed as the struggle to reproduce. This is problematic, since the winners in the natural selection game are viewed as being the fittest individuals. Fitness, in evolutionary biology, is not the number of press ups a peacock can do, but rather is all about being represented in future generations. Thus natural selection, in the end, is all about reproduction too. A second side of sexual selection, conflict among males, was seen, by Darwinian biologists at the start of the twentieth century, as a part of natural selection, since the winner generally had attributes, such as greater size and strength, which would suit them in the general battle for survival. One of the great challenges posed by sexual selection was that it could produce outcomes that were not in the interests of natural selection. If your tail feathers grew too big, you could become open to a greater chance of predation. For many decades, Darwinians downplayed sexual selection, preferring to put forward natural selection as the sole force responsible. Konrad Lorenz, the great Austrian animal behaviourist, in his book *On Aggression*, in 1966, wrote that female choice could lead to "*bizarre physical forms…which may easily result in destruction*", and that the crested argus pheasant, whose tail feathers stretch to an amazing 1.5 metres, "*has run itself into a blind alley*"! The concern of Darwinian thinkers, that natural and sexual selection could act against each other, the former for the good of the species, and the latter for the sexual gratification of the individual, led to a more radical solution. Adaptations may be of benefit to the genes, rather than the species. Could a selfish gene hypothesis explain the vagaries of sexual selection?

Certainly it can be understood why such extravagant and potentially harmful adaptations could arise. The argument goes as follows: a female is attracted by large tail feathers. She mates with a long-tailed male, and the resultant male offspring will have long tails, while the resultant female offspring will have their mother's desire for long tails. It becomes hard to disconnect this cycle, and it could lead to extremely long feathers. The problem with this argument is how did the desire for something that wasn't there originally come about in the first place?

Gender stereotyping in evolutionary theory

Another point worth raising is that competition for a mate is not, alone, the domain of males, and mate choice is likewise not the sole domain of females. There is, perhaps, more than a hint of old fashioned sex discrimination in the original concept, the female leading the male astray into profligate expenditure, akin to Eve tempting Adam into eating the forbidden fruit in the Garden of Eden. Indeed evolutionary theory has long been couched in masculine terms, such as *competition, fitness, conflict and evolutionary arms race*. Metaphors often relate to social context. The Victorian context was extremely different than today. Take, for example the following quote from Charles Darwin, who, in *The Descent of Man* (1871), commented that "*The chief distinction in the intellectual powers of the two sexes is shewn by man's attaining to a higher eminence in whatever he takes up, than can woman – whether requiring deep thought, reason, or imagination, or merely the use of senses and hands.*" This statement would be highly unacceptable in today's world, as evidenced by the response to the comments of Harvard University President, Lawrence Summers, in 2005, when he ascertained that women had an inherently lower aptitude in science and mathematics. The advent of Sociobiology, mixed with neo-Darwinism, brought feminism and science into conflict, where stereotypical female roles were deemed as being genetically fixed. These arguments followed a similar spiral to that of natural selection. We start with humans observing animals, and imprinting on to them human behaviour. Sociobiology then takes these animal models and applies them to humans, thus reinforcing outmoded human social context, via the natural world. Craig Stanford, the renowned primatologist, has suggested that our concepts of human social structure have greatly impacted upon how we understand other primates. In a recent book entitled *Feminism and Evolutionary Biology: Boundaries, Intersections and Frontiers* (1996) edited and introduced by Patricia Adair Gowaty, Distinguished Research Professor in Ecology at the University of Georgia, the whole issue of *genetic determinism* (that we are purely the product of our genes) is discussed, and a new emphasis on the impact of the environment upon genetic expression is emphasised as offering a way ahead, wherein feminism can embrace evolutionary biology. Those taking this stance are part of a school of thought called *Darwinian Feminism*. However the ever increasing emphasis of neo-Darwinism on the gene as the essential basis of the Biosphere must surely continue to create problems within the context of feminism, in terms of genetic determinism. Darwinian (and neo-Darwinian) thinking runs into significant problems in the real world, from eugenics to feminism.

While female-female competition (where two females fight for control of one or more males) and male choice (where the male weighs up the most attractive mate) appear to be less common than male infighting and female choice, there are examples. The two spotted goby, depending on the ratio of males to females in a population, either exhibits male-male competition (if there are more males than females) or female-female competition (if there are more females than males). Sea horses also show this response to sex ratio. As an example of male mate choice, male pipefish have been shown to prefer dominant females.

The pecking order and the limited gene pool

As hinted at already, populations of eukaryotes are often organized in a hierarchical way. In other words there is a pecking order. A vivid childhood memory of the author involved watching the lowest member of the pecking order in his grandmother's hen house, in rural Ireland, eventually succumb to continued attacks. Some individuals, like Top Cat in the Hanna – Barbera cartoon, are dominant over other individuals, such as Choo Choo. Social structure usually relates to resource acquisition; however there are also important structural implications for reproduction, and, therefore, gene flow. There are four main types of relationship in sexually reproducing animals: monogamy, polygamy, multimale-multifemale and dispersed. While each most probably involves sexual selection, the impact on gene flow, and, thus, the significance of the population, can be very different. Long-lasting monogamy leads to a realistic population of two individuals after initial selection. Polygamy, whether it is polygyny (one male mating with a number of females) or polyandry (one female mating with a number of males), again is often a stable multi-partner relationship, and so the population size is limited to a single individual providing half of the genetic material for the next generation, with the other fifty percent coming from a limited number of individuals. Even in promiscuous, multimale-multifemale or dispersed mating systems, pecking order will often lead to an actual limit upon gene flow. Thus, population genetic variation may not reflect the variation available. In other words, the gene pool may be smaller than it would appear. Highly structured reproductive populations will not have access to all of the variation in the population, while organisms that partake in horizontal gene transfer will have access to genetic material far beyond a population. Attempts at calculating the effective population size never include any allowance for such things.

Hierarchical structure can be extremely powerful. Mandrills are large Old World primates. The dominant males have fat deposits in their rumps and flanks, as well as dramatic skin colouration. The presence of a dominant male will suppress these secondary sexual characteristics in sub-dominant males, while the removal of the dominant male will lead to these characteristics developing in a previously sub-dominant male. Similarly, dominant orangutans sport long hair, fatty cheek flanges, large laryngeal sacs and massive size. The presence of a dominant male will, again, suppress the development of these traits in other males. We still do not fully understand how this suppression occurs, but the fact that it does indicates that most of a male population in these two species will be unable to contribute to gene flow at any given point. It is no surprise, therefore, that in orangutans, males tend to be solitary.

Another example of a difficulty in using the population as a meaningful way of understanding gene flow comes from plants pollinated by wind and animals. Wind-pollinated plants rely on wind speed and direction for transport of pollen grains, followed by fortuitous impact with a sexually compatible partner. The pollen grain cannot determine where it will end up. Obviously the location of a pollen-producing plant, in terms of exposure to wind, and the size of the grain, will contribute towards success or failure, but no mate choice can be made. Indeed, the original location of the plant will usually have been due to a random seeding event itself. The recipient partner may improve its chances of catching a passing bundle of genetic information by developing larger receptive surfaces, usually feathery stigma. However, again, this will not allow any form of selection. Wind-pollinated plants are some of the most successful on the planet. The Poaceae is a huge plant family (some 10,000 species), which includes sugarcane, bamboo and the grain crops, and serves as an example of this success.

Animal-pollinated plants rely on the movements of animals between plants, leading to an intermediary in the process. This may introduce less random mate selection, with the plant being able to exert influence on the animal, for example through colour, scent or nectar, thus ensuring a more reliable journey from source to destination. Individual plants may be able to compete for the attentions of a given pollinator. Certainly, many animal-pollinated plants have developed unique relationships with a single species of animal. Thus wind- and animal-pollinated plants are quite different in terms of pollen transport, and, thus, gene flow.

So given that there are varying restrictions upon gene flow within a population, and that the effective population size in terms of sexual reproduction may be heavily influenced by such things as social structure and pollination strategy, how valuable is the population as a unit of diversity? Added to this, the fact that a significant slice of the Biosphere is asexual, and the complexity of horizontal gene transfer, particularly among the prokaryotes, it quickly becomes apparent that no single model of population dynamics has any chance of providing an insight into the bigger picture. While individuals are often part of a population, the concept of a population as a standard, universal entity that can be used to understand gene flow across the Biosphere is weak, given the barriers and short circuits in gene flow, the difficulties in quantifying these barriers, and the species-specific characteristics that give populations their characters.

So where does this leave us? Species, populations and individuals are intertwined with each other; none can be extricated and called the unit of organization that explains all. Yet the Biosphere has other levels. We need to examine these in order to determine if any of them holds the key to understanding life on Earth.

Chapter Eleven

The Community, Ecosystems, Biomes and Gaia: Hopeful Contenders for the Throne of Diversity

How else can biodiversity be organized? Apart from interactions with members of their own species, all organisms also interact with members of other species. The organism and its set of interacting species are called the community. Originally "community" referred to species of a similar type, such as a community of birds, or a community of insects, but now the term more properly refers to the entire set of interacting organisms. Like all terms in biology, such as life, species and population, community carries its own baggage in terms of difficulties. One problem involves determining where a particular community ends. Communities are often connected by species that move between them. For example a bird might eat fruit in one community, and several hours later, the seeds may be ejected as droppings in a totally different community. Many species move between communities in this way. Another area of difficulty is the temporal aspect of communities. From season to season, different species may be present. For example, migratory species may only be part of a community for a short period of time each year. Some species are active only at night or during the day (nocturnal or diurnal species, respectively). Communities also change over time, but this change is very gradual. A grassland, over hundreds of years, may become a forest, but it can be difficult to decide *when* it has become a forest. How many trees make a forest?

Two interesting questions also arise. Firstly, do communities evolve? Neo-Darwinian theory strongly rejects this idea, but in this book we recognize each level of organization in the Biosphere as different, and under its own rules. So communities may be able to evolve. Secondly, what impact does a community have on the evolution of species within it? Again, we recognize that each level of organization impacts upon levels above and below it, and so the community may play a key role in the evolution of species. We will look at these issues in detail in Section V.

For almost a century, there has been an ongoing debate about what a community actually is. One major character in this debate was Frederic Clements (1874-1945) one of the founding fathers of modern ecology. Hailing from Nebraska in America, his work on community structure in the Great Plains led him to suggest that the community was an integrated, complex organism, whose changes over time were akin to development. Clements went on to provide a detailed classification of the stages of community development, and the species associated with these stages.

Another key thinker in community ecology, fellow American, Henry Gleason (1882-1975), felt that Clements' approach was too prescriptive and observed many deviations. He argued that the community depended completely on the individual species present, rather than it functioning as any kind of unit. The argument between Clementsian and Gleasonian schools of thought has carried on ever since. While Clements' view of a developing community organism has many attractions, and fundamentally is accepted as a mechanistic model of community development, Gleason's criticisms are also supported by observations around the planet.

To understand how a community develops, we need look no further than coastal regions that are found on either side of the mouth of a large river. The river disgorges its sediment (tiny pieces of material carried from the mountains, where weathering breaks down the rock) into the sea. The sediment moves in the sea currents, and forms sand banks. At low tide, winds blow the sand onshore, and sand dunes form. Over time, series of dunes build up, the youngest near the beach. If we start walking from the shore, inland, we undertake a trip through time, each step taking us further back. As we move, the community changes, from a young, highly opportunistic place, where short-lived, fast-reproducing creatures scurry and scamper to make ends meet in a dynamic, quickly changing world, to, eventually, a forest where change happens very slowly, and the dominant creatures are long-living and slowly reproducing.

All communities tend to do this, changing through time. We understand this change as being driven by the organisms that are there, each group of organisms changing its world, so that it no longer can thrive, but instead creating an environment that suits another organism. Gradually, one set of species replaces another, until eventually, the mature community is formed which is a stable, persistent group of species (what Clements referred to as a climax community). While each organism survives because it can make energetic sense of its environment, each will also impact upon that environment by its activities. As the environment changes, so do the entrance requirements for species. It is like a group of night club bouncers, some allowing you in if you are wearing a shirt, others requiring a hat and yet others requiring a pair of green shoes. As each group of visitors enters, they alter the night club's policy on entrance. Those wearing shirts convince the night club that only people with hats can enter. Anyone without a hat, even if they have a shirt, is then removed. The hat wearers then convince the night club that only green shoes are suitable attire, and so anyone without these shoes will be removed. Here we see that the club acts as an organism which, at any one period of time, has members with a piece of clothing in common, akin to the Clementsian argument. However the exact identity of the individuals who are wearing the correct clothing may vary, depending on who turns up that night, as Gleason would predict. The ability to fit the requirements will depend on the individual being able to match the current rules of the club.

Ecosystems as units of diversity

The biology of communities is tightly linked to the physical environment. Thus, the community may best be considered within the context of the ecosystem, which includes biotic (living) and abiotic (non-living) elements. So rather than discussing the fresh water community of organisms, we should consider the freshwater ecosystem and so on. Ecosystems have the same issues relating to their definition as do communities.

For example, when considering a lake ecosystem, should we include all the feeder streams and the water table relating to these? The rock type around a stream will have a profound effect upon the lake, as will biological processes on the hills and mountains from where the streams originate. The nutrient status of the lake will in large part depend on processes occurring on these mountains. If a forest is cut down, there will likely be a greater flow of water and nutrients into the lake. Thus, change in a montane forest ecosystem will have consequences for surrounding fresh water ecosystems.

Biomes

Ecosystems of a similar nature are clumped together into biomes. For example the desert biome comprises of all the deserts around the world, and the rainforest biome includes all the rainforests in the world. The Biomes act as units of diversity, in terms of providing a large scale energetic context within which life evolves and functions. Comparing differences between biomes can be a powerful way of examining the role of energy in the structure and function of communities, and thus allows us to tease apart some of the complicated influences that press upon nature. Again, it is difficult to delineate the edges of a particular biome. Where does a desert begin? Are savannas merely the edges between rainforests and deserts, or separate biomes in their own right?

Gaia

Taking this connectivity to the extreme, we return to the broadest scale of diversity, where the planet is viewed as a single system. This is the domain of Gaian theory, named after the Ancient Greek goddess, Gaia, the personification of the Earth, and, more intriguingly, the mother *and* wife of Uranus! James Hutton (1727–1797), the famous Scottish geologist, suggested that the entire planet could be viewed as a super-organism and that it was best studied using geophysiology, much in the same way as physiology is used to study human health. Vladimir Vernadsky, the father of biogeochemistry, revived this concept, but has largely gone unnoticed in terms of receiving recognition as a founder member of Gaian thinking. More recently, James

Lovelock (b. 1919), the British independent scientist, and Lynn Margulis (b. 1938), the celebrated American microbiologist, have revived the concept.

It was while working for NASA on a project that was trying to determine ways to discover life on other planets, that Lovelock suggested the atmosphere of a living planet would be different from a non-living planet. In other words, life will leave a fingerprint. On our planet, for example, nitrogen, oxygen and carbon dioxide levels are all products of the Biosphere. Thus a visitor from a distant world would be able to deduce that there was life on the planet, even from far away, because these gases reflect radiation in a particular way that represents their chemical properties, a sort of chemical signature. He then reasoned that, in fact, given the long term stability of things like temperature, salinity of the oceans and atmospheric content, the planet was a self-regulating system, where the Biosphere and the environment interact, and where temperature, acidity-alkalinity and the gaseous composition of the atmosphere are controlled by biotic modulation. From the Gaian perspective, the entire planet is thus governed by feedback processes, and is seen as a unit. However Gaia does not comment directly on diversity, but rather on the function of our planet as a whole.

The gene as the unit of diversity

What about the gene? Certainly every member of the Biosphere has genes, if we exclude prions, and these genes code for the proteins that determine key characteristics of organisms. The gene acts as the molecule responsible for crossing the divide between generations, and between species in a single generation, in the case of horizontal gene transfer. However genes are more generally limited within populations, and are very much the product of the environment. Furthermore, the structure of genes is determined by the interaction between proteins and their energetic context, and the "behaviour" of genes is determined by the proteins interactions within their organismal context. Genes are further compromised as a meaningful unit of diversity as they are tied in to the complex interactions that result from the other levels. For example reproductive strategies differ widely among species, and these are more often linked to resource availability rather than the optimum way to promote gene spread. Thus food webs and succession often play a determining role in how genes are spread. Also, population size can be limited by a wide range of things, often related to other levels of Biosphere organization, such as the habitat, resource availability and the biome. Species-specific traits also can greatly impact on genetic spread. The very concept of reproductively isolated species is a significant limitation to any selfish gene concept, as is the fact that genetic material in sexually reproducing organisms is diluted at each generation, and that genes in the end are part of an extremely large social structure where negotiation and compromise are likely to be key. No gene is an island!

Conservation of Diversity

Another way to understand diversity is to look at our response to it. Given that we are attempting to place structure upon what we observe, then our drives to do this offer an insight into what we end up with. Stemming from our recognition that the Biosphere is a wonderfully complex and diverse entity, has come the drive to conserve it. Conservation biology has become this response, and in recent years it has targeted three levels of organization: single species, ecosystems and ecosystem function.

Single species approaches are now the most outdated. Usually, the prettiest, fluffiest representatives have been singled out, such as the giant panda and the St Lucia parrot. A slimy nematode has little chance of such attention. The emphasis is on one species, and might involve captive breeding in zoos, and the sale of t-shirts and badges emblazoned with the cute and cuddly object of our conservation affections.

It was quickly understood that, in reality, a broader, ecosystem level conservation approach was needed, and so an effort was made to protect habitats like wetlands and rainforests, within which many species live. Moves were made to purchase large tracts of habitat.

The most recent advent has been ecosystem function. Here, it is not so much the individual species that are of interest, but rather the sustainability of ecosystems. The recognition that function is central to this, and that things like food webs and nutrient cycles are key, have shifted the emphasis of modern conservation biology. Now we think about the diversity of function and the function of diversity.

The International Union for the Conservation of Nature (IUCN) recognizes three types of diversity: species, ecosystem and genetic diversity. All three are important in terms of how the Biosphere is structured. Interestingly, each of these levels also has consequences for the others. Species limit genetic diversity, and yet genetic diversity can increase species diversity. It has been shown that if we take two woodlands with the same species of tree, there are more insect species associated with the tree population that has the greatest genetic diversity. Species are limited by ecosystem constraints.

We have recognized that defining diversity really depends on how we approach it. If we are driven by a desire to explain diversity in terms of its origin, we end up with a tree of life. If we base it on the organisms and their characters, we end up with kingdoms and domains. If we focus on function, we arrive at a different place, with key functions and their roles at the ecosystem or planetary level coming to the fore. Each of these is valid in its own way. Yet no single level of organization, from gene to biome, provides a satisfactory unit of diversity. Each level is compromised by its dependence on other levels, while providing its own influences. The Biosphere is a complex creature indeed.

In the end, however, we can only understand diversity if we understand what has driven the process of diversification in the first place. Why is the Biosphere shaped in the way that it is? The meaning of diversity ultimately depends on what it represents and how it evolved. We will explore this in Section IV.

Section IV

How Does Evolution Work?

We have been examining the structure of the Biosphere, this amazing, complex collection of living organisms that populate our planet. In order to understand it, we need to understand how it evolved. So what exactly is evolution and how does it work? Neo-Darwinian evolution puts forward the scenario that DNA is changed through time, in a process that is random. Random mutations occur when the sequence of the DNA is altered, often due to energy from ultraviolet radiation. Upon reproduction, the newly altered sequence, if inherited by the offspring may code for different proteins. This results from changes to protein sequence, which in turn can alter the form and function of the protein. The altered protein may then alter the form and function of the individual. These changes may make the organism better suited to its environment, and therefore more capable than a competing organism. As a result, the offspring of the mutated organism may be at an advantage over competitors. The family line of this organism may then come to dominate in a particular population. Gradually over time, mutations accumulate and evolution carries on, a seamless process driven by DNA, and random in its inventiveness.

Is this really how evolution works? In this section we will examine the process of evolution and look at the problems with this neo-Darwinian approach. We meet a small boy with a very heavy rucksack. We encounter contingency theory and the red queen. We look at problems with time travel and a movie starring Gwyneth Paltrow. We can understand much more of what has happened by understanding the constraints that have acted upon the Biosphere, and we then need to ask exactly how constraining are these constraints? In the end, constraints from physics, chemistry and biology significantly limit what is possible.

Chapter Twelve

Physics: The Ultimate Constraint upon Evolution

The "what" of diversity, although clouded in complexity, is straightforward compared to the "why" of diversity. Why is the Biosphere organized in the way that it is? Vertical gene transfer, competition for resources and a changing environment all work to provide a mechanistic explanation of how life has changed through time, via the process of natural selection. The gene has become the focus of attention in terms of the unit of selection. However there are problems with this approach. Simon Conway Morris, the renowned English palaeontologist, in his book, *The Crucible of Creation: the Burgess Shale and the Rise of Animals* (2000), has compared the reductionist view of evolution to an oil painting '*It has explained the nature and range of pigments, how extraordinary azure colour was obtained, what effect cobalt has and so on. But the description is quite unable to account for the picture itself.*'

So how can we account for this mesmeric painting? Evolution is a process of change. When something changes, three things happen. Firstly, something drives this change. Secondly, something permits the change to happen. Finally, something prevents a different change from happening.

Although the millions of species of organisms would appear to suggest that evolution has a free and unrestrained licence to paint what it wants, this is actually far from true. The diversity of life is, in fact, highly constrained. In the next five chapters, we will examine these constraints, and look more closely at how evolution actually operates.

The rudderless pedalo: what controls the evolutionary journey?

We can approach the huge question of why the Biosphere is organized in the form that it is in another way, by asking why the Biosphere is not organized in a different way. In trying to understand how we ended up with the situation we have today, we must look at the constraints that have acted upon evolution through time, limiting what is possible. The many paths taken by replicating organisms have led to millions of different types of representatives on this planet. What led them along their particular paths, and if we started again, how many of them would be here now?

Let us think about some of the great constraints, the fences and walls that prevent the Biosphere from going down some routes, while permitting travel down other paths. We can understand this by taking a trip down a river in a pedalo. So let's get on board. The first thing we notice is that the pedalo is rudderless, and therefore subject to the currents and constraints of the flowing river. Secondly, there are no pedals. As we leave the safety of the quay in our pedal-less, rudderless pedalo, we notice that there is a current, created by a number of things including the water itself, the shape of the river bed, and numerous objects in the river. Without a current, the pedalo wouldn't go anywhere. Above all, there is a brilliant blue sky. The Sun is shining, indescribably bright, and the heat from it warms your face as you grimace to see past its glaring radiation. If it wasn't for the Sun, our river would be solid ice and we wouldn't be going anywhere either, even with a set of pedals.

Cosmological constraints: Our Place in the Universe

Our star is, at present, about half way through its journey to becoming a very different beast indeed. In another 5 billion years, it will have used up most of its hydrogen and will expand into a red giant. Well before this time, in around 500 million years, its temperature will have risen to such an extent that life as we know it will no longer be possible. Eventually, the Earth's water will reach boiling point and disappear, along with the atmosphere. At present we are in an orbit that provides a temperature consistent with life processes to take place. Thus the occurrence of life on the planet is constrained, in time, by the evolution of our neighbouring hydrogen fusion reactor, from where most of the energy needed to fuel the Biosphere comes from. Life doesn't just need the right space, it needs the right time.

Interestingly, the early evolution of life on Earth was possible because of greenhouse gasses. At this stage, the Sun was 25% cooler than at present, and so liquid water would not have been possible if it wasn't for high levels of carbon dioxide on the planet. The decline of these greenhouse gases was accompanied by an increase in solar radiation, allowing continued liquid water to persist on the planet. The fact that our Sun is not part of a binary star system, is important, in terms of the existence and persistence of a Biosphere. Most stars occur in pairs, and this would likely create unstable orbits for associated planets, or lead to surface temperatures on these planets that would not be conducive to life.

At the level of our solar system, the presence of the giant planet of Jupiter is posited as having formed a protection against excessive meteor bombardment of the planet. Another cosmological constraint, in terms of the boundaries within which life has occurred, is our orbiting satellite, the Moon. Its presence, and origin, has had significant impacts on our planet. The Earth's mantle forms a wedding ring of metals. We would expect the core to contain most of the metal elements, but on Earth, we find much higher levels of metals in the mantle, and thus in the crust, than predicted. These metals are thought to have come from the dramatic events that led to the Moon's formation. Early Earth was impacted by a massive object, the size of the planet Mars, and the consequence of this brief fusion was the formation of the Moon, the two giant liquid spheres coalescing briefly, and then separating. However, during separation, the metal-rich core of the incoming object became subsumed in the mantle of the Earth, leading to an enrichment of metals. A consequence of this metallic veneer on the planet was the provision of accessible metal ores near the surface, which eventually led to the raw materials from which human technology would feed upon, leading to the industrial revolution, the recent greenhouse effect and much of the fabric of modern human society.

The oblique impact also likely led to a 23.5° tilt, on average, of the planet, which was stabilized by the orbiting Moon. Of course, the Moon has produced the tidal effect on our oceans, with all of its consequences for evolution. In its earlier days, the moon was closer to the Earth, and its pull was such that it would have led to tidal impacts on the molten crust of the Earth, possibly setting in motion early plate tectonic processes.

The presence of water is an important pre-requisite for the Biosphere. We now think that this water may have come from comets bombarding the Earth, prior to Jupiter having such a large effect upon the trajectories of these things. Again, we see a window that was open at one point, leading to water, and perhaps other more complex molecules, arriving on the planet, but then closing, thus greatly reducing the chances of further, damaging, bolides impacting on the planet.

Both the Earth's rotation around its own axis, and its orbit around the Sun, have placed constraints on diurnal patterning and the length of seasons. Venus, for example, has a day that is around 5800 hours long! This would create major problems for any kind of circadian rhythm, while working a night shift at a factory would be an extremely lengthy undertaking indeed. Statements like '*Let's wait until morning*' would have a much more serious consequence! Thus the rotation and orbit of Earth set particular constraints on the Biosphere, particularly relating to the time when solar radiation is accessible. A night longer than 100 hours would make photosynthetically driven growth and development almost impossible.

The four universal forces of physics

More fundamental and pervasive are the constraints placed upon our planet by the four universal forces of physics: gravity, electromagnetism, the weak interaction and the strong interaction. The events in the Cosmos itself stem from these forces. Gravity is the weakest of all the forces, but has the most visible effects. Gravity cannot be screened and acts at infinite distances and on all matter. From black holes to falling apples, gravity has a wide range of effects. It has major impacts on the Biosphere, posing challenges to support, balance and locomotion, with added challenges on land, where the support of a water body is no longer present.

Electromagnetism is extremely important, and fundamental, particularly at the molecular level. It describes the interaction between charged particles. It is a much more powerful force than gravity and is fundamental to a wide variety of crucial areas, from protein structure and function, through physiological transport, nerve impulses, DNA structure and a myriad of other atomic interactions.

The weak nuclear interaction is restricted to atomic nuclei, and is involved in decay, for example allowing neutrons to change into protons. While none of this is easily seen as having implications upon the Biosphere and its evolution, it determines the size of the building blocks of matter, quarks and electrons, a fairly fundamental issue! The strong nuclear interaction is what holds protons and neutrons together, and again is fundamental to the behaviour of sub-atomic particles. Much work is going into trying to unify these four forces into one theory of everything. The weak nuclear interaction and the electromagnetic force have so far been unified in what is known as the electroweak force.

These fundamental universal forces provide constraints upon all matter, with the latter three having significant effects on the elements that are the key personalities of the periodic table, and form the basis of chemistry. Ultimately, the games of chemistry are played to the rules of physics.

The Laws of Thermodynamics

The next important set of constraints comes from the laws of thermodynamics. Organisms need to acquire energy to stay alive, and need to reproduce copies of themselves to provide continuance of their lines beyond death. These two challenges shape the living planet, from the atomic through to the trophodynamic level. The laws of thermodynamics may come closer to accounting for the picture itself than the fundamental laws of physics. The impact of these laws is central in terms of how the Biosphere is structured. They explain the flow of energy through the Biosphere, and the presence of entropy throughout the Universe. They also place constraints upon which chemical reactions can and cannot occur spontaneously.

Physics is fundamental to our understanding of life. We have already reflected, in Chapter Two, that the New Physics differs radically, as a philosophy, from neo-Darwinian thinking, which is structuralist in its approach. Darwin was working long before we had an understanding of modern physics, and neo-Darwinism is built upon his foundations. This book is built on a much more modern set of principles, and as we shall see in Section V, finds its roots in physics. We will discover that by building on more fundamental scientific principles, we are dealing with an approach that is beyond the cave of limited thinking, and instead we are able to elucidate the true basis of life on Earth, its evolution, structure and function.

Physics sets the limits for everything else. The outcomes of these limits are realized in chemistry, which itself plays a significant role in shaping the living world. In the next chapter, we will explore the implications of chemistry upon the Biosphere, and see chemistry as the middle world that lies between physics and the cave wall.

Chapter Thirteen

Chemical Constraints: the Middle World Between Physics and Biology

Taking a deep breath, we now move on to the games of chemistry, which themselves provide the rules to which the games of biology are played. The games of chemistry play out in two ways, firstly in our environment, and secondly within the organism. It is all chemistry, but some of it is relevant to a single organism, while other aspects impact upon the entire Biosphere.

In many ways, the discovery of the periodic table is one of the most beautiful achievements of man. In this relatively simple diagram lies the essential information for understanding how things are put together, and why they behave in the way that they do. The periodic table holds within it the reason for many of the constraints that arise from chemistry, but the games of this table depend, ultimately, upon atomic and sub-atomic physics. The route that evolution has taken has been significantly constrained by chemistry. Take diffusion as an example.

The process of diffusion and its importance to the history of the Biosphere

If we have a high concentration of a gas in one location, and a lower concentration of gas in another location, then, provided that there is a clear route between these two locations, the concentration of gas will increase at the lower end of the gradient, and decrease at the higher end. Diffusion can easily be seen if you drop some dark liquid, such as ink, into a glass of water. As an important aside, it is key to note that diffusion is not directed. The atoms or molecules don't decide to go somewhere. They end up in different places by random movement. Rather, it is driven, by entropy. The end effect is a homogeneous mixture, but driven by random movement.

Diffusion of oxygen became a major constraint upon life. Early Earth had low levels of oxygen, which gradually built up due to photosynthesis (you will remember that oxygen is a by-product of photosynthesis). Thus if you were too big, oxygen would not be able to diffuse from your surface to your centre in sufficient quantities to meet the requirements of oxygen-dependent respiration. It is like a supermarket selling turkeys at Christmas or Thanksgiving. The demand in the shop will be high, but the ability to restock the shelves will be limited. If the distance from the cold store to the shelves gets too large, then there will be a shortage of turkeys. Also if the door out of the cold storage room is too narrow, only one person at a time will be able to leave the storage area, carrying a turkey to the shelves. In the same way, the surface area of an organism is the limit. As an organism gets bigger, the amount of surface area per unit volume will decrease. Think of a cube that is 1 cm wide. The volume will be $1cm^3$ while the surface area will be 6 cm^2 (as there are six faces to the cube). Thus there are 6 cm^2 of surface area for every cm^3 of volume. Now think of a cube that is 10 cm wide. There are 1000 cm^3 of volume and 600 cm^2 of area. So there is only $0.6cm^2$ of area for every cm^3 of volume. The bigger an organism gets, the less area is available for oxygen to diffuse across. In other words the door gets smaller. As oxygen levels increased on planet Earth, more oxygen could enter through the doors, and so larger organisms were possible.

Thus, oxygen concentration constrained the size of organisms. This is thought to have delayed the advent of multicellularity on Earth. The Biosphere eventually tackled this in two ways. Firstly, there was an increase in the surface area by creating folded membranes (a trick used in many such transport challenges, as our lungs and intestines testify, with their deeply folded surfaces) and, secondly, circulation systems developed, using haemoglobin that was pumped around the body, to bring oxygen to all parts of the body. Insects approach this differently with lots of tiny pipes running throughout the organism.

The mystery of multicellularity and Elkanah's eureka moment

One of the great puzzles facing biology relates to how and when multicellular life began on Earth. Earliest fossils of microbial life date back to 3.46 billion years ago. These Cyanobacteria were discovered in the Apex Chert in Western Australia. Claims of even earlier organic life, from Greenland, go back as far as 3.85 billion years ago. Yet it would be almost another 3 billion years before multicellular organisms would appear. In 1872, fossils were found by the palaeontologist, Elkanah Billings, in the Avalon Peninsula of Newfoundland, that were to become the first evidence of multicellular metazoan life on Earth. This was indeed a momentous event. Suddenly, a whole host of strange new organisms inhabited the planet, different than anything seen before. The later discovery of a large number of similar fossils in South Australia led to this group becoming known as the Ediacaran fauna (after the area where they were found). Surrounded in controversy, the sudden appearance of multicellular life forms some 570 million years ago has caused much discussion as to why they occurred when they did. Oxygen has always been at the top of the list of candidates for the position of the major constraint that held back multicellular evolution. Firstly, ultraviolet radiation was a significant problem, and it wasn't until atmospheric oxygen levels reached around 1% of the present levels that sufficient ozone (O_3) would be formed to block out this harmful radiation. Aerobic bacteria could function at only 0.5% of present levels, while single celled eukaryotes would require levels just above this. Organisms from the Ediacaran fauna such as *Dickinsonia*, variously described as a worm, a jellyfish, or even an ancestor of the chordates, would require between 10% (if it possessed a circulatory system) and almost 100% (if no circulatory system was present) of the present oxygen levels, due to their size.

Oxygen control hypothesis of multicellularity

One working hypothesis as to why multicellularity arrived when it did is the oxygen control hypothesis, or rather, the oxygen control group of hypotheses. This group of theories include the ice age hypothesis and the supercontinent breakup hypothesis.

Snowball Earth: the ice age hypothesis

It is known that cold water has higher levels of dissolved oxygen in it than warm water. Co-incidentally, just prior to the Ediacaran fossil record, a large glaciation event, called the Varangian, occurred. Named after the Varangian Fjord in Norway, which, incidentally, became the centre of Viking culture by the ninth century, this glaciation event, or series of events, spanned a time between 850 and 600 million years ago. At this time, the planet may well have been completely covered in ice, and this has been referred to as *snowball Earth*.

Ice formed on all land, which was clustered around the equator during this period in a huge land mass called Rodinia. This was important as, today, the tropical seas absorb the most energy from the sun. Land absorbs less heat than water, and so when the continents were aligned along the equator, a significant drop in absorbed heat would occur. Also, continents experience more rainfall than oceans, and, given that the tropics are the wettest parts of the planet, this rainfall would weather the rocks, which leads to the absorption of carbon dioxide, as it combines with calcium and becomes precipitated in the oceans as calcium carbonate, forming rocks like sandstone and limestone. It is thought that a significant decline in the amount of carbon dioxide (the opposite of greenhouse warming) may have led to a significant drop in temperature, as heat left the planet. Carbon dioxide in the atmosphere acts to absorb escaping heat, preventing its loss, and thus preventing cooling on the planet.

As ice began to form, it acted like a mirror, reflecting sunlight back from the planet, and further exacerbating the cooling effect. Cold water has higher oxygen levels than warm water, which would have allowed multicellular organisms to have greater access to oxygen, opening up the possibility of multicellularity. This runaway cooling may have finally been stopped by volcanic activity that would have needed to have raised the carbon dioxide levels to 350 times that of today in order to lead to a thaw. This led to a super-greenhouse effect.

Breaking up is hard to do: the role of plate tectonics

The second hypothesis centres on the break-up of Rodinia. Tectonic events accompanying this break up would have led to shallow seas, where photosynthetic plants could thrive, and where sediment from the increasingly large coastal area would pour into the sea, leading to organic carbon being buried. Thus, increased burial of organic matter during the tectonic events surrounding the Rodinia break up would also lead to an oxygen surplus. This is because during photosynthesis, while oxygen is produced, the organic carbon formed at the same time will use this oxygen when it is degraded. Increased organic burial means less oxygen consumed.

Only when this carbon is buried, will it be prevented from using up the oxygen produced. However it happened, oxygen levels did rise during this period, making multicellular life much more likely to appear, which it did. Of course the rise in oxygen, while allowing multicellularity and success for the aerobic life forms, was extremely debilitating for anaerobic organisms, such as the Archaea. Oxygen can be viewed as a pollutant from their point of view, leading to significant chemical constraints upon their distribution. Oxygen levels have remained toxic to them ever since, and many of these organisms can now only survive in low-oxygen habitats, such as swamps. Furthermore, oxygen can form dangerous free radicals, and only with the evolution of the peroxisome could eukaryotes cope with these. Peroxisomes are small structures found only in the eukaryotes. Surrounded in a membrane, they contain special enzymes that can detoxify poisons. For example, they are responsible for breaking down a quarter of the alcohol that we drink. They were first discovered by Johannes Rhodin (1922-2004), then a Swedish PhD student, in 1954. He would later go on to make huge contributions in the field of Alzheimer's disease.

Romer's Gap and a dearth of oxygen?

The constraint of oxygen upon the evolution of the Biosphere did not end with determining when multicellularity could begin and where the Archaea could live. Later on, it may have been responsible for a silent period in the record of vertebrate fossils. Vertebrates had colonized the land some 415 million years ago, but suddenly terrestrial vertebrates mostly go absent without leave in the fossil record, for about 50 million years. This is known as Romer's gap, after Alfred Romer (1894-1973), the American palaeontologist. At the same time, arthropod lineages stopped diversifying. After the gap, the vertebrates re-appeared and remained buoyant to the present day. Recent analysis of oxygen levels has shown that ambient atmospheric oxygen levels plummeted during this time, from twenty two percent to as low as ten percent. It has been hypothesised that the new terrestrial colonists could not cope with such low levels. At the end of this period, oxygen levels rose again. Conrad Labandeira, an American palaeontologist, of the Smithsonian Institute, postulated, in 2006, that only when O_2 is above twenty percent can land-based life diversify. This is further borne out by the low success of groups such as the mammals at high altitudes. It has even been argued, by Paul Falkowski of New York, that a later sharp increase in O_2 some fifty million years ago may have been instrumental in the diversification and increase in body mass of the mammals, although this is disputed by others who point to vacant niches left by the dinosaurs as the real reason for these developments.

Thus, the chemistry of the environment acts as a significant constraint to evolution. Through geological time, changes in the production and absorption of many chemicals have altered the amounts of these chemicals in the atmosphere and water, resulting in constraints upon the evolution of the Biosphere.

The constraints of chemistry within

So much, then, for the environmental impacts of chemistry. Chemistry of the organisms themselves also creates constraints. As well as limitations such as diffusion, the chemistry of key molecules within our bodies can place significant constraints upon the direction that evolution can take. One of the major processes in the evolution of the Biosphere is the mutation. Mutations work by altering the genetic code, leading, sometimes, to a change in protein function. Mutations are the main source of variation upon which natural selection can act. They are fundamental to understanding evolution. Constraints related to mutations will therefore be central to determining what is available for change.

Proteins: dancing chains of acid

To understand constraints related to mutation, we must first understand proteins. Proteins occupy centre stage in all organisms. They can form the actual structure, such as keratin proteins in the hair, nails, hooves and claws of many animals. Bird feathers, reptilian shells and scales, and non-bony horns are all formed from this group of proteins. Other proteins form small machines that can have moveable parts. These *transport proteins* control movement of material across cell membranes, acting as doormen. Another group of proteins are the enzymes. Enzymes speed reactions up, a bit like a dating agency! Fate may eventually bring two molecules together, but enzymes facilitate this. They can't make chemistry happen that isn't able to happen, but they smooth the introduction process.

For all the roles that proteins play, their structure is central. Their shape constrains their function, like a spanner, that can be used for a particular task only if it has the right dimensions. How is this shape arrived at? Proteins are long chains, made up of amino acids, like a string of pearls. However proteins are not just long chains. The chains fold and produce three-dimensional shapes. They form elaborate and elegant structures, which give them their function. These shapes can resemble complex landscapes, with peaks and caves. Some of the caves allow two or more specific molecules to fit into them. Squeezed in together, these molecules interact with each other and form a single product. This is how enzymes often work. Interestingly, the shape of the cave can sometimes allow more than the "right" molecules to enter. As mentioned earlier, RUBISCO, the key enzyme in making sugar in photosynthesis, usually joins carbons together, but can also join carbon to oxygen. This is because both carbon dioxide and oxygen fit into the cave. However things can be a lot more serious than that. Sometimes a chemical can attach to a protein but then refuses to leave, preventing the enzyme from being able to function. Hydrogen cyanide has its devastating effects in this way, attaching to a key enzyme in the mitochondria, and preventing the synthesis of the critical energy carrier, adenosine triphosphate (ATP), leading to a collapse in respiratory function. This protein inhibition has led to the deaths of many people including Alan Turing (the father of computing), Adolf Hitler and the Russian mystic, Rasputin.

So how does a simple string of pearls form into such a myriad of elaborate, intricate shapes? It is much more impressive than origami, where a two-dimensional sheet of paper forms a three-dimensional bird that can flap its wings if you pull its tail. Here, an essentially one-dimensional line forms a three-dimensional world without the input of an origami practitioner. The answer lies in the order and types of pearls used. There are twenty-one different types of amino acids available for each position in the chain. Chains can be of different lengths. The smallest known protein is twenty amino acids long. It is made by Gila monsters (*Heloderma suspectum),* a poisonous group of lizards from Mexico) and is found in their saliva. One of the largest proteins is titin, consisting of over 27,000 amino acids, and occurring in mammalian muscle.

What determines the shape of proteins?

Depending on what order the amino acids occur in, the protein will form a particular shape. Why is this? It is all to do with physics. As we have said, the games of chemistry are played to the rules of physics. Each amino acid is made up of a specific group of atoms, and the distribution of electrical charge leads to different ways of bonding. They have electrical personalities, with some amino acids attracting others, while others repel each other. Some parts have a fear of water (they are hydrophobic) and thus are buried inside, while others can't get enough of the stuff and proudly parade on the outside. It's like taking one hundred (or in the case of titin, 27 000) people and putting them in a room at a party. Over time, groups will form, as the partygoers settle into huddles where they feel happiest. Amino acids are similarly disposed. The only difference is that upon entering the room, everyone is asked to hold hands with the person next to them, forming a long chain. Then, they organise themselves in a complex way, with the line twisting and crossing many times, influenced by the desires and dislikes of each individual. Eventually a three dimensional structure is arrived at, that is thermodynamically stable. In the end, the protein conforms to physical laws. These laws act like the Greek god, Eros, firing a golden arrow with dove feathers, or a lead arrow with owl feathers, determining attraction or indifference, and thus in the end, determining the structure of the protein. If we change the energetic environment in which these proteins exist, they will change shape. This is how transport proteins work. If energy is added or removed from the protein, then the whole protein will take on a new form, just like a soldier when the drill sergeant shouts '*Attention*' or '*At ease*'.

The significance of sequence

So how important is the sequence of amino acids? Even a change in one amino acid can be disastrous, not just for the protein, but for the entire organism. Many debilitating diseases are caused by the wrong amino acid in the chain. Canavan disease is a terrible affliction, leading to cerebral degeneration in infants, with death often occurring by the age of four years. It can be caused by a single base change in the genome. Given that the human genome has around 3 billion bases, this is indeed an unlucky event. The change leads to a different amino acid in a protein. The loss of function of this protein leads to impaired insulation of nerve cells, resulting in an impaired transmission of nerve impulses. Sickle cell anaemia is another example of a debilitating condition resulting from a single amino acid change, arising from a single base change again. Diseases such as cystic fibrosis, Duchenne muscular dystrophy, haemophilia and retinitis pigmentosa are caused in a different way. A single mutation leads to a stop message occurring instead of an amino acid, thus cutting off the protein chain before it is complete. Sometimes an amino acid can be inserted where it shouldn't be. In Huntington's disease, a single amino acid becomes copied many times, leading to a long chain of it in the middle of the protein.

What happens more often is that a single amino acid change will not impact drastically on a protein. It may reduce the efficiency of that protein, and thus still be selected against, but it may not have a noticeable impact. Thus it depends on which amino acid is changed as to its impact on the structure and function of the protein. It also must be remembered that only part of the DNA is used in coding for proteins. In humans, this is as low as 1.5%, with the rest being considered as mostly junk. This junk is useful however, in terms of acting as a straw man for mutations. Like a herd of wildebeest, any single base is more greatly protected from a predatorial mutation by being in a larger group of bases, just like one wildebeest is less likely to be eaten, the larger the herd it hangs out in (provided that prey selection by the predator is random).

Deoxyribonucleic acid: a modern Canterbury Tale

So how do amino acids know what sequence to line up in? This is where the DNA comes in. It can be difficult to understand this molecular drama that is played out, invisible to us, deep within our cells. The actors in the drama have strange, exotic names, but it is important to understand these things, as they lie at the heart of modern biology. So let's try to get our minds around some biochemistry! We will start with deoxyribonucleic acid, or DNA. Once Gregor Mendel had discovered that the character of organisms was inherited from their parents, the search began for the molecule that was responsible for this. What actually passed from generation to generation, and led to the organism being shaped the way that it is?

The search for the chemistry of evolution

From its discovery, in 1869, by the Swiss biologist Friedrich Mieschner, it was initially thought that DNA was too simple to be the genetic material. However work by Frederick Griffith in 1928, and, in 1944, by Americans Maclyn McCarty, Oswald Avery, and Colin MacLeod confirmed that DNA was, in fact the key chemical of inheritance. After the Second World War, a race between two labs developed: in California, a team led by Linus Pauling at Caltech, and at Cambridge, the Cavendish Laboratory team led by Sir William Lawrence Bragg. The Cavendish Laboratory team was complemented by a group in King's College, London, composed, primarily, of Rosalind Franklin and Maurice Wilkins.

Intriguingly, the son of Linus Pualing, Peter, happened to move to the Cambridge lab just prior to the discovery, as did Jerry Donoghue, a long term colleague of Linus Pauling. It is thought that these individuals acted as an unofficial link between the two groups, as they both raced to be the first to discover the structure! Linus Pauling was the most important protein chemist of the Twentieth Century, and was the hot favourite to crack the structure of DNA, having already pioneered structural biology in proteins. Bragg was a Nobel laureate and had competed with Pauling in a number of previous occasions, including the elucidation of the alpha helix structure, a key type of protein folding. He had lost out in his previous attempts to beat Pauling's group. Both leaders had felt that genes were, most likely, proteins.

James Watson and Francis Crick ended up sharing an office in Cambridge. Their first attempt to solve the structure of DNA involved a triple helix, with the bases on the outside and the sugar-phosphate backbone on the inside. This was quickly shown to be impossible. Their project was disbanded, but they pursued it unofficially, not wanting to be beaten. They studied Linus Pauling's work in great detail. Meanwhile, Pauling, too, was of the notion that DNA was a treble helix. It was Rosalind Franklin, working with Maurice Wilkins at Kings in London, who finally made the breakthrough, producing clear X-ray photographs of much higher quality than before, and showing that it was a double helix, not a treble helix. Mixed in with the whole story was a problem relating to politics. The United States refused to grant Pauling a passport because of his leftist leanings. This was eventually granted, but it restricted Pauling from discussing the DNA work at a crucial time. On finally getting to Europe, he heard Avery and Chase's proof that DNA was definitely the molecule responsible for coding proteins. Now, Pauling turned his huge ability and resources to DNA. The race was underway. In an attempt to strike early, he published a treble helix structure, which proved to be wrong. Watson and Crick, using Franklin's newest images, after a number of trial and error attempts, came up with the right structure, with the bases matching and pointing inwards, like the rungs on a ladder, and the phosphate and sugars on the outside. It was an inside out version of that of Pauling, and with two rather than three strands in the helix.

The story of the discovery of the structure of DNA is fascinating, combining all the elements of context, competition, politics and teamwork. Such drama also contributed to the legendary status of DNA. The mystery and drama associated with the birth of this icon is akin to many mystical accounts of the birth of deities, and has been retold in a whole series of books, enveloped in suspense, tragedy (the early death of Rosalind Franklin), twists and turns. The participants have become sacred figures in science, and the tale has become a moral lesson to all, with pride coming before a fall. It resembles a sacred text, a modern day Canterbury Tale, a mystery play of the middle ages.

The chain that makes a chain

DNA is a long molecule, and looks a bit like a ladder. The two long supports are made of sugars (deoxyribose) and phosphates, while the rungs are made of chemicals called bases, which occur in pairs. There are four different types of bases. Different bits of DNA have different sequences of these bases. The bases are like letters. A simple language has evolved, which consists of three letter words. Each group of three bases represents an amino acid. The order of the bases in the DNA is translated into the order that the amino acids occur in the protein. The fact that there are only three letters in each word, and only four possible letters in each position in the DNA, constrains the complexity of the language. It also makes it susceptible to mutations. If a letter changes, it means that a new word will form, leading, potentially to a different amino acid. We have seen how much damage this can do.

But hang on a minute. If there are twenty one amino acids used in proteins, then how come there are sixty four possible words (each word has three letters, there are four possible letters in each of the three positions, thus 4 x 4 x 4 = 64)? Along with the three words meaning STOP, that gives twenty four words needed. What about the other forty words? What do they do? Intriguingly, some amino acids are coded for by more than one word. The code contains redundancy, or overlap. For example, serine is coded for by six different three-base words. Alanine has four words while methionine only has one word (which is also the word for START). It is not understood why there is this uneven redundancy. It's like a code within a code. Having a number of different words for one amino acid certainly reduces the likelihood of an amino acid being changed due to a single letter change in the DNA by a mutation, since the new letter may merely change the word into one of the other code words for the same amino acid. For example the code word GGG codes for the amino acid, glycine. If a change occurred in the last letter, due to a mutation, this might change it to GGT, GGA or GGC. It so happens that all of these words also code for glycine, so the mutation would have no effect on the final protein sequence.

However we would expect such a trick to be equally spread across all amino acids, since any change can be disadvantageous (or of course, advantageous if it improves the protein function). Yet this is certainly not the case. Indeed, many diseases are the result of a single base change, as we have already noted. So there is mystery here, to match the da Vinci code. Right at the heart of the Central Dogma lies an uneven level of redundancy, which must surely have been under the most intense of scrutiny during evolutionary history, yet we can't explain the pattern.

If we imagine a system where the code words had four letters, then much greater redundancy would be possible. In this case there would be 4 x 4 x 4 x 4 possible words, that is, 256 words, giving just over twelve words for every amino acid. That would surely provide greater protection against single base mutation altering amino acid sequence. However, longer words might provide a larger target for mutation. What if there were more letters available? If there were 6 bases instead of four, then even for a three letter word, this would give us a language of 6 x 6 x 6 words, or 216 words, or ten words for each amino acid. What is for sure is that the present arrangement of DNA, with its four bases and three letter words, and the limited and uneven distribution of redundancy, all place constraints upon the genotype and phenotype of an organism, and these constraints are all chemical in nature.

Chemical constraints upon mutation

So we can now consider the constraints upon the critical process of mutation. The journey from mutation to variation is a long and treacherous process. Mutations would have been much more common on early Earth. This is because there was no ozone, which effectively screens out ultra violet radiation, a major source of mutation. As we have seen, UV was so strong, that it was not until oxygen levels reached a level where sufficient ozone was created that life could move to the ocean surface and eventually on to land. DNA itself is a constraint, because it offers some resistance to mutation, whereas RNA is much more susceptible. This is often cited as the reason why DNA became the preferred store of our genetic information. If DNA was not the genetic material, how different would the mutation rate be, and what impact might this have had on how the Biosphere turned out? As we have mentioned before, what if there were five or six bases instead of four?

In multicellular organisms, the mutation also needs to happen in the right type of cell. Large organisms often have reproductive cells isolated in a small region, for example the testes and ovaries in humans. All the other cells, called somatic cells, play no part in reproduction directly. Mutations in these cells will therefore have no direct effect on variation. However, strictly speaking, mutations in somatic cells can have the ultimate effect – removal completely from the gene pool. For example a mutation in an epithelial cell can lead to skin cancer which can, in some cases, lead to death. It is the reproductive cells, however, that carry the information needed to reassemble the organism in the next generation, and so only mutations in these cells will carry through to the next generation. So already, we can see that mutations are constrained by the impact of multicellularity, with only some of the cells being meaningful targets. Single cell organisms, which make up most of the Biosphere, do not suffer from this constraint.

Having occurred in the right cells, the mutation needs to survive the proof-reading system. Special proteins check for mistakes in the DNA when it is replicated during cell division. These proteins can remove offending base pairs and groups of bases or repair faulty bases. The efficiency of this repair system forms a significant constraint, setting a limit on the number of mutations that escape detection.

Even if a mutation survives proof-reading, it then must make a meaningful change to the genetic code, changing an amino acid. To do this it must sidestep the redundancy within the code, creating a change in the three letter word that actually results in a different amino acid. Then, the change in the protein sequence must have some functional significance, providing phenotypic variation upon which natural selection can act. Of course mutations may occur that aren't detected in the phenotype, but may set in motion changes that will later have an impact. Imagine a single base change that led to the three letter code GGC changing to GGA. This would lead to no change in the amino acid coded for, in this case, glycine. Now imagine that a second mutation occurs, converting the first letter from G to T. Now we have TGA. This word codes for STOP, which will completely cut off the protein chain. Now if the first mutation had not occurred, and only the second one had happened, we would have moved from GGC to TGC. TGC will translate into cysteine. Therefore, we see that although the first mutation had no phenotypic effect, its occurrence meant that when the second mutation occurred, there was a very large effect. Without the first mutation, which was phenotypically silent, we would have had a very different outcome following the second event. Of further interest is the fact that even changes in amino acids at some sites have no effect upon function at all.

Dollo's constraint and the morning glory

Some mutations can cancel others out. In tryptophan synthase, the enzyme involved in making the amino acid tryptophan (a real chicken and egg story – which came first the amino acid or the enzyme that makes it?), a mutation at either amino acid number 175 or 211 leads to an enzyme that doesn't work. However if both mutations happen together, we have a working enzyme! This is of interest in that it allows resurrection of enzyme function. However, there is a more general trend of irreversibility in evolution that is known as Dollo's law. Louis Antoine Marie Joseph Dollo (1857-1931) was a French engineer turned anthropologist, who worked on the Iguanodon dinosaurs (in 1887 alone he published 94 scientific papers!). Iguanodons are named after the Iguana (a living reptile species) because of the similarity of the teeth in both animals. They roamed the Earth as giant herbivores, between 150 and 90 million years ago. They were first discovered in 1822 in Sussex, England, by Mary Ann Mantell, the wife of a local doctor. In later life, the doctor, Gideon Mantell, claimed it was actually he who made the discovery! Dollo's involvement came about when a remarkable find of 31 complete skeletons were found, in 1878, in a coal mine in Bernissart, Belgium. At that time, Dollo was working in the Museum of Brussels. Through his work, he came to the conclusion that there must be fundamental forces acting on the organic world, just as in the inorganic (physical) world, and suggested that these forces would prevent evolution from reversing, just like gravity prevents a falling apple from ascending back to the tree. For example, when horses lost their toes, they could not regain them. His insights have received mixed reviews in recent times, but a study on the morning glory plant has shed some interesting light on his law. Rebecca Zufall, while working on her PhD at Duke University, USA in 2003, managed to unravel a fascinating mechanism by which petal colour has changed in these climbing plants.

Morning glory flowers open in the morning and generally last for only one day. The original species was a bluish purple colour, produced by a series of chemical changes, forming blue and red dye. In some species however, the blue dye is not made. Research has shown that two different enzymes in the pathway that leads to blue dye are not working in the red plants. One enzyme not working would have been enough to stop blue dye being made, but this double failure means that even if one of the enzymes recovered its function, the second one would have to do this as well, a very unlikely combination of events. Why might this be? It is quite possible that the failure of one enzyme has contributed to the failure of the second enzyme. Once the blue pathway no longer works, then there will no longer be selection pressure upon the proteins involved in that pathway. Thus, variation produced by mutations occurring elsewhere in that pathway will no longer be under the beady eye of natural selection. So we can see that once a function has been lost, it is likely that this will become even less likely to be reversed with time. In other words, we see constraints coming, ironically, from the release from constraints. In this case the easing of selection pressure allows further mutations to occur, leading to a destruction of the rewind facility.

The increasing likelihood of irreversibility with evolution can be seen as a constraint upon the ability of organisms to respond to cyclic change, such as long term cycles in climate. It would be preferable to be able to return to a former state rather than have to necessarily re-invent the wheel. Certainly there is evidence that reversion to a previous state can happen at times, for example in long term examples of ecological release. Here, the removal of a competitor or predator can lead to significant changes, which may be reversions to some earlier state. Of course, while the failure of one protein can completely disrupt a process, it is much more difficult for a change in one protein to build such a process in the first place. This is a classic situation of one direction being much easier than another. It is easier to destroy than to build. This shouldn't be a surprise, as it conforms to the second law of thermodynamics. However, this bias is a further constraint to increasing variation via mutation.

The context of change: social networking of molecules

The new change generally needs to work within the organismal context, while the organism itself needs to work within the context of its surroundings. No molecule is an island and the social aspect of molecules means that they must co-evolve. The more complex the social network, the more difficult this is. Most of the differences between individual organisms (called *phenotypic variation*) are products of many genes rather than one gene. Mendel's work was a success because he chose extremely simple gene-phenotype systems, producing what is called discontinuous variation. In other words the pea seed was either wrinkled or smooth. More usually, phenotypic traits are products of many genes and the environment. Richard Lewontin (b. 1929), the American evolutionary biologist puts it this way: "*What we can measure is by definition uninteresting and what we are interested in is by definition unmeasurable.*"

The Spandrels of San Marco and molecular sociality

Another interesting outcome of the social nature of molecules is the idea of the spandrel. Lewontin and Stephen Jay Gould (1941-2002), one of the most important evolutionary biology thinkers of the twentieth century, set forth an analogy based on the spandrels of San Marco in Venice. A spandrel is an architectural feature that arises from the meeting of two arches. It is a consequence of the support structure for the great dome in San Marco cathedral. Gould and Lewontin argued that it is a bi-product, which has found use in having some beautiful and ornate murals painted on it, perfectly fitted to its triangular form. One could imagine that the spandrel was designed to have these paintings on it, but, actually, the murals were not the reason for the spandrels to be built. In a similar way, many adaptations may have arisen as by-products of molecular sociality, which then found uses. In the same way as mutations are not directed, *per se*, to achieve a particular change in a protein, so the evolution of pathways, through new interactions created by new protein structure, will not be driven by some end product either. They may, in the end, find a relevant role and be selected for, but were not fitted towards that role (the exact meaning of the word adaptation: *ad* towards, *aptation* to fit.). This is reminiscent of the origin of oxygen, as a waste product of photosynthesis, yet now a key player in terms of how our Biosphere functions.

Of course the mutation, if it is to be systemic, must have occurred in the gamete, or gamete-producing cells, in the first place. If the organism undergoes sexual reproduction, then the mutation must survive the process of sexual selection, either indirectly or directly. Whatever happens, its own survival will be down to its fellow genes too. Has the mutation occurred in a fit individual, or one that is likely not to reproduce anyhow? Also whether or not the new property is a dominant one or a recessive one will impact upon it. Finally, if a point mutation occurs in a cell before it divides, then only half the reproductive gametes will have it, as the DNA splits in two during cell division.

Directed mutations: altering the constraints?

So we see that there are many constraints upon the mutation process. Each limits the mutation rate at a particular level. Possible changes in mutation rates are dependent on changes of these constraints. Two interesting aspects arise from this. In 1988, John Cairns of Harvard discovered that bacteria under stress were more likely to experience mutations that would have beneficial impact. His work caused huge controversy, as it appeared to undermine a crucial premise of neo-Darwinian evolution, that mutations are random. The theory became known as *directed mutation.* Fairly soon after its conception, it was recognized that the mutations were not directed towards a particular goal, and so the term *adaptive mutation* came into use. Elevation in mutation rate in bacteria occurs when part of the proof-reading system is relaxed, thus allowing more mutations to slip through the net. Whatever the cause, the end product is an increase in mutation, and thus an increase in the variation upon which natural selection can act. This doesn't actually get in the way of the neo-Darwinists' requirement for random mutations, but does show that changing the constraints upon the mutation process can lead to a faster response to an environmental stress. This is taken to the extreme in viruses, which never have correction systems in place.

So we see that the constraints of chemistry, both outwith and within the organism, have a significant impact on what is possible, in terms of evolution. The games of chemistry are themselves limited by the rules of physics, but, the rules of chemistry determine what games biology can play. What then of biology? Does it also constrain what can happen or is it purely a pawn?

Chapter Fourteen

Biological Boundaries: Limits Imposed by the Living

Biological constraints, ultimately, are derivations, games played to the rules of chemistry and physics. It is difficult to separate consequences from causes. There are constraints, however, that are related to the whole organism, and the biological and physical environments within which they live. Biological constraints ultimately stem from the consequences of the first and second laws of thermodynamics. Energy cannot be created (from the first law) and so must be acquired, in order to sustain life within an entropic universe (second law). From these constraints, arise the two great challenges in life: survival and reproduction.

Survival requires the acquisition of energy, and the delay of death. Death eventually comes to everything, due to the inability of an organism to maintain its structure and function indefinitely. Some organisms can live a very long time. A creosote bush has been aged at 11 000 years old. This is nothing compared to *Bacillus sphaericus*, a bacterium whose resistant spores were recovered from the stomach of a bee, found in the Dominican Republic, that had been encased in amber 40 million years ago. These spores were revived in the laboratory by Monica Borucki in 1995, while working on a Masters degree in California. While not actively living during the intervening 40 million years, they were not dead! Another species of bacterium, *Bacillus permians*, was brought back to life after an estimated 250 million years by Russell Vreeland and colleagues in 2000, although doubts exist as to the validity of this latter finding.

The big restaurant

As Woody Allen once famously scripted, in *Love and Death*, "*To me, nature is...I dunno, spiders and bugs and, big fish eating little fish, and plants eating plants and animals eating…it's like an enormous restaurant*". In this restaurant, the majority of animals die before they can reproduce. Defending against disease and predation, and offending in terms of energy acquisition, are key processes along with attempting to limit the loss of energy. Maintenance of internal temperature has led to the evolution of warm bloodedness. For example, the arctic fox can maintain a body temperature of 30 degrees centigrade in an atmospheric temperature of -70 degrees centigrade, a difference of 100 degrees! However, this in itself accounts for up to 80% of the energy expenditure in mammals, thus putting a greater pressure on resource acquisition.

Reproduction is also energetically expensive. With the exception of asexual reproduction, it occurs in a population setting, and brings with it sexual selection, which, as we have seen, can create very different pressures from natural selection. These pressures lead to differences in the sexes, or sexual dimorphism, which again adds constraints upon evolution.

It is the fact that organisms, like molecules, are social that creates many of the constraints on evolution of diversity. They have to fit into a community setting, and their success is limited by the success of that community. If one part of the community suffers, then many organisms may be affected. The extinction of a pollinator may lead to the extinction of the plant reliant on its services. For example, many Hawaiian honeycreepers face extinction, often due to introduced bird malaria. As a result, the plants dependent on these birds also face extinction, as their flowers are specifically designed for their pollinator.

Constraints from the multifunctional organism

One of the great constraints upon evolution is the challenge of needing to find multiple solutions at the same time. Imagine an organism that wakes up one sunny morning and recognizes that it is the product of a long, long line of evolutionary steps over many generations. It is the sum of an overall sub-optimal set of solutions to a myriad of challenges in an ever changing world. The constraint of multiple challenges is a significant one. Rarely is there freedom to put in place the ideal solution to a single problem. Even if this was possible, by the time the solution was brought together over generations, it will usually lag behind the changing environment, both physical and biological.

The English author, Reverend Charles Dodgson (1832-1898), better known by his *nom du plume*, Louis Carroll, made an unexpected contribution to evolutionary biology when Alice, the leading character in *Through the looking Glass*, came upon an unusual character called the Red Queen, a chess piece that became alive. At one point in the story, Alice had gone to meet the queen. Alice discovered that there was a huge game of chess going on and asked the red queen if she could take part. It was agreed that Alice could be the White Queen's pawn. First she had to get to the right square on the giant board. The Queen and Alice ran as fast as they could, but made no progress. After running and running, all the trees and bushes and hills were in exactly the same place. The Red Queen explained: '*Now, here, you see, it takes all the running you can do, to keep in the same place. If you want to get somewhere else, you must run at least twice as fast as that!*'

In 1973, Leigh van Valen (b. 1935) recognized that in evolution, a similar situation exists. As each species evolves advantages, so other species will need to evolve in ways to cancel out these advantages. This has been termed a co-evolutionary arms race. Life forms can be seen to be evolving just to stand still; otherwise they will be left behind. Of course it isn't that simple. Due to the constraints related to the multiple challenges impacting on an organism at any one time, and the social constraints within and outwith the organism, rarely is it possible for a simple arms race to exist. Organisms cannot direct their evolution in terms of an arms race. They can experience changes, often highly constrained, that may or may not include a contribution towards military activity, but these changes are random and tested within a multidisciplinary arena. It is like a government whose foreign policy towards a particular nation is likely to be the product of many pressures, only a few of which relate directly to the nation concerned.

So there is an inherent constraint on success, due to co-evolution. This constraint is an essential component in the balance of things.

As systems evolve, a glass ceiling will be reached. This is called the Peter Principle, after Laurence Peter, a Canadian teacher. Peter developed his thoughts in 1968, showing that in many companies, people get promoted because they are good at what they do, and this continues until they reach the ceiling of their abilities, in a post where they are no longer very good. Because demotion is unlikely, that is where they stay. Thus, the positions of senior management are normally filled by people who aren't very good at the job! In evolutionary terms, organisms evolve to handle the easy issues, but eventually get stuck with some difficult challenge. Thus all life in the end struggles, no matter how advanced, because of the constraining principle of something always being one step beyond their level of adaptive potential.

Imperfection as a necessary constraint

This brings us to another constraint, that of imperfection. Many processes rely on imperfection or inefficiency. We have already noted imperfection in DNA sequence proof-reading, allowing some mutations to occur. A perfect proof reading system would severely restrict evolution. Many plants rely on imperfect granivory (eating of their seeds). Squirrels and ants will often bury stashes of seeds, and forget about some of them, allowing some seeds to germinate and grow into trees. The fig wasp lays her eggs in the developing seeds of figs, but doesn't lay them in every seed, thus allowing some of the seeds to survive. Of course, imperfection is a consequence of community level interactions. If the fig wasp destroyed all the fig seeds, then there would eventually be no fig trees left. Thus a balance is reached between efficiency and imperfection. This, by the way, forms another interesting argument against the concept of the selfish gene.

What is perfect for one organism in terms of maximising a specific process will not be perfect for the longer term survival of its later generations. The level of imperfection is critical here. Imperfection is often possible due to the fact that the context of life is not always a completely limiting environment. Although the squirrel uses energy in building up its stash of nuts, there is no need for 100% efficiency in converting this harvest into consumed food. The odd forgotten collection of nuts will not, generally, be disastrous. Indeed, it is this leeway that facilitates the tree species' success. The degree of imperfection attached to any task will have a huge effect on the wider community, and in the direction that evolution can take. I call this the *squirrel effect*!

As humans, we have started to make attempts at improving efficiency, and getting rid of imperfection. What impacts this may have are not known, but it is likely that many areas of imperfection actually have a function and by altering the balance, we will have a devastating impact. One example already noticed is the impact of increased perfection of harvesting equipment in agriculture. Formerly we would cut and bind sheaths by hand, and quite a few heads of grain would be left behind, which helped feed wild animals and birds. Now with much more efficient combine harvesters and the like, very little grain is left for wild animals, and this has led to starvation and death, even threatening some species with extinction.

The constraint of the organism

It is not just the outside world that the organism is racing against. The organism itself provides constraints to solutions. Every solution brings with it costs, both in terms of resources needed, and in terms of its impacts on other solutions within the organism. For example an organism may be faced with the problem of dispersing seed as far as possible. By making the seed extremely small, and therefore, light, this should lead to better dispersion. However by doing this, the store of energy on board the seed, needed to allow germination and initial growth, will be extremely limited. This will reduce its chances of competing upon landing. An organism may want to have a huge set of tail feathers, like the Argus pheasant, in order to attract a mate, but this in turn may slow it down when fleeing from a predator. Compromise usually is the end result, as natural selection may apply the brakes to an otherwise runaway train.

The constraints of history: the legacy of the past

Another set of constraints are the ghosts from Christmas past. The further down the taxonomic hierarchy we go, from domain, to kingdom, to class, to family, to genus, to species, we see increasing diversity and a shift in the constraints. It is like going down from the top of a pyramid to the bottom. At the top, there are a few kingdoms; each of them has a number of classes below them and so on, resulting in a huge number of species at the bottom. Of course, this whole system is set in place by the way in which we define and classify the Biosphere. Each level will be constrained by that definition. The categories often reflect big developmental constraints on everything below that level of organization. The tetrapod body plan, the vertebral column, the placenta, the flower, all offer great advantages, but also create constraints.

Take, for example, flowering plants that have evolved on land, developing pollination as the means of reproduction. Some of these lineages have returned to an aquatic existence. Erasmus Darwin, the grandfather of Charles, concluded that water was damaging to pollen and therefore "*it seems necessary that the marriages of plants be celebrated in the open air*"! While some aquatic plants have mastered pollination under water, others go to extreme lengths to continue with aerial pollination. The constraints on pollination, set in place on land, have led to some elaborate processes in maintaining this approach. One of the most sophisticated approaches is taken by *Vallisneria spiralis*, a species of eel grass. Eelgrass is dioecious, that is, male and female plants are separate individuals. Male plants produce short flower stalks, and the plant remains underwater at all times. Female plants have long stalks allowing the flower to break the water surface. The male flowers are released, unopened, and float to the water surface. They then open, and the stamens act as sails. Meanwhile, when the female flowers break the surface, still attached to their stalks, their unwettable stigmas bend backwards and form a meniscus. The free moving male flowers are blown about with their "sails" and tumble into the depression around the females, literally falling in love! Fertilization then occurs following which the stalk of the female flower coils, and draws the now fertilized female flower back under the water, where the fruit develops. Erasmus Darwin first described this process in 1790, and the Reverend William Paley, a proponent of Natural Theology, cited it as an evidence for the existence of God! *Hydrilla verticillata*, uses a similar approach, but when male flowers float to the surface, they catapult their pollen through the air into the female flowers. Whether god-given or not, these plants show how constraints in terms of past lifestyles can lead to extravagant efforts to overcome such limitations.

By the time we reach the species level of organization, things are fairly much in a straight jacket. Our little organism that has just awoken in a moment of self-realization, quickly recognizes that its future generations are limited by a number of significant developmental constraints. Like RUBISCO, the key enzyme in sugar synthesis, which is constrained by its oxygen habit, so there are many aspects of the design in each species that are not easily changed.

The constraint of the population

At the population level, there are significant limitations upon population density. The number of individuals that can exist is limited by resources, and a habitat has what is known as a carrying capacity. Above a certain number of individuals, the habitat can no longer sustain any increase in the population. The main limit is energy, although a build up of toxic waste products may also contribute, as can oxygen levels, particularly in water. Evolution is limited by such constraints. The concept of limitations upon the growth of human populations was first developed by Thomas Robert Malthus (1766-1834), the English political economist. This great Malthus effect of competition at the coal face, on the edge of the carrying capacity, supported by over-production, came to dominate early evolutionary thinking, especially in development of the meaning and power of natural selection. Yet the reason for the vast reduction in numbers in nature is, generally, nothing to do with selection within a tightly competitive, resource-limited arena. Most habitats are not at their carrying capacity for a particular organism. For a tree, many seeds will be infertile, many will be lost to habitats where they cannot grow, many will be eaten by granivores (grain eaters) and many will be eaten, as young seedlings, by herbivores, or die of disease. None of these are anything to do with competition for resources. The other thing to remember is that an oak tree may live for over 400 years, and so has plenty of time to produce seeds.

Humans, on the other hand, represent a different case. The population explosion over the last 250 years has led to us reaching and surpassing our natural carrying capacity. In order to sustain the population, we have had to use vast amounts of energy to artificially raise the carrying capacity of our habitats. By doing this we have created issues of pollution and altered our climate, impacting on many other species. Yet the key point is that our situation of overpopulation is not at all representative of much of the Biosphere over evolutionary time. No other organism has the luxury of altering its environment to allow population increase in the way that we have. Let's go back to our oak tree. Only one in every ten thousand acorns will result in a tree. However the reason for this is not related to competition. Acorns are predated upon. Their success will be determined by where they fall or where they are carried. Often an animal will bury them and forget about them. None of these things has anything to do with carrying capacity, and the surviving individual, while needing to be able to grow into a tree, may well be the only survivor, but given the ways in which the other members have met their deaths, not necessarily the fittest. Indeed, a healthy, big, fat acorn may be more attractive to a granivore than a weak, skinny one!

There is a significant difference between being alive and being the fittest. Of course there will be instances where the survivor would be among the fittest genotypes on offer. Certainly significant weakness, or lack of fitness, will reduce the chances of survival. However the ability of an acorn to determine its survival due to its fitness, in the face of random distribution, stony ground, fires and forgetful squirrels is a difficult concept to accept. Furthermore, if an acorn had a genome that improved its ability to influence the memory of the squirrel, direct its path from the tree to a nice patch of nutrient-rich ground and extinguish the fire, then why aren't some trees producing thousands of offspring each year? Or even a couple of trees? What other constraints may or may not be related to the population?

Island constraints

Speciation would appear to occur much more readily on isolated oceanic islands, or groups of islands, like Hawaii or the Galapagos islands, compared to the mainland. On the mainland, larger populations will often lead to the *status quo*, maintaining a given species in a stable way. On islands, small populations are more likely to contain extreme samples of the mainland group, and thus have the potential to breed and produce very different organisms. It is like imagining a whole set of people with different coloured hats. If we pick five people out, they may, by chance, all have the same coloured hats. When these people decided which colour of hat to wear in the hat shop, it turned out that their decision was related to other parts of their character, particularly what colour of food they liked to eat. So our five individuals all eat pink food. If we put them on an island, they will likely produce offspring who wear pink hats, and who also have a tendency towards pink food, which is very different from the mainland. Another constraint can be mentioned with this analogy. What if the island did not contain any pink food? In this case, they would either die, or have to develop a different diet. Thus, evolution on islands can be restricted in terms of the possibilities available.

One positive aspect of island life is that while you may have made it to the island, some of your competitors, predators or diseases may not, and so this may allow a release of some of the constraints upon future generations. The changes that occur can give us an insight into how constraints actually impact upon life. Fijian fruit bats become more active during the day in the absence of predatory eagles. Many lemur species on Madagascar are diurnal, even though equipped with the organs for night vision, and this is thought to be due to missing predators. Meadow voles in Canada become indiscriminate of habitat type if their predator, the northern short-tailed shrew, is missing. Birds on islands without predators often lose bright markings and revert to simpler songs than when predators are present. This is interesting in that it may be thought that bright plumage would be a disadvantage in the presence of a predator, attracting attention. Instead these findings point towards a role for bright plumage in deterring predators. Plants become less showy on islands, and this is often accompanied by a change from being animal-pollinated to being wind-pollinated, since the pollinating species may not have accompanied the plant to the island.

The altitude, area and remoteness of an island will have significant impacts on what can evolve there. Biogeographical considerations as a whole are important. One interesting example is the concept of ecological distance. The island of Mona lies half way between Puerto Rico and Hispaniola, yet of its forty two species of butterfly, nine are found in Puerto Rico, and none on Hispaniola. The reason for this is that the wind direction is constant, from Puerto Rico to Hispaniola, and so although Mona is geographically equidistant between the two land masses, the ecological distance is very different. From Puerto Rico, Mona is downwind, and so butterflies can reach it. From Hispaniola, as far as the butterflies are concerned, Mona might as well be on the far side of the Moon!

On the subject of butterflies and islands, the needs of a population of butterflies change dramatically during their life history. As larvae, they are leaf eaters (foliovores) and need to find plants that are suitable. As adults, they often feed on nectar, and this can involve using different plants. Thus, landing on an island is fine, but for the population to persist, both suitable leaves and flowers must be available, and these will need to be close enough to the plants with which the butterfly species evolved a relationship back on the mainland, since, usually, there are highly specific chemical and structural restrictions on both herbivory and nectar feeding. This limitation is thought to have reduced endemism in Pacific butterfly species.

Longer term constraints

Constraints can come from long term cyclical or at least re-occurring events. Many species carry with them aptations that are only used every few generations, and otherwise, form a cost. However when a sporadic event, such as a hurricane or a fire, occurs, species with particular investment in strategies related to surviving these will come to the fore. It's a bit like a little boy who is sent to school every day with a huge, heavy rucksack. The other students ask what he is carrying, and, looking in the rucksack, he explains it's a set of flippers, a wetsuit, oxygen tanks and a mask. His performance at sports day is never good, as he lumbers along with the extra load, and he returns exhausted from school each day. He finally plucks up the courage to ask his father why he has to carry this stuff around. After all, they are hundreds of miles from the sea. His father replies that he doesn't know, but that his parents made him carry the same stuff around all of his life. Then one day it rains like it never has before. The whole country is flooded. Only the little boy and his family are able to survive thanks to the heavy bag that each has carried. The little boy thought to himself that he finally understood the reason. Plants with expensive strategies, stored for a "rainy day" will often be at a disadvantage when in competition with invading species. While these invasive species may dominate for a number of generations, without the extra expense, they eventually may succumb to a sporadic event, which will restore the balance of nature over time. However this strategy may fail, if, in the intervening period, the native plants are out-competed to the point of extinction.

Constraints from the community

The community setting provides another key constraint, that of the successional stage. All communities fit into a bigger picture, called a time line. New communities, found, for example, on young sand dunes, in the aftermath of a volcanic eruption or where a glacier has retreated, gradually change through time, transforming into different units of diversity. Depending on the age of the community at which an organism thrives, certain characteristics related to that successional stage of community development will constrain the distribution and function of that organism. If we take a sand dune succession as an example, the organisms that can live on the young dunes near the shore are very different than those that live on the older dunes. Each set of organisms is geared towards the habitat in which they exist. Early successional habitats tend to be ruderal (that is, highly changeable and unstable, with high mortality rates), with opportunists dominating, while older communities are home to longer term, competitive strategies. Thus the freedom to evolve in one particular habitat will be constrained by the life history characters that are needed to match the challenges of that particular stage in community development.

Diversification is thus restricted by the community within which a species exists, and there are stringent job requirements. These are not controlled by the organism, or its genes, but rather are a product of ecosystem interactions, both physical and biological.

Specialization brings constraints of itself, and the necessity to fit within a particular community limits the range of specializations that are possible. In the end, each stage of community development must happen, otherwise later stages cannot occur. Thus all species in a particular level of community organization cannot evolve into a different level without being replaced. This is interesting, because it suggests that a change from being an opportunist to being a competitive strategist is somehow not feasible for most things. Think of a production line in a factory, where one group puts wheels on a car and another group puts steering wheels on. If all the guys who put wheels on decided to retrain to put steering wheels on, then the car would not work. The reverse would be true too – a car with wheels but no steering would not work either. Another way of looking at this is that if some organisms converted from one role to another, then there would be vacancies advertised for their original job. Thus the make up of the workforce is not determined by the members of the workforce, but rather by the jobs that need to be done. Just because a person who fits tyres on a car retrains as a candy floss maker, it doesn't mean that he will necessarily remain part of the workforce. There are significant constraints related to the niches that are available. Theodore Geisel, the children's book writer from America, who worked under the alias of Dr Seuss, summed this up in his book, *On Beyond Zebra!* in 1955:

"And Nuh is the letter I use to spell Nutches
Who live in small caves, known as Niches, for hutches.
These Nutches have troubles, the biggest of which is
The fact there are many more Nutches than Niches.
Each Nutch in a Nich knows that some other Nutch
Would like to move into his Nich very much.
So each Nutch in a Nich has to watch that small Nich
Or Nutches who haven't got Niches will snitch."

In the end, the job opportunities will constrain diversity. Of course, niches can be created by the activities of particular organisms also, but we generally see the vacant niche as being the key in many aspects of species diversity.

Shifting niches: the niche as a constraint

The constraint of the niche is also important to consider. Organisms can only exist in a specific set of conditions. If these conditions are not present, then this will not be possible. Evolution is constrained by the conditions at a particular moment in time. Given that the process lags behind the conditions, this makes response to the conditions even more difficult. Niches are likely to shift in space with time, and so we again fall into a red queen situation of sorts, with the organism trying to converse intelligently with its surroundings, but always finding that it is two sentences behind. Niches can also cease to exist. With climate change, many species are moving towards the North and South poles, in order to stay within the temperature range that they need for survival. If the species is growing on an island such as Ireland, eventually they will not be able to move any further north, or they will end up in the ocean, like lemmings heading for the cliffs. Their niche will, in effect, cease to exist. The same happens on mountains. As a climate warms up, species are forced further up the mountain, chasing the shifting niche, in search of the temperatures that they can survive and compete at. However, eventually, even the summit of the mountain may be too hot for them, and they will be outcompeted and disappear, due to their niche moving off the top of the mountains, in a sort of ecological ascension! Thus, no matter how well adapted you are to your niche, the niche will not necessarily be there for ever, leading to your extinction.

Mass extinctions: the ultimate in constraint?

Throughout the history of the Biosphere, there have been a number of events that have transcended all other determinants of diversity on our planet. In these periods, large proportions of living organisms were destroyed. The figures are quite staggering. Perhaps nothing has constrained evolution more than the mass extinctions.

There have been at least five great mass extinction events. The Ordovician event, occurring around 440 million years ago, and named after the geological period at the end of which it occurred, destroyed more than 80% of marine animals including many of the trilobites. Back then, South America, Africa, Australia and Antarctica were all joined together as one giant supercontinent, Gondwana. As mentioned in Chapter One, tectonic plates shift around the globe, and through the history of the Biosphere, the arrangement of land masses has altered, leading to significant impacts on the organisms. The map of the world is constantly changing, and 440 million years ago, a large chunk of land found itself moving over the South Pole. The result was a huge glaciation event, lasting up to 1.5 million years, where water was trapped as ice on land, instead of returning to the sea. Rivers dried, and the sea level fell dramatically. This led to the shallow seas around the continents disappearing, as water levels dropped below the continental shelves. As in all mass extinctions, disaster brings opportunity, and following the great extinction event, the invasion of land by animals and the appearance of more advanced plants on land began, along with the appearance of bony fish in the seas.

The next big event hit the Earth around 360 million years ago. Another global cooling is suspected as the cause, and the result was another significant extinction event, destroying 70% of all species, and particularly affecting corals and almost all of the jawless fish (Agnatha). Of these jawless fish, only lampreys and hagfish still survive to this day. Once again the extinction was followed by opportunity. Following this event, several groups of animals appeared, including insects, amphibians and reptiles, as the land fauna, in particular, took off.

Then, around 250 million years ago, the mother (and the big daddy) of all mass extinctions occurred. Called the Permian mass extinction, but also known, more appropriately, as "the great dying", its cause remains uncertain, with huge volcanic events in Siberia, an asteroid and glaciation all indicted. This event was to kill 90% of all marine species, and 70% of all land species. Trilobites, the ancient arthropods that had reigned on Earth for at least 250 million years, and that had survived the other two great extinctions, finally succumbed to the Permian wipe-out, never to return. The destruction was huge, and for millions of years afterwards, the Earth was occupied by mostly opportunist species in a scene reminiscent of the movies depicting the planet after a huge nuclear war. There was a massive restructuring of entire biomes, leading to the ecosystems that basically exist today. In this great rebirth of the Biosphere, mammals, modern reptiles and dinosaurs eventually emerged anew.

The fourth mass extinction, the End Triassic event, occurred around 200 million years ago. Its cause is unknown, but well may have been a volcanic eruption. Many mammal-like reptiles went extinct, thus this extinction is thought to have had a key influence on how mammals evolved after this point. Following on, the dinosaurs massively expanded their range, and we see the arrival of the birds also. Crocodiles, turtles, lizards and frogs also emerged.

The final member of the big five wipe outs is probably the most famous, the K/T mass extinction. It occurred at the end of the Cretaceous (traditionally abbreviated to K) and marked the beginning of the Tertiary (abbreviated to T), 65 million years ago. Dinosaurs were the famous losers, but flying reptiles were also lost as well as many marine reptiles, and many of the ancient groups of birds. While recent findings point to the existence of large predatory mammals, called *Repenomamus,* existing before this event, mammal and bird diversification did not really explode until after the K/T. There are two competing theories as to the cause, but in reality, both probably played a role. In

1980, Luis Alvarez and a team including his son, Walter, discovered that sediment samples from this time, from around the world, contained a higher than background level of the rare element, Iridium. The significance of this relates to the fact that Iridium is an extremely heavy element, and is rare in the Earth's crust. Most of it is in the mantle. However asteroids contain high levels of this element. A proposed impact site was determined, on the Yucatan peninsula of Mexico. The other theory is that the Iridium came from the mantle, resulting from a huge volcanic event in India and Pakistan, an area now known as the Deccan traps.

So mass extinctions have had dramatic effects upon the diversity of the Biosphere, removing whole groups of organisms and opening up parts of the canvas for new painting. Following these great catastrophes, it can take millions of years for the Biosphere to restructure. Recovery suggests a return to some former state, but the Biosphere is a very different entity following a mass extinction. As many of the mass extinctions have different causes, or combinations of causes, each one is different. Thus, there is unlikely to be a group, or groups, of organisms that are adapted to survive all of these. As we have seen, the trilobites made it through the Ordovician and Devonian extinctions, but came unstuck in the Permian.

The key challenge to the Biosphere is that it is not a matter of some ecosystems surviving and others not, but rather whole trophic levels and successional stages within each ecosystem are often destroyed. This means that it can take a very long time for an ecosystem to re-establish. This may well involve the need for new species to evolve, if there is no surviving organism capable of playing a particular role. However, the vacant niches left by mass extinctions also provide constrained opportunities, that is, openings in particular roles. Evolution may then be able to morph into these opportunities, but more of that in the next chapter.

So we have seen that there are constraints upon evolution, limiting what is possible. Physics constrains chemistry, chemistry constrains biology, and biology itself imposes limitations. What we need to ask now is how limiting are these constraints? As evolution operates within special and temporal contexts, is it destined to go in one particular direction, or is it luck that we have ended up where we are?

Chapter Fifteen

Contingency and Determinism: a Requiem for Lady Luck?

As we watch our river, and see thousands of pedalos released downstream, it is clear that the constraints that act at a physical, chemical and biological level have significant influence on what can exist. The Biosphere today is a product of all of these. It echoes historical constraint, and indeed, is more associated with this than with the present, given the lag that exists between species traits and the environment. The question we now have to ask is this: how constraining are these constraints?

Imagine going into a recording studio, and looking at a vast mixing desk, with hundreds of sliding control levers. Each lever represents one of the constraints we have mentioned. We can slide it up and make it stronger, or slide it down and make it weaker. If we start changing the positions of some of these levers, what impact would it have on what the present Biosphere looks like? Surely the alteration of some constraints would have a greater impact than the alteration of others. The absence of entropy or the weak nuclear interaction would have a much more significant effect than the impact of community development or imperfection. However, altering the strengths of any constraint will have a significant impact. Even slight alteration will have consequences. What then if we do not change the constraints, but rather set up a parallel universe, with exactly the same starting point, and let it run its course? How different would things be then?

The life and non-life of George Bailey

This question lies at the heart of contingency theory, developed by Stephen J. Gould in his book, *Wonderful Life* (1989). The book takes its title from the famous movie, made in 1946, of the same name, starring James Stewart and Donna Reed. We find James Stewart's character, George Bailey, on the brink of suicide, on Christmas

Eve, when an angel arrives to stop him. We then go through a number of snapshots of Bailey's life, each one showing a caring man whose actions helped the people around him.

The angel shows George what his hometown would be like if he hadn't existed. Everything was different and everyone was miserable. Many of the people George helped in his life are dead or ruined in this alternative world. George realizes that, indeed, his life was, in fact, wonderful.

Gould was struck by the huge diversity of body plans of organisms found in the amazing collection of creatures found high in the Canadian Rockies, called the Burgess Shale. This extraordinary assemblage had been discovered by Charles Doolittle Walcott (1850-1927), the American palaeontologist, while he was on a working holiday with his family in 1909. It was quite a fortuitous find. On the last day of his vacation, his wife's horse slipped, and Walcott dismounted to move some rocks out of the way. As he did so, he inadvertently cracked open one of the rocks, and there, encased for half a billion years, lay a beautifully detailed fossil. He returned the following year and began uncovering a remarkable collection of fossilized remains, representing a snapshot of life some 520 million years ago. Gould felt that the generation of so many diverse forms, and the subsequent demise of a large number of them, were products, and victims, of luck. In his famous analogy, Gould used the theme of the movie, where the film of George Bailey's life is re-run, but without him in it, to examine how things could be different if we re-ran the film of life on Earth. Would it always be the same? Would you be sitting reading this book?

Despite a revision of the Burgess Shale fauna that now indicates that many of the species may actually be related to existent species, the diversity is still immense, and many of the creatures represent completely different types of organism, the likes of which do not exist today. So the role of lady luck needs to be assessed. For example, when a mass extinction visits the Biosphere, do the survivors make it through design, or luck? Would evolution eventually produce similar replacements? If particular species went extinct, how different could life be on Earth today? Gould focused on *Pikaia*, thought to be an early chordate, and thus a potential ancestor to humans. If *Pikaia* had been removed (and we don't know if it was, or whether or not its demise would have halted chordate evolution), could there not have been convergent evolution from another group, possibly related to *Pikaia*, that would have taken its place? We can also ask to what extent is lady luck limited by the constraints that we have discussed in this chapter. How random is the evolution of the Biosphere? Are constraints sufficient to prevent contingency and act as a determinant force? Let us try to answer these questions.

Will lady luck's random but alluring dance be smothered by the damp blanket of constraint?

The impacts of constraints and of contingency work in opposite directions. If we take any moment in the history of the Biosphere and freeze time, then, surely, we predict what will happen next. Imagine the scene: the Sun hangs in the sky as a cat is frozen, mid-leap, and a mouse stares at its predator in fear and tension. This entire tableau, akin to some morbid nativity scene, with all of the characters poised but never fulfilling their potential, stripped of all kinetic energy, holds within it an inevitability. The Sun will set, the mouse will be caught and the leaping cat will land.

It is not a matter of running the film of life on Earth again, but rather, stopping it, looking at a single frame of the movie, and asking if, given the events in the frame, we can be sure of what will happen in the next frame. If we understand everything related to the events in the first frame, then what happens in the next frame will be completely predictable.

The constraints will act on every level of organization in the frame, with atoms and communities all coming under the laws of physics. Given an understanding of all things, and given that this state of omniscience can exist, then there would appear to be little room for contingency. If the next frame in the reel of film is a consequence of the previous frame, then if we re-run these two frames of the film of life again, we would get exactly the same sequence of events.

Interestingly, it is this predictability that allows life to exist at all. There would be no point in having a fairly rigid set of structures, of having DNA correction upon replication, of having predictable coding of amino acids, if everything was random. Changing conditions are not the same as random conditions. Yet this is the problem of factoring luck into the equation. How much luck do you insert? How random do things get?

Contingency and time travel

Contingency has much in common with the science fiction genre of time travel. The history of time travel fiction is as darkly hidden as the history of natural selection, but the first time machine appeared in *El Anacronópete*, by Enrique Gaspar y Rimbau, the Spanish writer and diplomat, in 1887. Time travel has always brought with it the fear that if you travel back in time, and change anything, there will be consequences for the future world from whence you came. A common theme is for the traveller, on returning to the point in time from where he first left, to discover a terribly contorted world, all thanks to his having crushed an insect, or having killed a small child. This difficulty with time travel has long been recognized, and reaches its perplexing apogee in the Grandfather Paradox, which reflects that if you went back in time and caused the death of your grandfather before he had met your grandmother, then you would not have been born, and thus could not have travelled back in time. This would have allowed your grandfather to meet your grandmother, therefore leading to your birth after all!

Igor Novikov (b. 1935), the Russian astrophysicist, in his Self-Consistency Principle, stated that any change that led to the alteration of the future could not take place. In the Biosphere, while the issue is not that of the future affecting the past, we still need to consider how constrained are the events that occur, with the future needing to be consistent with the past. This, in turn, finds resonance with fatalism and predeterminism, wherein the future remains the same even if change is attempted. Determinism, on the other hand, has room for the hypothetical possibility of an alternative outcome. It can be argued that if we knew everything, then there would be no unknown. Yet our lack of knowledge will have no impact on the outcome. Thus the world acts as if we knew everything. In other words, stochastic events are only stochastic because we don't fully understand them. Emergent properties in the end can be explained. This is a separate issue from the Heisenberg Uncertainty Principle, which has important implications for sub-atomic physics, but has negligible effects at the macroscopic scale. If determinism is merely accurate prediction, then an end point can be predicted if everything is known. This does not make the end point the cause or reason, but does lend an air of inevitability, and rather undermines the role of lady luck.

So we can argue that what has happened, in the end, is what has happened, and the present Biosphere is the product of these events. At any one time, of the range of options that may have been on offer, one happened and the others didn't. That is the reality. The cat fell to Earth, it didn't carry on at a tangent, nor did it disappear into the sky. An asteroid that collides with the Earth was always going to do so, given the series of events that occurred around it. Tectonic plate movement led to the separation of Madagascar from Africa. It wasn't luck; it was merely the result of physics. Indeed, the probability of getting heads when spinning a coin is one hundred percent, if the exact conditions of the spin are replicated. So if we run the film of life again, it could be argued that we would get exactly the same outcome.

Making and missing the train

Movies have explored this whole issue. In *Sliding Doors*, a 1998 film starring Gwyneth Paltrow, the plot explores contingency. Helen, the central character, is running for a train. The film examines what happens in her life if she catches the train, or she misses the train. Thus, in effect, we end up with two comparable Helens (played by one incomparable Gwyneth!). Would Helen have missed the train? It depends on how random the events surrounding her actually are. We don't have the luxury of a parallel universe, or two copies of Gwyneth Paltrow, with which to carry out this experiment.

Many of the constraints that we have discussed earlier can be seen to have a strong impact on the process of diversification in the Biosphere. It is hard to escape the logic of this, yet the thought of existence being completely determined, where freedom is merely a mirage, and choice just a state of mind, does not rest well with us. However the alternative is more difficult to defend. Also, if we do inject contingency into the process, how much do we inject? What could be different? How much would change in our parallel universe? Surely the asteroid would hit in the same spot as before, with the same velocity and with the same consequences. We may not be able to predict the future, but that doesn't mean that the future is unpredictable. So like Helen in the movie, if we make the train, then we make the train, and, if we ran the film of time again, there is a good chance that she'd make the train every time. It is not the randomness or otherwise of the process that is of real interest, but rather the process itself.

Leaving aside how the Biosphere might look if we did the whole thing again, we instead need to focus on why it looks the way that it does in the first place. In attempting to understand this, attention has focussed on natural selection, since Darwin and Wallace presented their work. In the next chapter, we examine their theory in detail and identify significant problems with it that point to a very different explanation about how evolution works.

Chapter Sixteen

Darwinism and Neo-Darwinism: Flickering Follies in Caveworld

Having seen how the diversity of life is structured, and how constraints play a key role in determining what diversity is possible, we need to now consider the engine of diversity. What drives the whole process forward? Obviously Charles Darwin's *On the Origin of Species by Means of Natural Selection, or the Preservation of Favoured Races in the Struggle for Life (1859)*, and the subsequent discovery of the gene, leading to neo-Darwinism, lie at the heart of the predominate scientific theory of why the Biosphere is shaped in the way that it is. It was Darwin who popularized the term *natural selection*. It is widely accepted that this term was inspired by the breeding of animals, such as pigs and pigeons, where artificial selection is carried out. Darwin used this analogy, nature selecting what would survive or thrive.

Historical baggage

Well before we had any knowledge of the basis of variation, Darwin posited that given the large number of offspring that are born, and the fact that only some of them continue to exist, survival would depend on how well the organism was fitted to the environment in which it operated. The English economist, Herbert Spencer (1820-1903), developed the term *survival of the fittest*, inspired by Darwin's work, but within the context of social economics. Both *natural selection* and *survival of the fittest* carried with them some baggage as is inevitable with any analogy or metaphor. A number of questions immediately come to mind, which we will endeavour to address in this chapter. If selection occurs, then what is selected for? How does this selection process work? What is the unit of selection? If the fittest survive, what determines fitness? The problem with introducing a new term, that then becomes the defining statement of an entire theory, especially one as important as evolution, is that once it is established, it becomes difficult to change. As a result, all debate and development of the concept becomes tied to this term. This is classically represented in what happened with natural selection. The problem is that the term has its origin in human choice, breeding of pigs and the like. Have we been limited in our understanding of it by being chained to its historic origin? We know more now, not just about the gene, but about the forces that determine success or failure within the living world. Therefore we seek to ask if natural selection is still the best way to think about the interaction between organisms and their environment.

Political and economic theory also played their parts in the development of Darwinian theory. *Survival of the fittest* aligns with the competitive marketplace, while group altruism stems from socialist thought. For example Prince Pytr Kropotkin (1842-1921) was an anarchist of some fame, having spent time in prison in both Russia and France, and argued that it was co-operation, not competition, that led to the evolution of man. Macroevolution and microevolution map on to macroeconomics and microeconomics. It is no coincidence that economic game theory led to the development of evolutionary game theory. It is interesting that economics, which deals with group interactions on a financial scale, should find a bedfellow in the subject of evolution. It reflects a resource-based, market-driven common ground that is often not recognized by the very proponents of theories using this terminology.

The basics of neo-Darwinism

The present understanding of evolution boils down to a simple set of processes. To recap, individual organisms interact with their environment, and are largely made up of proteins and the products of proteins. These proteins are long chains of amino acids, and the sequence of these amino acids is critical to the functioning of the protein. The order that the amino acids occur in is determined by the DNA, which codes for the amino acids. Random mutations in the DNA, and movement of bits of DNA to different locations, change its code, and this can lead to a change in the sequence of the amino acids, which in turn can lead to a change in the protein function. This, in turn, can lead to a change in the organism, altering its ability to interact with the environment.

In sexually reproducing organisms, each organism will be different than either of its parents, because it is made up of DNA from both of them. Thus a child is never identical to either of its parents, but rather shares half of its DNA with each of its parents. Organisms that do not sexually reproduce are completely different. They form copies of themselves, but these copies may differ if horizontal gene transfer allows some genetic material to be moved into them. Some organisms reproduce vegetatively, by producing clones that are identical to themselves, challenging the concept of individuality. The bulk of evolutionary theory focuses on sexually reproducing organisms in the Eukarya domain which, as we have seen, did not exist for the majority of time over which life has evolved.

The basis of selection

Natural selection results in the differential survival of individuals. The question is: what is selected for and against? This has caused much controversy among biologists. It comes down to how we view the Biosphere in terms of its organization, as we have discussed in Chapter Eight. The genes are part of the genome. The genome is within the individual. The individual is within a population, which is part of a species. The population is also part of a community, and the community is part of an ecosystem. The great difference in viewpoint stems from two origins: firstly, whether we believe that each level of organization is purely the product of the previous level (reductionism), or whether each level of organization has properties that cannot be reduced to a simpler level, and secondly, whether we see the key question as being about replication or interaction with the environment, and which one is the basis of understanding how evolution works.

The unit of selection: candidates and crises

Darwin very much saw the individual as being the key target of selection. The fitter, better-adapted individual will have a greater chance of surviving and reproducing than one less adapted. It is thought that the tragic death of his young daughter strengthened his belief in this. Spencer's *survival of the fittest* came to represent this view. Mendel's work, and the subsequent discovery of DNA, led to a re-evaluation of this area. The DNA was seen as the unit of inheritance, producing the phenotype, but persisting through time. The individual was merely a vehicle, a servant, the public face of the DNA. The DNA was the replicator, while the individual was the interactor. Therefore natural selection, in the end, operated at the level of the DNA. Of course, natural selection could not directly act upon the DNA. However the success or failure of the individual in the end resulted in the success or failure of the DNA.

An early problem became apparent. In sexually reproducing organisms, only 50% of the DNA from any one individual is normally passed to the next generation. Two generations down the road, only 25% of the original DNA is present, and after ten generations, only 0.1 % of the original genome would be present (provided that each generation resulted from the mating of two unrelated individuals). So the genome of an organism is not a long lasting entity, but is mixed at each generation. This being the case, it was decided that it must be the individual genes that were in fact selected for or against. The gene became the currency of variation and the unit of selection, rather than the genome.

Natural selection may identify the gene as the unit of selection, according to this reductionist stance, but the gene is not the level at which selection acts. Genes are dependent for their survival on the interaction of their products, the proteins, which also determine the replication of genes. Within an organism, the proteins interact in a social way, and their usefulness to the organism is usually dependent on a whole lot of other proteins. Conversations occur, groups of proteins operate together, and any change to one protein can have implications on other proteins. There is a great pressure upon the proteins not to change, as very few changes will work to help the organism. We only have to look at a pharmacist's shop to see evidence for this. The medicines available, either on the shelf or on prescription will work for most of us. That is because the large bulk of each of us is basically the same. We have nearly identical biochemical and physiological responses to medicines. We are also psychologically very similar, and so psychologists can generally provide treatments that work for most of us. We are similar in how we learn, thus education is generally delivered in a classroom, often using a national curriculum, and examined in a uniform way. Of course there are subtle differences, but the differences, such as facial details and hair colour, disguise the fact that we are more similar than different. We are also very similar to other species of primates. Diseases that can afflict other primates can be passed on to us. Gorillas can contract measles and bronchopneumonia from humans, and AIDS and the Ebola virus are thought to have possibly infected humans from non-human primates originally.

Why all the drama?

Speciation generally needs dramatic change to occur. Geographic barriers, such as mountain ranges or tectonic plate movements, are often called upon, as is dispersal to a distant oceanic island at the edge of the dispersal range of the species. Mass extinctions lead to spectacular speciation following recovery. Generally, there is a greater pressure to remain as a species than to undergo speciation. The theory of punctuated equilibrium, where long periods of little speciation (equilibrium) are interspersed (or punctuated) with speciation events, points to this same issue. Without some outside agent, the process of evolution is not driven forward by the gene. This all relates to a problem at the heart of our understanding of evolution. The gene is part of a complex whole, and there are many different levels of organization, of which it is only one. Each of these levels is made up of parts from lower levels (e.g. populations are made up of individuals), and forms the building blocks of higher levels of organization (e.g. populations of different species make up communities), but each level also has interactions within itself. It has become clear that each level of organization has properties that cannot be explained by adding up the components of what it is made from. In other words there are emergent, new properties associated with the level itself, only found at that level. Of course, without the gene, there would be no community, but without the community there would be no gene. No man is an island, as John Donne (1572-1631), the English Poet, famously observed, in his *Devotions Upon Emergent Occasions* (1624). Sociality is a core concept, from molecular biology through to psychology, and in each realm it has significant impact. Things interact with other things at every level. The interaction is not always open to reductionism.

The levels of organization

Let us look at the different levels of organization of the Biosphere again, and the concomitant levels of selection that exist. In sexually reproducing eukaryotes, each individual has two copies of most of its genes, usually one being from the father and one from the mother. Exceptions include the Y chromosome (with only one copy in males, and none in females) and the haploid mitochondrial genome. Like two partners in a dance, each pair of genes may be exactly the same (homozygous) or different (heterozygous). We will take an imaginary pair of genes in an imaginary rabbit species. They come in two possible types, one coding for a protein that leads to the rabbit having pink ears, while the other leads to the rabbit having blue ears. As for most genes, one type will be dominant over the other. In this case, pink genes dominate blue genes. If both copies of the gene are the same, then there will be blue or pink ears. If the individual has one of each type, because the father gave one type and the mother gave the other, then the individual will always have pink ears, because the pink ear gene will dominate the blue ear gene. Thus the impact a blue ear gene has, will depend on its partner gene. Imagine now that two individuals of this species live in two different woods, one with a deadly carnivore that only eats creatures with pink markings, and one that only eats creatures with blue markings. The fate of the organism, and thus the genes, will depend on the environment, not the gene. Although the combination of genes determines the ear colour, it is the woods that will determine if the predator can exist in it, and the predator that determines the fate of the gene. This is a very simple example, but clearly shows that the ability of a gene to have any impact is out of its direct control. It depends on the group of two genes, and the environment.

Genetic interactions

So the genome can have an impact on the gene, based on what character its partner gene has. There may also be other pairs of genes that exist in the genome that can over-write the impact of this pair, or there may be yet other genes that colour the rest of the animal blue or pink. In this case, even if the ears are blue, the rest of the animal could be pink, and so the predator that has a taste for pink food will eat the animal, even though the blue ear gene pair was present.

Genetic interactions can be very complex. Generally, genes are part of a genome, and each gene not only finds a new dance partner in each generation, but discovers a whole new set of other pairs of dance partners. As we have said before, most genes stay fairly constant from generation to generation, since any one species (and indeed higher taxonomic levels) are made up of broadly similar characteristics. The dance is not ballroom, where partners pair up for the duration. It is more like a complex céilidh. A céilidh is a type of Scottish dance, which can involve a whole group of dancers in extremely complicated interactions. The author has been based in Scotland for nearly 20 years, but still takes part in these ritualistic celebrations with fear and trepidation, usually creating havoc on the dance floor! Furthermore, it is not just the multiple interactions that demand consideration. The music can change from generation to generation. The environment is always changing, and so this bundle of genes is exposed to new challenges from the environmental orchestra. The stronger the interaction between genes, the more resilient will be the species.

Populations as interacting units

The individual organism finds itself a product of its protein interactions, which identify it as a member of a particular species. It also forms a part of a population, and as such is subservient to a number of population issues. Its ability to find a mate, as we have previously mentioned, will be determined by the options available within that population, as will its quality of offspring. While any one individual is not particularly important to the population, unless, perhaps it is an alpha male in a unimale polygynous structure, the character of the population is key to any one individual in terms of reproductive fitness. Thus the population context is just as important as the genetic context for a gene within any given organism. The size of the population may also have repercussions in terms of its competition for resources and with respect to its ability to defend resources, to defend against predation, or to work together in order to hunt. The population itself is reliant on its individuals to provide genetic variation, and to behave in particular ways. For example if some members act selfishly, that population may be less effective than if they all work together. The population is also affected by the habitat, in terms of how much food is available. This will be a product of biology and geography (location, location, location!). So the habitat will impact upon the individual, not only directly, but through the population. It is a misconception to think that any one individual is significant; it is the group that provides the meaning of a population, and which gives each individual its meaning, particularly within the context of reproductive fitness, in sexually reproducing organisms. Finally, stochastic events, such as volcanic eruptions, drought or flood may have an extreme impact.

Community level interactions

The community is dependent on its populations for its players, and will function only if there are the right types of species present. These species are dependent on each other, either directly or indirectly. If bacteria, fungi and other recycling species are not present, then the nutrient cycle could grind to a halt. If this happens, the whole system would collapse. Similarly, the absence of a top predator could have disastrous consequences for the balance of nature. The community is heavily structured around feeding, and the flow of energy is a key part to community structure. If we think of ecological succession in sand dunes, although the individual species involved at each stage of community development may differ from site to site, the same directional process occurs. The genes are different but the environmental feedback leads to the same procession to a climax community.

The contextual dogma

At this point, we should introduce a new dogma that is more relevant than the Central Dogma (that DNA makes RNA makes proteins). We will call this the Contextual Dogma. Inspired by Karl Popper's writing, it starts with the statement that context is central to any perception of reality. Furthermore, context is central to any process. Gene products must make sense within the context of the organism. In turn, the organism must make sense within the context of the environment. Finally all levels of organization are within a context of the chemical and physical laws, which pervade everything simultaneously, with the last word, '*simultaneously*', being particularly important.

The problematic species again

The other key level of organization in traditional Darwinism is the species. This problem child creates its own set of complexities. The species is a barrier to gene flow, as it will, under the most accepted definition of the word, form a reproductive exclusion zone to genes outwith that species. Speciation that splits one species into two species will prevent future matings between these two species, at least theoretically. Therefore it acts to reduce gene movement. Selfish genes that emerged in one species through mutation and selection may lead to the demise of a competitive species, but will be unable to spread into that species, thus greatly reducing its ability to benefit from useful traits in that second species. A gene trapped in a small population of a species will be unable to bail out into another species. Reproductively, a population can be like a desert island, trapped with its favourite record, book and luxury item, where the genes are stuck. A key question can be asked, the basic format of which can be applied to any subject in order to enhance our understanding of the processes that are important. How different would the ultimate selfish gene machine be from what actually exists? Imagine a group of genes going on strike and demanding better working conditions. What would be written on their placards as they gather around a fire on a cold winter's day? "Down with speciation"? "More speciation"? "Gaia stinks"? "No to sex"? "No to vegetative reproduction"? "No to altruism"? "Love thy neighbour, even if he is a different species"?

Why diversify at all?

The other question to ask is why have all living creatures not merged on the one body plan? Surely, there will be a single bauplan that is optimal? Why bother with anything else? Why diversify at all? A whole world of organisms that can interbreed would be heaven for a gene, allowing the best options to spread universally, with competitive exclusion leading to the fittest organism dominating. Indeed, horizontal gene transfer offers this option, but much less so in eukaryotes. This brings us to one conclusion: there is more than one way to exist, to make a living, to succeed in solving the multiple challenges faced simultaneously. In spite of competition, the way of the world is not to exclude, to have complete victory. The genes and their proteins form many types of individuals, called species, each of which can exist in their own way. The laws of physics and chemistry allow for a wide number of players in their games. There is no ultimate answer, but rather a whole suite of sub-optimal solutions. Interestingly, as we increase the number of problems requiring simultaneous solutions, there will be an increasing number of solutions available. This happens because, there being no single optimal solution, and so no attainable perfection for any one solution, there will be increasing numbers of increasingly sub-optimal solutions.

The stability of the species – a new explanation

So how does evolution work? How come speciation occurs, but yet species themselves are relatively stable entities? Mutation-driven natural selection leads to two kinds of events. Firstly there is stabilizing selection that basically maintains the *status quo*. This lies at the heart of why a species remains as a species. What is interesting about this is that many species have populations that are separated across the globe, so called *cosmopolitan* species. They do not find themselves in identical communities (there are few if any identical cosmopolitan communities), yet their populations are maintained and kept within the species over many generations. Thus the species, while not a part of the hierarchy linking genes, genomes, individuals, populations and communities, has an identity and is often long-lasting in spite of the gene shuffling, mutations and population dynamics. I suggest that any given organism is the product of a central core of genes that are at equilibrium across a species, and a more peripheral set of genes that display greater variation. This is akin to an idea of Hal Caswell, an ecologist working in Woods Hole Oceanographic Institution, in 1978, when he observed that communities of organisms are built of a central group of dominant species which are strongly interactive and are at equilibrium. These are surrounded by a second group of non-equilibrium species. Here we would see the first group of genes as defining the species, and providing a stable core that allows this level of organization to be maintained, whilst non-equilibrium genes lead to individual and inter-population variation. We have seen before, for example in RUBISCO, the carbon gluing mega-protein, that some proteins just don't change, even over millions or billions of years. Thus there will be a key set of proteins that remain unchanged. Indeed, most of the core metabolic pathways of the Biosphere have remained largely unchanged for billions of years, since they were originated in the ancient prokaryotes. This comparison between species and proteins also offers an interesting, but as yet unexplored suggestion that as genes are to species, so species are to communities, with groups of tightly interacting species giving communities their identities and resilience, while other less connected species interact more loosely.

Speciation in spite of the species

The second kind of event is speciation, but this is reliant on a definition of what a species actually is, which is not straightforward, as we have seen. What is clear is that dramatic events such as mass extinctions lead to greater levels of extinction and, subsequently, of speciation, than is normally found. So something happens here that increases speciation. Something breaks the binds that hold a species together. Oceanic islands also are hotbeds of speciation, with high levels of species only found on them, called endemic species. Around 90% of plants found on Hawaii are only found there, and have most likely evolved there. The figure for New Zealand is 80% and for St Helena is 79%. Ninety nine percent of the snails on New Caledonia are only found there. Here again, something is triggering speciation. In all cases, the driver of speciation, and therefore of diversity, is not the gene.

At the heart of neo-Darwinian evolution, lies the Central Dogma. Random mutations alter the DNA, which can lead to altered amino acid sequences in proteins. These in turn can impact on the fitness of individuals, and natural selection acts upon individual variation. It seems simple and straightforward. Yet there is a central difficulty at the heart of this dogma that becomes apparent, a difficulty so significant that it undermines the entire production.

Speciation does not occur at a constant rate through time

The mutation rate is viewed as being constant over evolutionary time. The molecular clock is seen as ticking at a steady rate, as good as any Swiss timepiece. The longer a species exists, the more mutations it picks up. As the cuckoo pops out of the clock every hour, so a mutation occurs at regular intervals. The cuckoo pecks at the DNA and changes a base. Two related species can be compared to each other to see how long ago they separated. The more base changes, the longer ago they separated. The only problem is that we don't see a constant rate of speciation to reflect this constant rate of mutation. In fact it is anything but constant. There have been dramatic periods of speciation interspersed with long periods when not much happens at all. This is not what neo-Darwinian theory predicts. The constant pecking cuckoo doesn't drive evolution. Something else does. Now that *is* a problem.

Speciation is a problem for the selfish gene, whatever way we look at it. In a way, the most surprising thing is that species are generally so stable through time. If selfish genes prefer speciation, possibly as a way of protecting themselves against competition (a small fish in a big pond can be a big fish in a small pond), then the stability of species works against this. If selfish genes fare better without speciation, allowing them to access more individuals, then speciation events work against this. Of course in the end, the species is the unit of diversity and evolution. *The Origin of the Species* marked the importance of the species concept, even though Darwin himself struggled to define what a species actually is. Speciation is the ultimate result of evolution. Yet there is another problem at the heart of Darwinism. The theory actually predicts no evolution!

How Darwinism predicts stasis rather than evolution

Natural selection mostly acts to select the fittest. The fittest will be produced by selective pressure acting against other options. This is called stabilizing selection and is argued to be the dominant form of selection. If we imagine a population of individuals of differing heights, selection will favour the average height, acting against tall and small individuals. It thus stabilizes the population. The only problem is that the more selection acts, the greater the stabilization, and thus the less varied the population will be. So natural selection reduces variation. There it is in a nutshell. I'll say it again. Natural selection reduces variation. Since the whole thing works by natural selection acting upon variation, then we end up with a dog chasing its tail. Selection leads to a loss in variation, which leads to a reduction in evolution. Over time, even with environmental change, there will be increasingly less variation to allow for significant evolutionary response. So that is a really significant problem.

The species is a fascinating level of organization, an offshoot from the main hierarchy, whose definition is ripe with controversy. Since the species is the central player in evolution, the ultimate product of the process, then are there such things as species-level characteristics that can form a target for natural selection?

Species selection

Species selection is a hotly debated topic. Certainly the persistence of species, some for many millions of years, testifies to their claim as a unit of selection. Species certainly replicate (speciate) and die (go extinct), but are they subject to selection?

Species level traits would be found within a population of species (as opposed to a population of individuals) that share a common ancestor (are monophyletic) and that are maintained by survival and reproduction of component species. Species in a particular setting will speciate, but only those with a particular suite of characteristics will survive. Certain trait combinations may also make extinction (species death) more or less likely, particularly during widespread events such as mass extinctions. Thus the lineage of species will be pushed in a particular direction, based on shared characteristics. If a species is defined by strong interactions of a subset of genes, then the group of interacting species is more likely to be a unit of selection than is any one of these genes by itself. Thus, the species represents this consortium, and would itself form a unit of selection.

There are two ways in which a group of species can thrive: by reduction in extinction (the museum hypothesis, borrowed from community diversity theory), or by increasing speciation (the cradle of diversity hypothesis, again from community diversity theory). I would suggest that survival of a species during heightened extinction of other species leads to the possibility of proliferation. Survival depends on the nature of the extinction event. Thus species level characteristics can influence the potential of that species to come through some dramatic extinction event, and thus to open up the opportunity for a dramatic speciation event in the subsequent, simplified Biosphere.

How group selection created the selfish gene

We see that DNA is a macromolecule, incapable of directing diversity, but capable of generating options. Natural selection, acting at all levels of organization determines if the invention will sell. What we need to ask is where does natural selection come from? What lies behind this selective process? Before addressing this, a final few words are needed on why the debate over evolution, in terms of the subjects of natural selection, has detracted from any meaningful discussion of the engine of diversity. For too long the argument over the unit of selection has taken away from an understanding of why the world is the way it is. It is an irony that the popular notion of the selfish gene was a product of group selection theory.

Vero Wynne-Edwards, the Leeds-born naturalist, a champion of group selection and a record holding cross country skier to boot, had written a book in 1962, entitled "*Animal Dispersion in Relation to Social Behaviours*" in which he argued that group selection favoured populations that self-regulated themselves in terms of territory and reproduction. He emphasised the role of group selection over individual selection, the Darwinian view. This led to a mighty backlash from neo-Darwinists, led by George Williams. In his repost to Wynne Edwards, entitled "*Adaptation and Natural Selection*" (1966), Williams stressed that selection worked primarily through the individual, and this led to the establishment of the gene as the unit of selection.

Why is it that both sides continue to argue over this? When we get a position where two or more clear and logical arguments are made in opposition, it is often the case that neither is right, but that both contain part of the truth. We shall see in the next chapter how this represents the debate over group and individual roles in evolution. The years since these two books were published saw an ever-strengthening drive towards placing the gene at the centre of things, and focusing on it as the basis of evolution. It became almost religious, a totem, and anyone who detracted from it was quickly labelled a heretic, anti-Darwinian and as foolish as Lamarck. Groups were out, genes were in. Yet the group argument has crept back in recent years, regaining some lost ground. Even at the level of a gene, as we have mentioned, in a diploid organism, the fate of a trait (excuse the poetry!) is a consequence of the group of two genes.

Genetic relativity

More profoundly, the contribution of a given pair of genes upon the individual's fitness will be dependent upon the organism's other genes. This is called *genetic relativity*. This group of genes provides the phenotype, which is therefore an object of group selection. Given that a genetic sequence may exist but that it may be silenced in the overall phenotype, its contribution, and functional essence is dependent upon the group of genes in which it is part. In other words, just like the tree in a forest falling without being noticed, if a gene sits in an organism, and no-one actually notices it, then does it exist at all? It certainly can't be a unit of selection if its phenotypic input is muffled by the overall group of genes. In terms of natural selection, it ceases to exist. Group selection should not be seen as an alternative to selection at the level of the gene, and this has been a significant issue due to the polarization of viewpoints taken after the Wynne-Edwards/Williams starting point. Rather, selection at every level is part of the greater whole.

So what is selection?

The best way forward is not to focus on the unit of selection, but rather on the basis of selection itself. What is selection? Rather than defining it within a context of its effects, we need to consider what it actually is. By understanding the basis of selection, we can determine upon what and where it actually impacts. This great force, all pervading throughout the Biosphere, whose effects are spread across many levels of organization, and whose impacts reach across all taxonomic units, needs to be more closely identified. Is it a collective expression, encompassing many different and unrelated pressures? Is its definition dependent on how we view the Biosphere, or is there a single selective pressure? The concern in actually facing up to these questions is that if we recognize selection as a single identifiable entity, then we may have defined God. We may be left with a world that is subservient to some greater force. If this force is active, we find ourselves in a deterministic, or worse, fatalistic existence. As the sand dune communities are inexorably drawn towards their climatic conclusion, so, too, the Biosphere could be under some sinister influence, drawn onwards by the singing of the Sirens of selection!

Complete funk?

The birth of neo-Darwinism, where the genetic material is seen to provide the necessary framework through which evolution acts, led to a great debate as to the unit of selection. At what level(s) does natural selection act? Typically, the debate has arisen because of the human need for one answer. In an attempt to explain all things with the one theory, the emphasis has been placed on the gene. The gene-centric view was first put forward, in 1958, by Colin Pittendrigh, also known as the father of the biological clock, for his work on diurnal rhythms, and developed by, among others, George Williams, John Maynard Smith and William Hamilton. Present advocates include Richard Dawkins. Lynn Margulis decries this gene-centric argument, claiming, in the journal *Science* in 1991, that its advocates "*wallow in their zoological, capitalistic, competitive, cost-benefit interpretation of Darwin - having mistaken him... Neo-Darwinism, which insists on the slow accrual of mutations by gene-level natural selection, is a complete funk.*"

It has been argued that, in the end, everything above the gene is merely the environment of the gene. Thus we can reduce the whole show to bits of DNA and the rest. Everything channels down to the gene, akin to a funnel. Whatever happens at any level above this in the end comes down to the ultimate unit of selection. This does not help us to understand why we have the diversity that we have. While emergent events at any level will result in a change to the gene, the gene is powerless to control many of these events. This is because the world is more than genetically programmed machines. While the gene is subject to the impact of higher levels, the higher levels are not explainable in terms of the gene alone. In fact the gene can be viewed as the manipulated, harassed servant of layers above it, since it alone is subject to influence from all the other layers.

Either the gene does its job, or it ceases to exist. There is no more an argument for a selfish gene than there is for a selfish community, or a selfish individual or a selfish atom. It is no less significant nor is it more significant than anything else. It is a collection of atoms, dancing to the tune of a much greater entity, playing a game to the rules of chemistry and physics, a shadow on the cave wall. The engine of diversity lies outwith the gene. It is only when significant outside influences act that the equilibrium is punctuated, and large-scale evolution actually occurs. Indeed, Darwinian evolution is most likely to lead to no evolution at all! This is really what happens through most of the history of life on Earth. The current theory does not account for what we observe. Given this, it is time to look for a better explanation.

In the next section, we will look for the key force that drives communities, individuals and genes along the paths that they take, the real explanation as to why the Biosphere exists in the way that it does. It is time to break out of the chains that have kept us in the cave, transfixed by shadows, and walk out into the sunlight.

Section V

Energy as the Architect of Structure and Change

We now come to the big idea of this book. We have realized that there is a significant gap between evolutionary theory and what actually happens in the real world. We start with a conundrum: what has an impact at every level of the Biosphere, the impact being different at each level, yet with each impact at any one level affecting those above and below?

By starting with what we observe, and with no initial theory, there is no need for a unit of selection. Freeing ourselves from this, we look at how life is organized. Each level, from gene to biome, has properties that rely on their building blocks, but also has properties that are unique to that level. Energy is the agent of organization, and speaks differently to each level of organization. Energy reaches into biomes, communities, individuals, proteins and genes in completely different ways, which allows us to have one agent, but many different units, each displaying its own response to that single agent. We explore the responses and apply our understanding to some of the great debates in evolutionary biology. We show that evolution works in the empty market place, not in the crowded back alleys.

It is energy that determines the shapes of proteins and the functions of enzymes, and energy that lies at the core of biochemical processes such as photosynthesis and respiration. It is energy that flows through the definition of the niche, thus driving succession and speciation. It is energy whose river runs through food webs. It is the perturbation of the energetic context that punctuates evolutionary stasis. The Biosphere, in the end, is merely a shadow on the cave wall, a brief, fleeting representation of the energetic context.

Chapter Seventeen

Chasing Shadows: One Foot in the Cave

In this section we want to uncover what lies at the heart of the Biosphere. We will discover how the whole thing ended up the way it did, and why it is organized in the way that it is. We ask why reductionist (Darwinian) and holistic (Gaian) arguments both appear to hold water, but yet neither has prevailed over the other? An alternative explanation is needed to understand the way that the Biosphere functions and how it came about. Can we find such an explanation? Certainly there is a need to find one, as existent theories struggle to provide a meaningful explanation beyond their immediate backyard. Attempts to use such theories to understand broader issues often lead to very stretched, contorted strands of thought that are far from home, trying to sing with the aardvarks, swim with the dolphins or dance with a bee who has found a new source of nectar.

Francis Schaeffer, the late, great American philosopher, who founded L'Abri, beneath the Dents du Midi in Switzerland, where many young thinkers, including the author, could find the time and space to question and challenge accepted dogma, had a key test of any explanation: does it work at the bottom line? In other words, how does your theory stand up to examination across the spectrum of situations that share common ground with it?

Many theories can explain a small part of a larger whole, but run into problems beyond this. We have seen plenty of examples in our journey so far. We have noted the difficulties that a theory can run into once it has become established into the centre of a belief structure, irrespective of how it arose in the first place. Natural selection and survival of the fittest are two such embedded phrases, both of which carry uncomfortable baggage. We have also recognized that attempts to apply evolutionary theory to the human race have produced conclusions that do not sit comfortably with our perception of the world. Among humans, many alpha males and females presently live in prisons. Is this good for the human gene pool? Dachau and Auschwitz stand as horrific reminders of human cruelty, yet fit more comfortably within the context of the second part of the title of Charles Darwin's *opus grandis*, "*favoured races*". Is the despotic rule of a dictator, who massacres the innocent and his enemies alike, merely the emblem of the fittest surviving and the weak being removed? Is law and order merely a means of survival of the weak, rather than the fittest, thus standing in apposition to Darwinism, and weakening the human gene pool? The cycle of inspiration, with artificial selection initially inspiring the concept of natural selection, and then natural selection inspiring the concept of eugenic artificial selection, is a classic example of a derivation driving the expansion of the initial concept.

If spectator sport has replaced direct conflict, then is hooliganism such a surprise? Surely, it is merely a tribal behaviour that represents both a bonding event and a territorial situation? Humans are sexually dimorphic, in that males are, on average, larger than females. Modern theory points to this being linked to male-male conflict in resolving competition for females, yet the average fight to the death at a local bar over the issue of a female human will end up in the courts. The system of belief that is neo-Darwinism finds itself at odds with human society in the same way that many other belief systems do. It doesn't work at the bottom line. When we try to apply the explanation as to how the rest of the Biosphere works to our towns, cities and homes, we run into difficulties. Is it acceptable to have a societal structure that is immune to the basic driving force that we understand as underpinning the present structure of life, and that we use to understand every other organism on the planet with the exception of ourselves?

So we come to a conundrum. What has an impact at every level of the Biosphere, the impact being different at each level, yet each impact at any one level affecting those above and below? To understand what impacts upon the Biosphere in such a way as to be the organizing force at every level of organization, from sub-atomic particles through to biomes, we must first understand the organization of the Biosphere. If we look at our planet and its biology, we see a number of clear levels of organization. Going from large to small, we have the Biosphere, the biomes, the ecosystems, the communities, the populations, the individuals, the cells, the molecules, the atoms and the sub-atomic particles.

Each level is organized in the way that it is for three reasons:

a) the bits that it is composed of;
b) the level-specific context;
c) the level into which it fits.

Above, below and within. We can imagine each level as a room, whose walls, floor and ceiling are full of holes. Organizational driving forces can come down from the ceiling, up from the floor, or through the walls. Imagine a group of people calling instructions from each surface, '*Move to the left*', '*Touch your toes*', '*Jump up and down*', '*Put your thumb on your nose*' – like some bizarre game of *Simon says*.

The voices from below remind us of what we are made of, and the limitations that this impinges upon us. The voices from above remind us of our responsibilities to a greater order. The voices around us give us the rules appropriate to our level. However, most importantly, these voices, above, below and within, are all speaking the same language and come from the same source. The voice from below is the voice of the building blocks, and is an outcome of the room beneath the one under consideration. In this lower room, voices from above, below and around it set in place the sounds that emanate from this room to the room above. Unlike a reductionist system though, the voice that comes from the room below is only one of the contributing elements. Thus, the voice from the floor below does not determine the floor above, but only contributes to it. Running through the entire building is the temporal context, the historic lineage and the genetic history of the organisms concerned that constrain the possibilities, and reduce the opportunities to express the energy context. Thus, we have the same language setting the context and acting as the driving force, organizing each level and determining how these levels are structured.

So lets get down to it, the nitty gritty, the new approach. Here it is straight up: *energy*. In this section of the book, we will free ourselves from the bonds that have forced us to look at the cave wall. We'll walk past the people carrying the cardboard cut-outs, past the fire, out of the cave and stare at the real explanation that lies behind, in front of and within the Biosphere. The thesis of this book is that, in fact, it is one voice, speaking above, below and within; that voice is the voice of energy.

Chapter Eighteen
Energy as the Architect of Structure

In this chapter, we take a look at every level of organization in the Biosphere and discover that energy is the prime agent of organization in each case. Each level is structured by energy, acting above, below and through that level. Energy is the architect of Biosphere structure.

The Biome

At the top of our organizational pyramid sits the Biome. Each biome consists of a group of ecosystems that are similar, such as the rainforests, deserts, savannahs, or tundra. For example, the rainforest biome contains all the rainforests of the world. The biomes are generally found in bands around the planet and are fundamentally determined by rainfall patterns, which are, in turn, determined by solar energy. The basis of the biomes is energy. While different biomes share similar food chain characteristics with decomposers, photosynthetic organisms, herbivores and carnivores all usually present, these patterns are expressed differently depending on the energetic context of that particular biome. In other words, things are always eating other things, but depending on the biome, there are differences in the way that the restaurant operates. The biome is different from every other level of organization, in that its structure comes only from a voice from above, literally and metaphorically, the sun. Biome traits are determined, in the end, by solar density, the interaction between the events on a star, and the curvature of the planet. These voices come together to set the stage and determine the context of the Biosphere at any particular location on the planet. The organisms have little effect on the biome, so it is strictly a top-down set up, organized by solar energy, and then impacting on the levels below. However the biome, just like the gene, is not the single unit of organization. It plays an important role in shaping the other levels in the

Biosphere, but each of these other levels has its own story to tell, as we shall see shortly. First though, how does energy organize the biomes?

How energy organizes the biomes

At the equator, there is a greater density of solar energy than further north or south. Imagine three parallel beams of light, travelling along through space. In one situation, they hit a wall that is straight up, at right angles to the beams. In a second situation, they hit a wall that is sloping away from them. Draw this on the back of an envelope if you want to. The important observation to make is that the distance on the wall from the top beam to the bottom beam is less if the wall is upright. Another way of thinking about this is to take a French baguette, that wonderful, cylindrical bread, and slice it straight down the middle. Now take one of the halves of the baguette and slice it at an angle. The surface area of the slice that is cut straight down is less than the surface area of the slice cut at an angle. If we spread the same amount of jam on both surfaces, the jam would be spread more thinly on the angled slice.

Why are we concerned about this bread-slicing, jam-spreading thing? This is because it lies at the heart of why biomes differ in the way that they do, and, ultimately, why the Biosphere is partitioned between these biomes in the way that it is. Just like the jam, the same amount of energy arrives at different angles on the planet, depending on where, on its surface, it impacts. The amount of energy per unit area (the thickness of the jam) is greater at the equator than north or south of it. Thus, obviously, it is warmer at the equator than elsewhere. However, something much more complex occurs. The heat at the equator warms the air, and creates water vapour. This warm moist air rises. As you know if you have climbed a mountain, or checked the temperature on the screen inside a jet at 30 000 feet, it gets colder the higher you go. So the rising air gradually cools and, as it does, the water vapour precipitates and falls back down to Earth as rain. Thus the rainforest biome is formed – warm because of the direct impact of the high energy density, and humid, due to a combination of the temperature and the rainfall, all driven by heat energy.

The air, unlike the water, doesn't precipitate and fall to the ground, but keeps rising. It then is forced north and south from the equator, by air that is rising from the surface. This movement takes place high in the sky above us, and the moving air is now low in water content. It continues to cool and becomes denser, falling as dry air. When it reaches the ground, the air picks up moisture. This area becomes dry, and forms the desert biome, in two bands, north and south of the equator. It is still warm, as the surface of the planet here is only slightly angled. In between the deserts and the equator are the savannah bands, formed as an intermediate region, not as wet as the equator, but not as dry as the desert. Over time, the expansion and contraction of the savannah is thought to have played a significant and fundamental role in the evolution of the passerine birds and greater apes.

So the dry air that falls upon the desert becomes moist, by removing water from the surface, and moves north and south of the desert biome. Thus, it either returns to the rainforest, and enters the whole cycle again, or goes in the opposite direction (north in the Northern hemisphere, south in the Southern hemisphere). Here, it brings moisture to the temperate rainforest bands. The deserts contribute moisture to the two wettest biomes on the planet. In turn the temperate areas experience a lesser version of what happens at the equator, with air again rising, water falling, and dry air moving north and south, to the deserts or the Polar Regions. Here it falls and draws moisture from the surface, and moves away, drying these two areas. Interestingly, the Arctic and Antarctic are as dry as the traditional sandy deserts. Thus we see that the energy density is all-important in determining temperature, precipitation and evaporation, which in turn determine the biome character.

The ecosystems and their communities

The biomes, in turn, have a huge impact on the evolution and diversity of the ecosystems within them. The ecosystems exist within a space that is permeated by three voices of energy. The voice from above is that of the biomes, now formed and functioning to speak to the level below them. The biomes have a huge impact on the evolution and diversity of the ecosystems within them. This driving force is not a product of the organism, the population or the gene. It is an energetic force, realized in the form of the biomes.

There are other voices, coming from the walls of the room. Life in any biome falls into the same broad set of job descriptions, be they photosynthesiser, predator or decomposer. These roles have characteristics that will mostly be aligned to the energetic context surrounding them. Within the ecosystem itself, a voice relevant only to this level occurs – the voice of trophodynamics. Ecosystems are composed of communities of organisms that interact with the physical surroundings, be they soil, rock, water or air. Energy must flow through these communities, and the structure and function of these communities is tied up in the food webs that they form. The key drivers here are the requirement for and the resulting acquisition of energy, mostly derived from the Sun, in the form of light energy converted to chemical energy in photosynthesis. The rest of the food chain involves the movement of this chemical energy throughout the food web, with leakage at each stage. This energy is needed to maintain life, and to replace energy lost through growth and activity. Like the biomes, the structure of these food webs is determined not by the organisms themselves, nor their genes, but by the laws of thermodynamics, that demand payment, and forbid the *de novo* creation of energy. It is like an economy, where no-one is allowed to produce money by making coins or bank notes, but instead must earn it, and where everyone must pay tax on what they earn, and must pay rent and buy food. Thus they must continue to earn money. There is no social security in nature. Existence comes at a price, and that price is energy.

The voice from below the ecosystem and its communities comes from the populations that make up these communities. Depending upon the health of the population in terms of numbers and variation, the community may be defined differently, as we shall see when we consider the impact of energy on populations. Furthermore, the number of primary producers will limit how high the food pyramid can be. In other words, a small population of photosynthetic organisms will mean less energy entering, and therefore less higher levels in the food chain.

So the ecosystem is a very dynamic entity, with energy defining it through the ceilings, walls and floors. However there is a fourth voice here: time. As communities age, they change in character, and the conversations between energy and matter shift to new subjects.

Populations

Like ecosystems and their communities, there are three voices of energy that apply to this level of organization. The voice from above represents the community, and is extremely important. How the population will be structured will depend on the age of the community and the resources available to it. It will also depend on the other members of the community, in terms of predators and prey. The size of the population will very much depend on these things. Too many predators or too few prey items may mean that the population will be wiped out. Too many prey or not enough predators may mean that the population over-expands.

A whole separate level of interactions with the community also will play an important role. A disease organism may require a second host to complete its life cycle. Depending on the numbers of this second host, the population may be more or less susceptible. For example, mosquitoes and humans both act as hosts for the malaria parasite, *Plasmodium.* By exterminating either humans or mosquitoes, the chances of contracting the parasite for either host will be reduced. Another important community issue is the issue of competition with other species. If a predator preferentially eats your competitor, then your own population will benefit, but if a predator that is specific to your main competitor goes locally extinct, then your competitor may drive your population to extinction, because it has been freed from the predator. All of these issues relate to the trophodynamics of the community, that is, the energetic context of the population, and none relate to the genetic make up of the population.

Within the population runs the voice of energy that relates to the energetic quality and quantity of the habitat. The energy available to a population will determine its structure and function, and has a huge array of impacts, as we shall see in Chapter Twenty. Populations are limited by energy, in terms of their growth rates and densities. Every habitat has a carrying capacity, that is, there is a restriction on the number of any given population that can be carried or sustained by a given habitat. There is feedback from the environment, called density-dependent feedback. In other words, the higher the numbers of a given population, then the greater is the pressure upon it. Eventually, the increasing pressure, due to increasingly limited resources, will prevent any further increase in the population. At this point, the population is said to have reached its carrying capacity. In the end, carrying capacity is an energetic concept. The only way to raise the carrying capacity is to increase the available energy, or improve energy use efficiency.

Historical population genetics: a record of energy through time

The genetic makeup of the population is the main way in which the voice of historical energy communicates with the present. The genetic makeup acts as a record of how things have been. A healthy environment will have led to a healthy variety of genes within the population (what we call *heterozygozity*, meaning a mix of different genetic solutions), whereas a stressed environment will have led to a paucity of variation, with small populations and inbreeding leading to all sorts of problems, including a dramatic reduction in the options available for subsequent generations. It was energy that spoke to the population over millennia, and these conversations are recorded in the genes.

Individuals

The population depends on a width and depth that is supplied by its individual members. Spoken to by the level above, the population, it finds itself a captive to this population in many respects, and yet is itself responsible for helping to define the population. If the population is at or near the limit that its habitat can sustain, then the voice from above may greatly limit the individual, in terms of its chances of mating, and in terms of the chances of its offspring surviving. The size of the population may also impact upon the ability of the individual to find sufficient food, and to avoid predation. At the individual level, energy speaks in a clear way. Here, the voice is all about resource acquisition. The individual is the only level of organization where energy intake and loss is the key. The individual organism must meet the bills, and face up to the laws of thermodynamics that prevent the creation of energy, and demand a continued payment to satiate the appetite of entropy. The individual is also the level at which physiology operates. A living organism is a physiological system, and physiology is merely the handling of energy, be it sensory, metabolic, heat management or water management. The organism is designed to acquire energy, and is formed from the proteins that speak to it from below.

Species: a brief detour

Species do not live within the organizational structure, and yet lie at the centre of evolutionary theory. We have shown that the species concept is problematic in many ways, and, since it is not really part of Biosphere organization, its role is questionable in our attempts at understanding evolution. We have seen that the species is a taxonomic term, and the over-emphasis upon taxonomy, which actually has no direct bearing on the biosphere, has led Darwinian thinking astray, driving it to ignore all of the other levels of organization. However, if the species has any significance, then it is the representation of a group of aptations that represent the organisms approach to its energetic context.

Proteins

Proteins and their products make up the organism. They give function, character and structure to each individual, and convey the stored information from past generations to the present. We are, in the end, a storybook of times past, but, more importantly, an historical record of the energetic history of our planet. Our structure reflects the voices below and their history, but our survival represents our response to the voices above. The protein is dependent on the voices above it for its context, and is formed from the coding information of the nucleic acids that code for it. But the energetic voice that speaks directly to the protein is the one that determines its shape. It is the energetic context that determines how the protein folds, and, as we have seen in Chapter Thirteen, any change in this context will lead to a change in the protein structure, even though the sequence hasn't changed. Here we can see that energy is the boss of structure. The protein, in the end, represents an energetic space, described by the voice from the walls surrounding it. This voice is dominant and speaks also to the level below, determining what structure will work. The nucleic acids are forced to dance to this tune, because, in the end, the protein will only work if it fits the energetic demands. Only the right sequence will work in a given energetic context, and this context therefore places the demand on the DNA to provide this sequence. Thus energy dictates sequence. It creates and selects the structure and so is the ultimate causative agent of sequence. The sequence and structure are physical expressions of the interaction between energy and matter.

The lord of the dance

The room, whose walls, floors and ceilings are permeated by the voices of energy, forms the configuration space at each level of organization. Hence, the organism, its molecules, the community and the ecosystem all contort themselves to the demands that are shouted through the walls. The Biosphere, ultimately, is a response to the energetic chorus that pierces through it. The journey taken by the Biosphere through time is a journey directed, scripted and produced by the rules of thermodynamics. Chemistry also dances to these rules, while biology takes the chemical dance and expresses it further in tune to higher voices, energetic communications unheard by the chains of amino acids, and only relevant to those who can hear its words. It is like a dog whistle, unnoticed by us and therefore apparently non-existent, but very much an issue for the dog. We can see the effect upon the dog, but if we have not seen the whistle being blown, we will have no idea what caused this effect. In this way, this book presents a theory that accounts for emergent properties in biological systems. When we find properties that cannot be accounted for by the sum of its parts, it is because each level of the Biosphere is not a sum of its parts. Rather, it is a responsive unit in itself, and the totality of its parts is merely the starting point. Each level responds uniquely to the energetic voice that is relevant to that level, and so will exhibit properties that appear emergent, just like the dog that turns around when the "silent" whistle is blown. The blindfold and earplugs of reductionism have diminished our ability to understand these things, as we deal in shadows that fall well short of the real thing.

The organism will be an expression of an appropriate, resonating system, a chemical dance to a musical score, designed around that score, moving to the energetic tune that runs through space and time. It is this quality that makes energy such a unique force in terms of shaping our Universe: its ability to act at different levels of organization, in different ways. It has left many smoking guns such as vitalism, the selfish gene and emergence, fleeting shadows that have been wrongly interpreted through the ages. It is because of this that humans have become somewhat polarized in their view of how natural selection works, and how the Biosphere operates. Reductionists argue that there is a bottom up system wherein the genes extend their influence outward, and that only the gene can be considered as the unit of selection, the rest acting as some sort of extended phenotype. On the other side is a hierarchical viewpoint, wherein each level of the hierarchy has independent qualities from others. Finally there is the top down view, where the higher levels of organization control those below. All of these belief structures have elements of truth to them, as is so often the case in apparently diametric arguments. We see that energy fulfils all of these roles. From determining protein structure, and thus sequence, through to trophodynamics and biome structure, each level of organization is defined by its energetic context, but also informed by levels above and below. The organizing force runs throughout the Biosphere. As we have seen, its impact is not only on many different levels, but in many different ways. Some of these are consequences of lower levels, some are controlled by higher levels, and some are unique to the given level under consideration. Yet it is the one force. Molecules contort in obedience to this force; organisms behave in line with this force, while biomes are located where this force dictates.

We have seen that energy is responsible for the structure of the present Biosphere, from biomes to food webs, and from populations to proteins. We now examine how energy can explain changes in the Biosphere. In the next chapter, we explore how energy is responsible for the evolution of life on Earth.

Chapter Nineteen

Energy as the Architect of Change

We have seen energy as being responsible for the levels of structure in the Biosphere, but how do we explain change? Why doesn't everything just morph to fit the energetic demands and then stay like this? There are two types of change: ecological change and evolutionary change. Energy drives both of these.

Ecological change

Ecological change is classically represented by the process of succession, where a bare area of land gradually moves through a series of community types to a final, climax community. In the case of terrestrial succession, this usually involves a move from communities dominated by ruderal, opportunist species, with short lifetimes and high reproductive rates, to a more diverse, stable stage, often a forest, with lower reproductive success, and with longer-living species. Beyond the climax community, no substantial change occurs without disturbance, and the final community is stable for many generations.

Eugene Odum (1913-2002), known as the father of modern ecology, has insisted that succession is a developmental process. We have already recognized that the niche is central to understanding what species can exist and where. The niche is the job description. It asks the questions. If you can supply the right answers, then you will persist. So the change in community type during succession can be seen to be driven by a change in niche. Plant seeds of all types rain down on a given location, falling evenly on early and late stages, yet at each stage of development only certain species are found. That is because only certain niches exist at each stage. Of interest is the fact that just as communities change through a succession, so do niches. The interconnectedness and developmental processes related to succession reduce, finally, to niches.

Obviously different niches must occur as succession continues, but why does the process stop? Why do communities come to a halt at climax? Is this a destination that is reached, an end point? If so, are the intermediate stages merely there as stepping stones, or necessary parts of the journey? Let us consider a determinate organism that develops from an egg to an adult. Here we have a series of developmental stages ending in adulthood. Each stage is a product of the previous stage, a consequence of the events that occurred earlier. Yet, only the final stage does not change into something else. Communities do the same thing, hence Eugene Odum's dictum. Yet communities are not organisms. They are composed of organisms, fitting into niches, and these organisms are part of the trophodynamic structure within a given biome. Thus the community falls under a very different energetic context than the organism. Voices which are specific to the community level of organisation place different demands upon organisms here.

Energy forms the basis of trophodynamics, both in terms of the cause and the process, as well as determining the identity of the niche. Traditionally, the changes that occur between one stage of community development and another have been viewed as an interaction between the biology and the environment. However this does not explain why succession comes to a halt. It is to energy that we must turn again. Niche change is an energetic event, and the biology, genes and all, merely provide a vehicle through which niches can transform, along a path that is energetic in its essence. Succession is directional, and is independent of biomes. Be it rain forest, savannah or temperate grassland, while the specific animals and plants involved may differ, the same basic changes occur. This is important, as it strips away the likely suspects from the crime scene. What we are left with is the energetic framework that expresses itself in the niche, which can be viewed as the *energetic phenotype*.

D'arcy Thompson and the Law of Transformation

The set of niches at any one stage are linked in terms of expressing the energetic framework at that stage. They are then transformed to a new set of niches. To understand how this transformation works, we need to visit the work of a famous Scottish scientist, based in the cities of St Andrews and Dundee in Scotland, D'arcy Wentworth Thompson (1860-1948). D'arcy Thompson was a scholar of Greek, mathematics and biology. He founded the field of biomathematics. Thompson's great work, *On Growth and Form*, published in 1917, contained his law of transformation. He stated that, in examining the relationship between the shape of an organism and its evolutionary history, '*a comprehensive law of growth has pervaded the whole structure in its integrity, and...some more or less simple and recognizable system of forces has been in control*'. Thus he understood that there was some underlying relationship between pattern and signal, a concept later developed by Brian Goodwin, Alan Turing, Louis Wolpert and others. By transforming the co-ordinates of a particular structure, he was able to generate another structure. What do I mean by this? Imagine a graph with two axes, the x axes along the bottom of page, and the y axis pointing upwards. Now imagine a square drawn in the middle of the graph. If we stretch the square, pulling its right hand side further right, we can change its shape, making it twice as wide as it is tall and forming a rectangle. We can do this mathematically, by doubling the value along the x axis, so that x = 2x. In other words, the shape is now twice as wide as it was before. This is what we call a mathematical transformation. If we doubled the y values instead, it would be twice as tall as it was wide.

D'arcy Thompson compared closely related species with each other, and found that he could transform the shape of one species into another by stretching them in different ways, just like the square. Thus he cleverly deduced that there were forces pulling at biological structures, and these forces could transform one species into another.

He did this on a wide range of objects, from whole organisms to bones. Transformation represents the forces that determine final morphology, and combines the influences of genes, material, laws and constraints. A key element in transformation theory is that development does not work in a vacuum, but rather, physical laws and constraints play significant roles in the forms produced. The properties of matter represent the forces controlling form. Again, returning to Thompson's own words, '*Cell tissue, shell and bone, leaf and flower, are so many portions of matter, and it is obedience to the laws of physics that their particles have been moved, moulded and conformed.'*

Physiological transformation

In work that I carried out in 1999, I suggested that his idea of morphological transformation can also be applied to metabolic pathways. I was studying two different species of plant that were closely related, but had very different types of root behaviour. On closer inspection, it turned out to be a simple change in the way the plant responded to a shortage of iron, and the change was a small, but crucially important alteration in a single biochemical pathway, a metabolic transformation. Here, the shape of the metabolic pathway is transformed, rather than the shape of the organism, but the same principles apply. Just like morphology, it is an energetic transformation, and allows us to map the evolution of pathways in a similar way to morphology.

As we have already noted, by altering a small number of the amino acids in a protein chain, the shape that the protein folds into can radically change, often affecting the function of that protein. Evolution most often works through such morphological changes at the molecular level as the new form of molecule is transformed into a different shape under the influence of the energetic context within which it finds itself. The new interactions made possible by these new molecular shapes can alter the pathways in which they act, leading to metabolic transformation. Interestingly, these changes are also structural in their basis. Biochemistry and physiological sciences are all about shape, just at a smaller level than morphology. This shape, in all cases, is a representation of the energetic phenotype.

Niche transformation

However niche transformation differs in important ways from the transformations of molecules, metabolism and morphology. The niche lies between the organism and the community. It is the energetic structure that is transformed, and this transformation is predictable and directional. It doesn't happen without the organisms being present, but it isn't fussy which organisms these are. The organisms are merely the vectors that translate the physical representation of the energetic context at any given point. As these organisms dance and contort themselves to the energetic rhythms, they facilitate niche transformation. They do not control it, but are nonetheless essential. Like a puppet government, the powerful puppeteer behind such a façade could not exert the influence it does without its puppets. Another interesting point to make is that the climax is reached because, energetically, the system is finally transformed into the end game, a set of niches that are at peace with the energetic context. The drive to change is no longer there. Finally, by recognizing that organisms can nether create nor destroy energy, but merely facilitate its transformation and passage, in agreement with the First Law of Thermodynamics, we see that the organisms are best viewed within an energetic structure, independent of their particular taxonomic labels.

Is there direction in evolutionary change?

What drives evolution? Certainly there is a huge difference between the world today and the world of 3.85 billion years ago, when the Biosphere is thought to have begun, deep beneath the water, far from the ultraviolet radiation that rampaged upon the surface of the Earth, in an ozone free world. Is there a directional force in evolution? Humans have always liked theories that give life a special meaning, from Vitalism to the tree of life, from the origin of the species to the creator God, from the Eukarya as the special domain, to the selfish gene. Man still considers himself as separate from the rest, as different. Law and order is not based on a scientific dogma, but usually finds its origin in religious writings, such as the Ten Commandments of Judaism. There is a significant gap between the neo-Darwinist dogma and moral and legal authority, though arguments have focused on attempts to align belief with dogma (capitalism with the selfish gene, and group selection with socialism, for example).

The over-riding message, most often subconscious in its delivery and motivation, is that bacteria are more primitive than fungi, which are more primitive than plants, which are more primitive than animals, which are more primitive than humans. We see this time and time again in terms of the killing of members of each kingdom. The July

2008 edition of National Geographic had the headline: '*Who murdered the mountain gorillas?*' Yet the deliberate spraying of insecticides to get rid of an insect feeding on a crop of wheat does not receive the same weight of response. Killing a tetrapod is more significant than killing an invertebrate. Killing an animal is generally more significant than killing a plant. Vegetarians believe that eating animals is different from eating plants. Genetic cloning of sheep, other animals and plants is acceptable to many, but much less acceptable would be the cloning of humans. Elimination of invading plant and animal species is fine, but not of humans. Terms like *higher plants*, *primitive forms* and *advanced forms* all reflect a concept that life has steadily improved and become more sophisticated over time, resulting in the apogee of evolution, humankind. Whether it is a creation belief system or a *de novo* evolutionary approach based on spontaneous generation, life is viewed as being represented by ever increasing complexity. Survival of the fittest, leads to ever-fitter organisms, and ever-improving *bauplans* (designs) and functions, with ever more sophisticated behaviour.

Yet is this really accurate? As we have recognized, two thirds of the domains, the Bacteria and the Archaea, are not Eukarya, and differ hugely in terms of their reproduction, structure and function. Additionally, the eukaryotes would not survive without these other two domains, both because they rely on the mitochondria and chloroplasts directly, and because the Bacteria and Archaea run the life support system of the planet, and are the key environmental engineers. These domains are still with us. They haven't been replaced by more "advanced" life. They are doing just fine. From the energetic point of view, the Biosphere has expanded into available niches, with chemical reactions developing, some in direct response to the demands placed upon them, and others exploring new energetic space. Chemistry fills the reaction space available and allowable, and, like a domino effect, runs on as far as is energetically feasible. Evolution works in parallel with this. Energetic niche availability, in the end, forms the driving force of evolution. This is clearly demonstrated by the tempo of evolution over time, adaptive and non-adaptive radiation and ecological release.

Shadows on the Cave Wall

Niche availability

If we look at the tempo of evolution over time, we find that natural selection has little impact upon speciation for most of the time. It is only when significant disruption occurs to the energetic context, for example the blocking of solar radiation by dust from an impacting extraterrestrial object, or from volcanic activity on the planet's surface, that we see the stasis punctuated. At other times, the Biosphere appears relatively stable. It is disruption, with the concomitant liberation and transformation of energetic niche space, which drives evolution. Primary niche space is completely new, possibly produced as a consequence of novel habitat development. As chemical societies (organisms) form into super-societies (communities), they come under higher levels of organizational control, the energetic voices that speak at that level. New niches become available as a consequence of systems being able to hear the new voices. It is a bit like a video game, where each level of the game brings a whole new set of rules and conditions, and allows for new moves and strategies to be exercised. New niches offer new challenges and lead to new structures. The build-up of ozone, and increased competition for diminishing resources in the aquatic environment, allowed the development of terrestrial niches. These niches became realized when they were wired into the circuit. What is interesting is that primary niches can be liberated or realized by a range of events. Whatever leads to the primary niche being realized, it will have its origin within a succession of existent niche types.

A secondary niche is one that already exists, but is secondarily vacant, due to the demise of its occupant. The demise is not just of an individual organism, but of the entire group of individuals that occupy that niche. In other words, the niche must be fully vacant, and not within reach of the species that had previously occupied it. Mass extinctions are extreme occurrences, and it can take millions of years for niches to be refilled. Indeed new types of niches may well replace old niches.

Another consequence of a large scale disturbance is that niches that have been emptied may be disconnected from the Biosphere, due to significant extinction of related niches. This greatly delays recovery of secondary niches. In other words, if we imagine a niche as a parking space, then after a mass extinction the entire parking lot has been reduced to rubble. Thus, the Biosphere would have to slowly re-establish itself, in a process akin to succession, but this time there would be no rain of seeds bringing pretenders to the niche throne. Rather, the species would need to evolve into the new niches, re-establish trophic connections and, possibly, even biome identity.

The process of recovery: ecology meets evolution

Of course, such a *tabula rasa* means that there is a greater likelihood of speciation during the process of recovery, since many species that formerly occupied niches now vacant will no longer exist and neither will their close relatives. Furthermore, the temporary disappearance of particular niches, possibly for millions of years, means that the organisms that would have filled these, as well as the species dependent upon these organisms, will have long gone. Increasingly disconnected niches will cease to function, and empty themselves of their occupants.

Energetics will insist that specific niches are re-created in a specific sequence following a mass extinction. Succession must occur, and the climax community must be reached. However, depending on what has survived the wipe-out, the organisms that fill these niches may be very different than the original tenants. This brings another important point to the table. A given niche can be occupied by completely different types of organisms. For example the aye aye, a strepsirhine (wet-nosed) primate from Madagascar, has an extremely elongated third finger which allows it to reach under the bark of trees and capture insects. This opens up a niche normally filled by the woodpecker, a very different type of organism, which uses a very different approach.

Thus, eventually, a structure will be rebuilt that will be functionally similar, if not species-similar, to that previously in existence before the mass extinction event. Function is the key here. Many ecosystems display functional redundancy, where more than one species can fulfil a particular role. This can bring protection to the ecosystem. Imagine two outdoor factories in a warm sunny country, where there is a production line in each factory that makes cars. In the first factory, there is one person doing each job, whereas in the second factory, there are five people for each job. Now in this sunny land, there is a great and terrible bird, the giant, polka-dotted, dancing chicken, which loves eating production line workers. If this monstrous bird chooses the first factory for a spot of lunch, it will be disastrous, as no matter who is removed from the production line it will prevent the manufacture of cars from being completed. The factory with five people at each position is still functional after the loss of an individual to the chicken. In the same way, an ecosystem with redundancy will be less susceptible to damage, due to species extinction.

Of course a factory with more workers must divide its profits up between more people. Interestingly, on many islands, there are less species per unit area than on the mainland. In these situations, there are often higher numbers of each species, so, less means more. Less redundancy means less competition between similar species, which means that each species can be supported at a higher population density. Increased numbers of individuals in any given species will bring protection against stochastic, random extinction, but will not protect against, for example, epidemic disease. More species will mean less of a risk of a disease taking them all out while still providing a reasonable total number of individuals as protection against greater wipe-out. Thus, the island situation is more likely to be the limited condition, less protected against total system breakdown, and thus more vulnerable, than the mainland example with its greater functional redundancy, but smaller populations.

The energetic landscape

An animal in a particular habitat will experience that habitat in a particular way. A predator will be interested in the presence of its prey. A frugivore will take note of the fruit trees and shrubs. A granivore will perceive the habitat in terms of seed availability. They will all note spatial and temporal distribution. For example, fruit will likely only be produced by a given tree species at one time in the year. Also once it is eaten, it won't be there anymore. Thus any given habitat exists as an energetic landscape, and, depending on the species and its chosen resource, this landscape will differ in its appearance. It is the energy that dictates the value of the landscape. Subtle changes from a human perspective may be devastating for another species, either directly or indirectly. This is extremely important. As we alter habitats, our actual impact upon the energetic landscape may be extremely different from our perception of that impact. This also applies to our attempts at conserving habitats and at synthesising artificial habitats, because the habitat is actually not a single entity, but a complex multiple set of different habitats occurring simultaneously, like the faces of a multifaceted object. Thus, we see that the energetic landscape represents the resource world for a given species. However the action of altering the energetic topography of this landscape may have far-reaching consequences. Thus our energetic theory of evolution sends a warning to us as a sub-species. By altering the energy flowing through the planet, we will create a different world. We will see the consequences of this in Chapter Twenty-three.

Energy is the architect of change, driving ecological succession and evolution. It provides the best explanation for the tempo of evolution. Change in energetic context transforms the structure of the Biosphere quite simply because, as we have seen in the last chapter, that structure is a response to the energetic context.

In the next section, we examine how our energetic theory of evolution addresses some of the great debates of our time in Biology, debates that have remained unresolved until now. We will take our theory for a test drive, seeing how it shapes up to the challenges of explaining some of the key aspects of evolutionary thinking.

Section VI
Resolving the Great Debates in Evolutionary Biology

Having seen how we can understand both the structure and evolution of the Biosphere through energy, we now turn to some of the big questions relating to how the Biosphere works. Our approach is completely different to the neo-Darwinian theory, and we will see just how different it is as we apply its principles to questions relating to behaviour, speciation, altruism, multicellularity and exobiology. We emerge with a new understanding that represents a much clearer way of reconciling many of the issues that relate to being alive, and we will discover that these issues are turned upside down when viewed from an energetic perspective. We meet a new species of elephant, a dominant starfish called *Pisaster* and a monkey who prefers to help non-relatives rather than his kith and kin. We visit a slime city to learn about multicellularity.

We then take our theory for a test drive to, literally, another planet. Given the universality of the laws of physics, we can examine what predictions we would make for life on a distant world. The rules of physics and chemistry are the same throughout the Universe, and so given the constraints that we encountered in Section IV, we can begin to describe the games that are likely to be played by alien biology. We use our knowledge of energy, acting to direct organization, function, ecology and evolution, to consider what our aliens might look like. We then reflect upon our own Biosphere, and ask what are the universal elements that it shares with other worlds.

Chapter Twenty
The Energetic Basis of Behaviour

Behaviour is the response to, and manipulation of, our environment. The neo-Darwinian approach is to understand behaviour in terms of the selfish gene. Thus we behave in ways that are expressions of our genetic drive, and the gene lies at the heart of every action. This book presents a completely different explanation. In this chapter we will explore the consequences of an energy-driven Biosphere upon how we behave, focusing on migration, social structure and reproductive behaviour.

Migration

Within the energy theory that this book presents as the best explanation for the diversity and function of the Biosphere, migration represents a classic example. It is driven by energy, and, usually, is related to the need for realignment between the organism and its energetic surroundings. This realignment is necessary because either the organism's requirements change at different stages of its life history, or because the habitat changes due to seasonality. Young animals have completely different energy requirements than adults, mainly due to the additional costs incurred by growth, but also, more subtly, because they are smaller than adults. The smaller an animal is, the greater the surface area to volume ratio. If the surface area is relatively larger, that means there is a greater surface across which heat can be lost. This is exemplified by the gray whale (*Eschrichtius robustus*). These mighty creatures normally live in the waters around the Bering Strait, but in the winter they undertake a 9 000 km round trip, swimming to the rather attractive destination of Baja California. Including the stop over, the journey takes 8 months, and during this time the adult gray whales do not feed. Why do these whales undertake such an energy-expensive journey?

It is all to do with the characteristics of baby whales, and the energy context within which these characteristics make sense. Young whales have no blubber. Thus, as mammals, and therefore as warm-blooded organisms, in the cold Bering Straits, they would use so much energy just keeping warm, that there wouldn't be enough energy left to grow. Being small, they have a larger surface area to volume ratio than the adult, and this exacerbates the heat loss issue. By changing the energy context through migration, adults can ensure that the offspring can grow. In this case it has nothing to do with food availability, since the adults don't feed during the migration, and, because the gray whale is a mammal, the baby whales are fed on the mother's milk. The difference is in temperature, and its interaction with the energy budget of the young whale. Why bother swimming all the way back up to the cold northern seas? Surely it would be better to stay off the coast of Mexico? The reason is that there is not enough food in the south. Once suckling has finished, the young whales will need to find their own food, and so the trip back to the north is essential. The parents also need to restock their energy supplies.

Distribution and hibernation

Energetic context also limits distribution, and many organisms are governed by temperature in terms of where they can live. In nature, energy budgets are very delicately balanced. On a winter's day, the early bird gets the worm so early, because if it didn't, it would run into energy deficit. Even then, many birds have to undergo nightly torpor, where they slow their metabolism down overnight to save energy. In seasonally polarized habitats, with cold winters, many animals hibernate for much longer periods to cope with this, in order to reduce their energy needs.

Home range

Migration and hibernation are all examples of behavioural responses to the energetic context, either physically moving, or physiologically down-sizing. The energetic landscape also has significant repercussions for how large a home range an animal requires. Let us consider three animals that all weigh around 100 kg: the American elk, the brown bear and the Sumatran tiger. The American elk has a home range of 100 hectares, the brown bear uses 1 000 hectares, while the Sumatran tiger's range is 10 000 hectares. Although they are the same weight, the energetic landscape for each one is extremely different. The elk is a herbivore, the brown bear an omnivore and the tiger a carnivore. Thus they occupy different positions in the food chain. Energy passes upwards, and at each stage, energy is lost. Thus, the higher we go in the trophic pyramid, the fewer animals there are, and the fewer prey items there are. From a Sumatran tiger's perspective, it has to travel far and wide to find sufficient food.

The energetic basis of social structure

However energy plays a much more significant role in shaping how an animal functions. It shapes social structures. As resources become more limiting, the ability to defend a territory, and to hang out in large social groups, diminishes. While a large population may be beneficial in terms of possessing greater genetic variation, and thus offering a sexually reproducing animal a greater choice of mate, as well as allowing for a greater variation in the next generation, it also brings negative elements to the table, with greater competition for resources. In the end, it is the resource distribution that determines how many organisms can live in a given area, and, therefore, what size of social group can form. In turn, this will determine the reproductive structure of a population. The reproductive life history of an animal is also influenced by the energetic landscape. A classic study of African ungulates has shown the importance of an animal's energetic landscape upon behaviour and social structure.

Kirk's dik dik (*Madoqua kirkii*) is a tiny antelope, reaching a maximum height of 40 cm, and weighing in at 3kg. It lives in woodland, and eats fruit as an important part of its diet. The problem with fruit is that once eaten, it is gone, and the plant will take a long time to replace it, often a year. Thus the energy landscape is not one where a large group of these antelope can survive. As a consequence of this, they occur in monogamous pairs. The energetic landscape determines the social and socio-sexual structure. A different situation is found in the Impala, a larger species of antelope, weighing in at around 80kg. These species live in African savannah, and graze and browse on continually growing leaf material. When the grass grows more slowly in dry periods, they switch to shrubs. As a result they form large herds, where males cannot rely on being able to form stable harems, since the resources are widely spread, and so females can wander around over a large area. In this case, males have to enforce temporary harems by actively herding the females at given times.

The wildebeest, weighing around 100kg, is a grazer, and undergoes a nomadic movement across Africa, driven by the rainfall patterns. As areas of grassland become dry, they must move on to other areas in huge herds of up to 600 animals. These migrations are therefore driven by changes in the energetic landscape. The outcome is that males can only form harems when the group stops moving. Reproduction is again restricted by energy, in that only when females are well nourished will they enter into the reproductive cycle. As a result, births occur in a narrow two to three week period each year. All the birthdays are in a small window between December and January, so if a wildebeest set up a greetings card shop, the business would only run for a very limited time: extremely seasonal employment when Christmas cards and birthday cards would be for sale for only one month in the year!

Another example of the impact that the habitat has on animals is exemplified by an amazing discovery made in the last few years concerning the African elephant. It has always been recognized that there are two species of elephant on the planet, the Indian and African elephant. As is well known, elephants are illegally hunted for ivory. In an attempt to catch these poachers, Nicholas Geogiadis, a biologist working in Kenya as the director of the Mpala Research Centre, in 1997, took ivory tusks that were confiscated from poachers, and subjected them to DNA analysis in order to discover where they originated from. The results produced an unbelievable outcome. Of the tusks tested, there were huge differences between some of them and the rest, a difference so large as to demand two different species. Further research revealed that a new species of elephant had been discovered, the forest elephant, delineated from the savannah elephant. Closer inspection of these two species revealed many differences that had previously gone unnoticed, even in an animal as big as an elephant. The forest elephant is smaller and lighter than the savannah elephant and lives in small groups of two to four individuals, compared to savannah elephants, which live in groups of four to fourteen individuals. The most revealing difference is that the forest elephant is a frugivore. Thus, like the much smaller dik dik, once the fruit has gone, it has gone. Hence, larger populations would be unsustainable. Here we have two species of African elephant, the closest living relatives to each other on Earth, with the same basic anatomy and physiology, and yet the social structure is extremely different. Once again it is the energetic landscape that creates that difference.

Energy and sex

The whole topic of sex in biology has been cast within the confines of the gene in recent times. Sex is also at the centre of the definition of the species, as we have seen. However, whatever the merits and costs of sexual reproduction, it is only the chosen approach of a limited section of the Biosphere. Indeed, many species of plant and animal either do not use it at all, or switch between sexual and asexual selection, depending on the environmental context prevailing. Also, the type of sexual structure of a population and the phenology (timing) of reproductive events are highly variable, not only between closely related species, but also within a given species.

As mentioned earlier, the red colobus monkeys, for example, may give birth in synchrony with each other if their predator, the chimpanzee is absent, but in communities where the chimpanzee is present, birthing is not seasonal. Thus reproduction is very much constrained by the energetic context, in terms of trophodynamics (both relating to resource availability, and the presence or absence of organisms that would consider them as a resource), and this context determines the sexual structure of the population as well as the type and timing of reproduction. We can see this effect, if we consider what would be the ideal type of reproduction, in terms of evolutionary fitness. Here, genetic information should be combined to provide the fittest offspring, and also maintain variation within the population.

Since sexual reproduction is a simple process (the combination of two parent genomes to produce the next generation), and since genes are cosmopolitan in their essence across the entire Biosphere, then why are there so many different methods employed, from serial monogamy to serial promiscuity? The answer to this lies at the heart of understanding what reproduction is. Yet to reach this answer we need to consider where reproduction came from. The simplest form of reproduction can be visualized as a crystal, which can seed other crystals, such as in a supersaturated chemical garden that we used to make at school. Dropping one crystal in to a jar with a very concentrated solution would lead to a rapid occurrence of crystals, copies of the crystal blueprint that is determined by the chemicals involved.

Simple organisms replicate asexually, by splitting in half, or budding off the parent organism. The mitochondria and chloroplasts in eukaryotes also do this, reflecting the fact that they were originally independent organisms. As multicellularity developed, some cells took on the role of reproduction, while others specialized in other profiles. Yet the process is, in the end, simple, coming down to a fusion of two cells in sexually reproducing organisms, accompanied by the asexual reproduction of mitochondria and chloroplasts. Thus every organism undergoes asexual reproduction, at least in terms of these key organelles, while a subset also combines sexually.

The added complexities reflect the games that biology plays, always to the rules of physics. However although the process is simple, the Biosphere has not settled on an optimal way to do this. So at the heart of the matter, lies the reality that reproduction is under the same hypnotic dance to the rules of physics as everything else, often not theoretically the best, but rather it is dragged along by the dance, and that dance sways and pirouettes to the energetic context that permeates below, above and throughout every organism on the planet.

Reproduction has become important for one simple reason, death. The grim reaper visits all of us eventually. If living organisms were stable, perfectly controlled and maintained, then there would be no need for reproduction. Furthermore, if spontaneous generation continued to occur, again reproduction would not be necessary. From the perspective of our atoms, life and death are merely part of the cycling of material through one compartment of the Universe, the Biosphere. The laws of thermodynamics bring an exacting task master whose demands will eventually lead to death.

Most animals die before they can reproduce. Most of these are eaten. Disease also plays a significant role. Ironically disease symptoms are often the side effects of another creature's attempts to reproduce. So we die, either as meals to satiate the energy demands of another's attempt to remain far from equilibrium (another definition of life), from 'natural causes' (possibly a defect in design or just old age), from dramatic change in our environment, as resources for a parasite or from overpopulation, again caused by the reproduction of others. During our lives, our focus tends to be upon survival, and this survival is all about one thing, energy acquisition.

We need to acquire energy to maintain ourselves and pay our rent to entropy. It is a rent, rather than a mortgage, because we can never pay entropy off. All the while, energy must be lost. Of course, we not only need to pay rent, we need to gain an overall net profit, in order to do things like purchase and build replacement parts, transport material, defend against predators and respond to environmental change. Thus energy is the key basis of survival, both in terms of acquiring it and in terms of avoiding being the target of something else's energy acquisition programme.

All members of the Biosphere play out their lives under the rules of physics. As a result they must acquire energy to live. Eventually they will die. No matter how good they are at surviving, they will, in the end, fail to pay the bills, and will begin the journey towards equilibrium with their surroundings, from whence they came. The energy that they have accumulated during their lives will be re-distributed, partly to pay entropy, and partly to form an energy source for something else.

More than one way to waltz?

A final point on this issue relates to the energetic freedom available to organisms. While energetic context clearly operates differently at each level of organization, there will be some freedom of expression. The energetic argument allows for this. Resources are not always limiting, and given the social nature of everything from molecules to communities, it is not surprising that the Biosphere is made up of many millions of types of response to the calls of physics. Also, sub-optimal solutions are the natural outcome of multifaceted challenges, and this leads to a greater number of final outcomes. It is the survival of the functional rather than survival of the fittest. This is no more clearly demonstrated than by Robert Paine (b.1933), not the signatory of the American Declaration of Independence, but the ecologist who coined the term *keystone species*. He worked on *Pisaster ochraceus*, the purple ochre sea star: a predator on the west coast of America. By comparing communities that included this starfish with those where he removed the organism from the communities for one year, he discovered a remarkable thing. When the predator was absent, species richness collapsed.

The sea star predominately ate the mussel, *Mytilus californianus*, an extremely successful competitor that would dominate its habitat, excluding other, weaker, species, and would lead to their local extinction, if it were not kept in check by the starfish. Hence, the predatory *Pisaster* allows weaker species to survive, by blunting the competitive edge of the potentially strongest competitor. By shifting the goalposts, it pays to be less successful – quite the reverse of survival of the fittest. Here, interactions between trophic levels (predation) actually alter the balance within a trophic level, thus impacting on interspecific competition. The genetic fitness of the weaker competitors is largely influenced by their weaker design, relative to the mussel, thanks to trophic interactions. The predator allows sub-optimal experiments at a different trophic level to succeed. These weaker competitors exist, not because of their inherent (genetic) strength, but because of community interactions. The voice above dictates their fate.

Plant roots are now looked on partly as consequences of energy overload. Margaret McCully, the Canadian botanist, famously demonstrated that plants can survive on a tiny fraction of the roots that they possess. Years earlier, Howard Thomas from the University of Aberystwyth in Wales, had suggested that exudation from plant roots, which is central to providing energy to the soil microbial community, was actually a strategy to dump excess carbon. Photosynthesis is inhibited if too much sugar is made, so plants get rid of the sugar. Thus the key starting point for energy entering the Biosphere often runs at an excess, and so there is a profligate shedding of this energy. This is not the strategy of an energy-constrained system! We now see a world that is functioning within the rules of physics, but where things do not need to be completely optimized. There is room for luxurious excess, and the dance is not tightly choreographed. The Biosphere explores energetic space, and acts under constrained opportunism. Interactions within and between levels of organization allow for success that is not explicable at an individual or population level alone.

So the evolution of the Biosphere can be seen as a chemical game that expands into energetic opportunities, and is limited by constraints. We have discussed the whole concept of constraints in Section IV, and recognized that many of these constraints are energetic in their essence. Thus the direction that evolution takes is sketched out by energetics, at every level of organization, from the sequence of DNA, whose role is realized, ultimately, as protein folding, through to biome characteristics, such as where deserts, rainforests and grasslands can occur. The pervasive nature of energy, intrinsic to everything from diffusion to trophic structure, from behaviour to reproduction and from reaction kinetics through to energetic landscapes, is clear to see.

Energy is the key to understanding the Biosphere, both present and past. It provides the best explanation for evolutionary tempo, through the perturbation of energetic niches and their re-establishment. It gives the answer to why genetic sequence is important. Proteins dance to the energetic tune, and the sequence of the amino acids, and therefore of the nucleic acid base pairs that code for them, ultimately respond to this tune. Natural selection based on competition does not explain how evolution works at a mechanistic level, and neither does the inappropriate aphorism, *survival of the fittest.*

Shadows on the Cave Wall

Structure, function, behaviour and change in the Biosphere are all directed by the single agent of organization, Energy. We now turn to some of the great debates relating to the evolution of the Biosphere, and examine how our theory provides a new way to understand these.

Chapter Twenty One

Speciation, Altruism and Multicellularity

Speciation

Speciation occurs at much higher levels at the geological moments when vacant ecological niches become available and when intraspecific and interspecific competition is relatively low, and far from equilibrium. I like to put it another way: evolution occurs in the empty market place, not in the crowded back alleys. After a mass extinction, it takes millions of years for recovery to take place. This is not due to resource limitation, since even an impact winter is not thought to last more than a few decades at most, with ocean cooling, which results from this, lasting only two thousand years. This is enough to vacate many niches, and it is the process of evolution, the re-establishment of community succession and the formation of trophic interactions, that takes millions of years. Niches need to be re-established and re-connected and organisms need to evolve into these niches. Competition-based theory does not provide a workable explanation for the direction and structure of these speciation events, just as it fails to explain the developmental direction of ecological succession.

To understand speciation, we must first understand populations. Individuals within populations experience two types of competition: intraspecific (competition from other members of the population itself) and interspecific (competition from members of other species). A given species will occupy a particular niche, and the niche will dictate the character of that species. If a member of a population deviates in character from the rest of its population, it will most likely perform less well than the other members. This will be tested by intraspecific competition. Depending on the deviation, the particular individual may find itself more suited to another niche. However, if this niche is already occupied by a different species, it is likely that the deviant will not be as well suited to this other niche as the existing population of the other species.

Thus there is pressure, from both intraspecific and from interspecific competition, not to deviate, and. As we have already noted, this pressure (stabilizing selection) actually reduces variation, the very stuff of Darwinian evolution! Imagine, now, that this second species was no longer present. The deviant from the first species may be able to use this empty niche. It may not be perfectly suited to it, but because there is no competition, this is not important. Furthermore, it will be more likely to succeed than if it remained in its original niche, where competition from its original population would most likely lead to its failure. Thus, the easing of interspecific competition, leading to available niche space, drives speciation. The driver is not the intraspecific competition, but rather the absence of interspecific competition.

We have seen that natural selection actually is a term without an agent, defined by its outcome rather than its mechanism, and based on entities such as species that are not relevant to our understanding of the Biosphere. It runs into difficulties in terms of defining a unit and an agent of selection, and this is largely because the agent of selection remains poorly defined. It runs into further problems, because of the recently mesmerizing effect of the gene as the unit of selection, combined with being caught in the headlights of reductionism.

Attempts at trying to explain everything in terms of the gene have become so construed as to move well away from Occam's razor. Occam's razor states that '*Entities should not be multiplied beyond necessity*' or that the simplest explanation is the most likely. Attributed to William Ockham (1285-1349), a Franciscan Friar and philosopher, it has, ironically, been associated with reductionist thinking, in order to explain the evolution and structure of the Biosphere. Energy is a better, and, in the end, simpler explanation, working as it does as an organizational force, and upon matter as the unit of organization, not based on outcome, but on agent. The simplest, but also the most convincing, explanation for why the Biosphere has evolved the way that it has, how it functions in the way that it does and why it is organized in the way that it is, finds its basis in energy.

Could it be argued that energetic considerations are merely a part of natural selection and that the fittest survive because in the end they respond to the demands of the environment? On the surface this may seem like a reasonable argument. However what we have set out here is very different.

Firstly, our energetic theory does not act upon any single unit of selection. It acts at every level of organization. Secondly, competition cannot explain the structure of the Biosphere, or why it has evolved in the way that it has. Rather, evolution acts to fill available niches, and is driven by vacant niche space. In effect, it is the removal of interspecific competition that leads to speciation. Competition maintains the *status quo*, rather than leading to evolutionary change. It maintains the equilibrium and keeps species intact. We can see the force of speciation as a see-saw. On one side sits competition, maintaining the species, and on the other is decrease in competition, leading to speciation. Thirdly, the Biosphere is a product of the interaction between chemistry and physics, purely and simply, and everything, from genetic sequence through to behaviour, finds its meaning within the energetic context. However, just because physics lies at the bottom of the whole thing, our theory is not reductionist, because physics, in the form of energy, also lies above and around the entire thing as well. The major constraints and opportunities arise not as the result of a single unit of selection, but are energetic in their essence.

So what place is there for the gene? It is a group of chemicals, key to the games that biology plays. The beauty of its simplicity reflects the simplicity of its role, as a means of storing protein structure, and as a means of facilitating the production of another individual. Errors occur, and these may lead to changes in the next generation's proteins. However it plays no part in the direction taken neither by evolution, nor of succession. The gene cannot explain why biodiversity is arranged in the way that it is. It is only one of many levels of organization that dance to the energetic piper's tune, and finds itself at the mercy of dances at higher levels too.

Diversity within the energetic context

One of the fun things about biology is the huge array of structure, function and behaviour that we find in the Biosphere. There are so many different organisms, with so many different ways of doing things. The diversity of life on Earth is truly amazing. There are, of course, many shared characteristics, found across many different species, but there are also many variations. Take for example, reproductive behaviour in primates, from monogamy to promiscuity, seasonal to non-seasonal births. Sexual dimorphism can throw up males and females that display completely different morphological features. For example in many moths, females are flightless while males can fly. In fig wasps, males never leave the fig and are flightless, while females emerge and fly. This huge range of variation is possible because the energetic rules are not overbearing. There is no single way to meet the requirements, but there are definite constraints. There are demands at every level of organization, creating the opportunity for many solutions. If we had a reductionist reality, it would be less likely that there would be this variation in design, as competition at the species level would lead to exclusion.

A problem with the Competitive Exclusion Principle

The competitive exclusion principle states that any two species that use the same resources, or occupy the same niche, cannot co-exist. The problem is that individuals of the same species, which, obviously, do occupy the same niche, can co-exist. So why can't identical members who happen to be of two different species find themselves unable to live in the same way? There is actually little evidence of a competitive exclusion principle operating in any but the most derived situations. Functional redundancy, as we have already noted, can be extremely useful for a community, in that there is backup for particular functional roles. The reliance of the Competitive Exclusion Principle upon the species concept, which we have discovered to be an extremely problematic concept (or set of concepts), is its Achilles heal. By removing the hypnotic obsession with species, we can better understand the Biosphere.

Most habitats are richly diverse. There is functional redundancy at every level. In other words, there are species doing very similar things. Energy as a basis of the Biosphere and as the mechanism operating throughout the Biosphere explains this. If you fit the bill, you can earn your living with a bit of freedom to express yourself. Since being the fittest is not always a demand, then being fit for purpose will be good enough. Indeed speciation occurs when previously uncompetitive individuals can find room to exist. Since competition is not the explicator of everything, the absence of exclusion does not need to be excused. The Clements versus Gleason debate on succession can now be resolved. There is an overall pattern to succession, but there is no need for exactly the same species to fill the niches in similar successions. This is because the main role of the organism is to facilitate the flow and transformation of energy. With energetic constraints acting at different levels, multiple solutions will be possible.

Altruism: the origin explanation

Altruism has been a topic of hot debate, taken as a testing ground for group versus gene selection. It was argued that group selection, and activities that promoted the group at the cost of the individual, an idea originally suggested by Darwin, was unlikely to be a strong evolutionary force. William Hamilton (1936-2000), a leading British evolutionary biologist, made a significant contribution to the neo-Darwinist interpretation of altruism. This brilliant man, who nearly died at the age of 12 while playing with explosives, later put forward a much more controversial theory than his views on altruism, when he suggested that HIV had arisen from polio vaccines in Africa in the 1950s. It was while researching this in the Democratic Republic of Congo, that he contracted malaria, and died shortly afterwards. In 1964, he suggested that a gene that led to altruistic behaviour, strengthening the group, but weakening the chances of the individual passing on its genes, would work if those that benefited from the behaviour were close relatives. Much evidence was cited in support of this, showing that altruistic behaviour was more likely to occur between close relatives than between more distant relatives or unrelated individuals. This approach led to the term *kin selection*. However there are also examples of organisms behaving altruistically to non-relatives. In 1984 in a much overlooked paper in the science journal, *Nature*, Dorothy Cheney, a leading American behavioural biologist, showed that un-related vervet monkeys were more likely to respond to each other's calls for assistance if they had groomed each other than if the grooming occurred with related monkeys. This represented the opposite result that would be expected from kin selection. The bond was not relatedness, but grooming. Grooming between non-related monkeys overcame the expected need for relatedness when it came to responding to a call for help.

Reciprocal altruism, as put forward by Robert Trivers, the American evolutionary biologist, suggests that an altruistic act can be justified if there is a likelihood of a reciprocal act being returned upon the original contributor, thus, balancing the books. You scratch my back and I'll scratch yours, whether you are a relative or not. This covers more situations than inclusive fitness. The outcomes that point towards shared genes being key (inclusive fitness), may merely be a case of relatives being more likely to be encountered, and thus being involved in more mutual back scratching. There are many examples of altruistic acts between different species, let alone related members of the same population. We can take a different approach to altruism, by recognizing that it is a point on a line that runs from independence to dependence. For example, the move towards multicellularity in some forms of life leads to some cells giving up some responsibility for certain things, such as reproduction. They altruistically carry out life support processes that allow the reproductive cells to carry out their roles. Let's examine multicellularity in a new way.

Multicellularity in a new context

As we have said, life forms face multiple challenges from many directions. The voices of energy call at lots of different levels of organization. It can all be too much for a little cell to handle efficiently. If cells can live together, and split the workload, then they can focus on particular tasks, and divert their energy budgets and machinery to this task. We have around 210 cell types in our bodies, ranging from nerve cells to hair cells, from hormone-producing cells to red blood cells. Of course, all cells types have many things in common, but some are more specialized towards their particular roles. A multicellular organism is not just a close knit community. None of our cell types could live in isolation. They have relinquished this ability, and become dependent on each other.

However the origins of multicellularity and of altruism are interesting areas of research, and the origin and meaning of both are most likely tightly linked. Although cell specialization in multicellular organisms finds its roots in a shared genome and a united reproductive unit working towards a single set of objectives, and is pictured as the ultimate example of kin selection, this line of thought is erroneous. The origin of multicellularity is not found in kin selection, but in community dynamics. The sponge is basically a community of different species, working together based on mutual benefit. The driver is, in the end, energy, in its multiple forms, that encourages division of labour. Thus, the need to be in more than one functional place at one time drives multicellularity and altruism. In terms of reciprocity, the likelihood of return is the key thing, and any kind of recognition of this will lead to mutual back scratching. In the end, we remember who our mother is, not because we run a gel of both of our mitochondrial DNA, but because, in the early years of our life, she was the one who changed our nappies, fed us and comforted us when we fell over and bumped our head on the coffee table. An adopted child will respond to their non-genetic mother in a similar way to a child with their natural birth mother or, as the trendy term labels them, their tummy mummy.

We now know that microbes can live in two different ways, either as free living independent cells, responsible for their entire existence, or in aggregations, such as biofilms, which can be free floating rafts, or, more often, attached to a substrate. A classic example of a biofilm that we have all experienced is plaque on our teeth. When a microbe becomes part of a biofilm community, huge changes occur, including to the types of proteins that they make. More than 99% of bacteria live in biofilms, so they are actually the normal state of existence of these organisms (and, of course, microbes are the central players of the biosphere, in terms of evolution and function). In fact the biofilm may be essential for survival. Take the plaque communities. The decision to leave the biofilm here will lead to attack by salivary enzymes, followed by an acid bath in the stomach!

Biofilms form by the production of a slime that protects them, and forms a medium for chemical communication with fellow members, as well as movement of nutrients and genetic material. Individuals may also take on specialized roles. The biofilm is not just a random pile of cells, but can have elaborate passageways that are formed from programmed cell death of some individuals, creating channels for the distribution of nutrients and for the excretion of waste products. These structures have been nick-named "Slime cities". Modern microscopic methods reveal complex structures.

Certainly, division of labour is seen to occur in these bacterial films, which can be made up of more than one species, and even include fungi. Roles relating to metabolism, dispersal and reproduction become the domains of only certain individuals in the collective. For example, *Myxobacteria* form fruiting bodies when resources become low, where only some of the individuals get to form spores, and thus actually reproduce. The individuals making up these colonies are usually not clonal. Thus, some individuals really do lose out as result. To facilitate this multicellular function, in terms of communication, signals reflecting population density, the local environment and spatial distribution are used, in what is called *quorum sensing*. As a result of all of this, individuals can gain access to otherwise unavailable niche space. A fascinating example of this is in the bacterium, *Myxobacteria xanthus*. Living in ponds, its enzymes that it uses to digest its cyanobacterial prey would become too dilute in the pond water, and be unable to work. So these *Myxobacteria* act as a pack of wolves, forming a spherical colony with pockets in it. They trap the cyanobacterial prey in these pockets and squirt their digestive enzymes into them, thus avoiding the problem of dilution. Living in a biofilm also provides benefits in terms of protection, either from particular predators, or from physical stress. Finally, due to specialization, it will allow more efficient operation.

Interestingly, multicellularity appears to have evolved many times. For example, the sponges, red algae, brown algae, fungi and seed plants are all thought to have become multicellular in separate events, as have the slime moulds and *Myxobacteria*. In all cases, three main advantages seem to emerge: feeding, dispersal and protection. The first two of these relate to trophic levels below the organism (i.e. their energy source and *its* distribution) and the latter to the level above the organism (i.e. the predator) or the energetic context within which the organism is found (physical stress). Thus multicellularity emerges from an energetic context. Therefore, we might expect multicellularity to arise as a response to resource availability issues. A cell that forms part of an artery wall, for example, has given up many other functions. However it relies on the reciprocal gifting of things that are critical for its survival.

Of course, altruism spreads beyond the multicellular single organism. Organisms can live with other organisms, in a loose multicellular relationship, while maintaining their integrity. A bacterium in a root nodule will give some of its hard earned fixed nitrogen to the plant, while the plant donates sugar and a nodule to the bacterium. Mycorrhizal fungi give phosphorus or nitrogen to the plant, while taking sugar from the plant. Around 90% of all plant species have these fungal partners. Corals are composed of animal and protist partners, but in a relationship of enforcement, where the protist partner is starved into submission. Thus, mutualistic relationships are common in nature, even between organisms from different domains or kingdoms. Surely altruism can be seen as part of this continuum, a meeting of two organisms, separated in space and time, but driven by a basic drive? In the same way that a multicellular organism works because of division of labour and altruistic behaviour, so a population or a community of organisms participates in this.

Monogamous relationships are usually based around reproduction, and here it makes sense to work together in order to successfully rear offspring. It may also relate to resource acquisition. However there is often no, or little, genetic relatedness between monogamous partners, and thus the driving force for working together is not related directly to kin selection, but rather to resources or offspring. It is much more likely that altruistic behaviour is based purely on the likelihood of re-encounter, and mutual benefit. Frequent reciprocal success will likely strengthen the exchange of assistance, and the more closely related you are, the greater the likelihood of encounter.

We can see this in human behaviour. Occasionally, babies have been mixed up at birth, and given to the wrong set of parents. If this is not detected for a number of years, parents and offspring recognize each other as kith and kin. More extreme than this is the use of parent mimics for conservation of rare species such as whooper cranes, where humans dress up like adult cranes, and successfully rear chicks, teaching them to fly and even leading them to new migration areas. Close kin relations can be short circuited easily without any recourse to genetics. After all, Bob and Suzy, the conservation workers, are not exactly closely related to the whooper crane chick. Their common ancestor stretches back to the stem reptiles, possibly the one found in Elgin, Scotland, just north from where this book was written! Yet the cranes respond to their surrogate parents as they would to their real daddy or mummy crane. Think cuckoos and dunnocks if you need another example. The small dunnock feeds and cares for the cuckoo chicks assiduously, in spite of the chicks quickly becoming larger than the dunnocks. The exploitation of altruism is common.

Life is, in the end, hot wired to resource acquisition and the rules of physics. Trying to explain this by using the gene is a less straight forward, and unsatisfactory approach. The bottom line is that organisms do what they do because they are chemical machines that are responding to the demand that the energetic context places on them. Experiments within the free space that is available will lead to organisms trying lots of things, some of which work and some of which do not work.

Levels of organization – same agent, same modus opperandus?

There have been attempts to examine how different levels of organization compare to each other, including Eugene Odum's already mentioned dogma, that succession is a developmental process. Biochemical pathways have been compared to societies, as have multicellular organisms. This, of course, fits well into reductionist thinking, in that each level can be seen as not only similarly constructed, but also that the reason for this is because each level is a result of the level below, and merely an outcome of the conglomeration of the building blocks of that lower level. Thus we would expect some sort of similarity at each level.

We do see patterns of organization replicated at each level. However it is important not to confuse the existence of similar patterns with similarity of cause. Similarity does not necessarily represent cause, just as correlation is not causation. Let us consider proteins again in terms of the key players and the agents of organization. The sequence of the amino acids exists in the order that it does because the DNA bases exist in the order that they do. However this is not the reason for the sequence. The DNA exists to produce the amino acid sequence, which exists in order to fold in a sequence-dependent way within the energetic context. To achieve a particular structure, the sequence must be responsive to the energetic context. In fact, as we have seen, many proteins are actually designed to respond to two or more different energetic contexts, such as some transport proteins. In any case, the individual amino acids while important, find their significance within the sequence in which they occur, and their position derives its meaning from the energetic context. A protein will attain its three-dimensional shape, and thus its functional meaning, only due to an interaction between its amino acids and their energetic surroundings.

Ultimately, it is the energetic context that determines the sequence, and not the other way around, and, likewise, the sequence of bases is subjugated to this context. This same understanding can be applied to each level of organization. The components of that level contribute to the level as a whole, but the energetic impact at each level is completely different. What makes an amino acid what it is, the chemical pieces and their relation to each other, is an energetic issue. The folding of a chain of these amino acids is also an energetic issue, but a completely different one. The trophodynamic interactions of a community and the succession of an ecosystem are again structured by energy, but involve totally different processes than other levels. These different voices, or tunes, that can only be heard by any single level, produce the apparently impossible – a single organizing force responsible for so many completely different outcomes acting on completely different entities. Like a more complex version of the Holy Trinity, these many voices are one, but this one voice is many.

It is energy that flows through the structure of proteins, and drives the function of enzymes. Energy lies at the core of biochemical processes such as photosynthesis and respiration. It is energy that flows through the definition of the niche, thus, in the end, determines speciation. It is energy whose river flows through food webs, defined as trophodynamics. It is the perturbation of the energetic context that punctuates species equilibrium. If we need a central dogma at all, then the games of biology are played to the rules of chemistry, and the games of chemistry are ultimately played to the rules of physics. All of nature dances to the tune of energy that pervades everything, and flavours all. The light on the hill is, truly, the salt of the Earth. The Biosphere, in all its beauty and complexity, is, in the end, only a shadow on the cave wall, flickering and undulating. Ultimately, it merely acts as a brief and fleeting representation of the ultimate essence. Walking out of the cave, and gazing skyward, as Plato did, leads to the greater truth, the source of it all, represented by the Sun. Even the Sun merely represents the deeper voice of energy.

Since our theory is based on universal laws of physics acting upon the universal elements of the periodic table, we can now examine a final great debate. If there is life on other planets, then what does our theory predict that it will look like? There are two reasons for asking this question, and devoting a chapter to it. Firstly, exobiology, the scientific discipline that attempts to predict what life on other planets, exobiospheres, might look like, is a burgeoning field of study, with many of the leading minds in biology now contributing. Indeed the Gaian theory took on its most recent form when James Lovelock was working in this area for NASA. So we need to investigate what our book's new approach offers to this field.

The second reason relates to our own planet. By examining a completely different planet, we can identify the universal aspects that our Biosphere shares with all other possible biospheres, and gain a different perspective on the nature of life on Earth.

Chapter Twenty Two

Exobiology: A Thought Experiment with Universal Appeal

From the *Third Rock from the Sun* to *Star Trek*, and from *Mork and Mindy* to *ET*, we have been fascinated by the possibility of life on other planets, and what these life forms might look like. Would they resemble us? Would they be aggressive towards us? Are unidentified flying objects possibly coming from other planets to observe us? Some even claim to have been captured by aliens and taken away in their spacecraft for a period of time, before being returned to Planet Earth! This chapter aims to understand what an exobiosphere might be like, using the energetic explanation that we have developed.

The first question we need to ask, again, is: '*What do we mean by life?*' We have seen that life is difficult to define, and the term may actually not be that useful at all. In many ways our thoughts on life are very much influenced by our experience of it. However most of life, in terms of diversity, is divided between the two domains of Archaea and Bacteria and, thus, is mostly invisible to the human eye. Indeed most of life is not sexually reproducing, and does not rely on vertical gene transfer as the sole method of genetic transfer. We also have a biosphere dominated by cellular structure (with the exception of viruses) and DNA (with the exception of some viruses that can have RNA as the coding system). The physical conditions on this planet may also be unique, and again this has had a large impact on how the Biosphere has evolved and functions. So the best starting point must be the common ground between our planet and other planets.

Firstly, other planets outwith our solar system do exist. With improved telescopes, we are discovering new planets on a regular basis. A recent estimate, by astronomer

Michael Meyer, predicts that between 20 and 60% of stars similar to the Sun will have Earth-like planets. So what is the common ground between our planet and other planets beyond our solar system? The answer is energy, and, more specifically, the universal laws of thermodynamics.

Energy can neither be created nor destroyed, and the Universe is an entropic system. Assuming these laws hold for all planets within the Universe, we have a starting point from which to explore the nature of exobiology. Aligned with this, we can assume that the periodic table of chemistry will be universal, and so the elements available for building molecules will have the same identities and properties as those on our planet.

If we take James Lovelock's definition of life, from his paper in the scientific journal *Nature* in 1965 (often viewed as the rebirth of the Gain hypothesis, the original birth being in 1789 with James Hutton), which states '*Life is one member of the class of phenomena which are open or continuous reaction systems able to decrease their entropy at the expenses of substances or energy taken in from the environment and subsequently rejected in a degraded form*' and recognize that energy flow is essential for life processes, we then begin with an energy source being required. This does not necessarily mean that the radiation energy from a star is essential. It is believed that the Biosphere of the early Earth lay deep under water, to evade powerful radiation prior to the formation of an ozone layer, and that this early biosphere was chemoautotrophic, that is, deriving its energy from inorganic material. The simplest life forms on other planets could be of this form, and may involve no other trophodynamic levels. They would live by getting their energy from material on the planet, reproducing and dying. This is the simplest food chain imaginable – a single link! Certainly, using, for example, hydrogen sulphide to make sugars (as some chemoautotrophs do) requires less energy than using water (as photosynthetic organisms do). Thus it would be more energetically likely to occur. However, it is also very possible that the biosphere on another planet will be driven by energy from a local star. Photosynthetic organisms open up the portals to a much greater source of energy. Again, they could be the only things on the planet.

There may be two links, with decomposers recycling dead autotrophs. This two-link chain could also incorporate disease organisms infecting either chemoautotrophs or photosynthetic organisms. Three links could involve this latter two-link chain along with decomposers.

Cellularity in outer space

Will these organisms be cellular? This is an interesting question, and relies largely on the presence of water. Cells primarily control reactions by setting up specific chemical concentrations, often different from outside the cell. Water has probably played a huge role in determining cell structure on Earth, given that it is the major solvent on our planet. Cell membranes (the skins of cells) are designed from two different sets of chemicals that are either attracted to, or repelled by, water. Thus the very structure of the cell is water-inspired. As we have already mentioned, water may well have arrived on Earth from comet impacts. What if no comets impacted on our distant planet? Water may not be present. However reactions need to occur in some sort of medium, and the second law of thermodynamics sets rules for what is energetically feasible and what is not. To make something happen that is not feasible initially, either additional energy is required, or the concentrations of the reactants need to be increased. Cells provide the possibility of adjusting concentrations of things to allow certain reactions to occur.

Multicellularity

Will there be herbivores and predators? What are the chances that some terrible monster from outer space might exist, that could threaten to eat all of us? What about ray guns? Well more about ray guns later! First of all, what about that monster? A big extra-terrestrial organism will most likely be (though not necessarily, as discussed above) of a multicellular structure. Diffusion processes are limiting. However the drive towards multicellularity is most likely not just about becoming big! Instead, it most probably finds its drive in terms of the benefits of specialization. As we mentioned in Chapter Twenty One, having more than one cell type would allow division of labour, thus potentially offering more efficient solutions to the many problems faced by the organism. As we have seen, on Earth, even supposedly single-celled organisms, such as bacteria, actually mostly live in multicellular communities.

Our multicellular monster will only be a tormentor for us if we fit its energy requirements. If the exobiosphere consists of only photosynthetic organisms, and maybe their disease organisms and their decomposers, then since the energy is derived from the local star, there will be no need to eat us. However light, gas and water are not the only requirements. Nutrients are also needed. On our distant planet, it is likely that this will also be the case, and that these nutrients will be made of the same elements as on Earth, with the same properties. Some photosynthetic organisms on our planet also eat meat. Carnivorous plants require diet supplements from the Animal Kingdom in order to obtain sufficient nitrogen. If nitrogen is needed, and is in short supply, there may be photosynthetic multicellular organisms that also hunt.

I know a lady who swallowed a fly, and changed the entire planet

Most plants do not kill animals. Therefore a green planet is likely not to be a direct threat to us (aside from poisons and barbs, but these are not necessarily present if there is no herbivore on the planet). The reason why we have herbivores and carnivores on our planet is an interesting question in itself. It goes back to where the eukaryotes came from, the Protista. The protistan Kingdom is a real mixed bag, but basically contains two kinds of organisms: things that swallowed (or, more likely, were infected by) Proteobacteria alone, and things that swallowed (or were infected by) both Proteobacteria and a Cyanobacterium. What do we mean by this? Well, Proteobacteria are thought to be the origin of mitochondria, found in all eukaryotes, while Cyanobacteria are thought to be the origin of chloroplasts, found only in photosynthetic eukaryotes. Thus if you only had the mitochondria, you couldn't make your own sugars, and would need to find an energy source elsewhere, whereas if you had both mitochondria and chloroplasts, you didn't, generally, need to look elsewhere. Protists with only mitochondria led to the Kingdoms Fungi and Animalia, whereas some of those whose ancestors had swallowed both types of prokaryote led to the Kingdom Plantae. If all the protists had evolved from an ancestor who had swallowed both types of micro-organism, and none of them had "lost" their photosynthetic invader through time, then there would be no fungi or animals.

So the acquisition of key organelles has shaped the phylogeny of life on Earth. Is this likely to happen on another planet? Eukaryotic photosynthesis and respiration depend on swallowing an already functional unit. How likely is this to happen in other biospheres? The emergence of eukaryotic organisms without the ability to photosynthesise has played a significant role in how our biosphere has ended up. Of course, there could be another reason for animal-like creatures to exist. Perhaps the switch to eating photosynthetic creatures occurred because of a shortage of space or other resources, meaning that they couldn't get enough energy, or associated minerals needed for the handling of that energy, to survive. Possibly, being starved of resources led to the emergence of predation. We have seen already that plants can develop traps and enzymes to capture and digest animals. Perhaps once carnivory was in place alongside photosynthesis, the ability to photosynthesise could be lost completely, thus producing an animal or fungus-like organism. This can be seen in some parasitic plants, such as beechdrops (*Epifagus virginiana*), dodder (*Cuscuta* spp) and *Rafflesia* (one species of which has the largest flower in the World, in spite of being a parasite – surely a lesson here somewhere. In addition, these flowers smell vile, hence the common name "corpse flower"), which have relinquished the process of photosynthesis completely. So we may have marauding aliens who started of as perfectly respectable photosynthesisers, but now, eat other organisms instead. The aliens could, of course, have maintained their ability to photosynthesise as well, acting as hemi-predators. Mobile photosynthetic organisms should not be ruled out either.

There could easily be a planet with only autotrophs on it, a veritable daisyworld. Freed from the need to find energy, these would probably be similar to those on Earth. Of course, life may have remained underwater or underground. If water was not split in photosynthesis, oxygen would not be released, and so ozone would not be formed. However, the need for a block is only significant if the biology is UV-sensitive. A non-sensitive chemistry would mean that there would be no dependence on water, or on ozone, for UV blockage. Indeed, maybe the exobiosphere could actually use UV as an energy source. It might also provide a better basis for Panspermia, since high energy radiation is viewed as one of the barriers to interstellar travel of "seeds" of life. Given these advantages, it may well be that somewhere in the Universe is such a system, possibly populating a wide volume of space due to its ability to disperse.

So, on our imaginary planet, we can postulate that organisms will need to absorb energy. A food web will only build if there are organisms present that cannot absorb sufficient energy from their non-living environment nor from the recently dead. You only eat if you are hungry. Of course, decomposers may be essential if dead organisms do not become available as resources under "natural" non-active means. Otherwise, resources will become locked up in the dead, and may become limiting. It will depend on the kind of organism that exists as to how easily it will dissimilate, and how limiting resources are.

Alien predation

So we have things that "capture" energy and maybe things that recycle it. What else can there be? If there are organisms that can't capture their own energy, and don't recycle the dead, then they will need to get their energy from other organisms. It does not necessarily mean that these killers have to be mobile. This brings us to our understanding of what we mean by being mobile. It very much depends on the timeframe used. Pine trees have swept back and forth across the British Isles as ice ages came and went, travelling thousands of miles. In Scotland they have been as mobile as the animals during these times. In a given day, a single pine tree won't move at all, no matter how long you watch it. But it is only our definition of the individual that limits our appreciation of the large-scale movement of plants. Every time you sneeze due to a pollen grain, you should remember that you have interrupted a journey.

Since our predators will capture living creatures, they will likely be modified in terms of sensory detection. Motility may arise and bring with it heightened sensory detection aimed at three things: feeding, reproduction and survival. Thus whatever the planet, energy is paramount in understanding what kind of exobiosphere might exist. There will be a level of organization that taps into the energy of the physical environment, equivalent to photosynthesising organisms on Earth. Depending on the situation, heterotrophy might arise. If it did, these life forms will need to be designed to obtain energy from other organisms.

The rest will be the elaborate games of biology, played out and dependent upon the chemical context. Yet if the laws of physics hold universally, then similar constraints will be in place on other planets as on Earth, and energy will be the determining agent, running throughout the exobiosphere, at every level of organization. There will be a food web, and there will be associated senses related to resource acquisition and defence. There will be reproduction. So if you arrive on another planet, full of enthusiasm and energy, but more importantly, fat, protein and carbohydrates, supplied, recently, from your spacecraft's in-flight meals, you could well find yourself viewed as a resource, a package of free energy ripe for acquisition. Exobiology will either detect your presence as a spike in the energetic landscape relevant to that particular organism, or you will go unnoticed – an irrelevant object that is not a suitable addition to its diet. If you fit the bill, you will be handled and some of your energy will be taken in to the exobiological organism, allowing it to continue its existence in a Universe where energy assimilation is essential.

What else can we predict, using the energetic approach? Given the assumption that the periodic table is a universal representation of the chemical constituents available, molecules formed from these elements are also predictable. What we cannot know is the availability of particular elements on the planet. On Earth, for example, the presence of many metals in the crust may be accounted for by the traumatic birth of the

Moon. These metals allowed the industrial revolution and the birth of technology to occur among humans. If they had not been available, how different might the technological history of humankind have been? More complex molecules involved in replication and metabolism will function based on structures that are determined by the energetic context. They will fold within this context, and so energy will drive sequence in any DNA-like and protein-like molecules. In the end, structure of molecules is determined by energy.

Extraterrestrial sex

Predictions relating to reproductive systems are difficult. To explore the possibilities, we must first begin with some basic considerations. Reproduction will be most likely necessary, in terms of continuing lineages, if death occurs, and is needed for increasing population size, and in terms of diversification of life forms. An exception to this would occur if there was continuous spontaneous generation of life forms from non-living constituents, which is also possible, as is suggested in terms of the origin of life, independently from the influence of outside agents, on Earth. There may be asexual or sexual reproduction or both. Sexual reproduction may involve two or more individuals, and the process itself will depend on whether or not there is a DNA-type molecule that acts as a coding unit for the organism.

If the basis of life was cellular, multicellular organisms would most likely need some kind of developmental process, involving cell division and differentiation, and underpinned by some kind of coding molecule, or there would need to be aggregation of different types of cell. Single cell organisms could replicate by fission. Of course, there may be no coding molecule of inheritance, and instead, each component of the organism could replicate to produce copies of themselves. Disease organisms could utilize resources and molecular machinery of other organisms to replicate, akin to viruses on our planet.

Just as on this planet, sexual structure and behaviour will most likely be heavily influenced by the energetic context in terms of patchiness and density of resources.

Furthermore, reproduction will be within the context of population dynamics, in that the habitat will have an energetic carrying capacity, which will have a huge influence on the reproductive fitness of individuals. If the habitat is sparsely populated, growth rate will be more likely to be rapid. Organisms living in habitats that are saturated with other organisms, interpreting niche space in similar ways (as is the case with functional redundancy on Earth), will be under greater competitive limitation, and the population will have a much lower reproductive output due to this.

Reproduction on Earth is intrinsically linked with water. Internalization of early development and production of cleidoic eggs (eggs encased in a relatively impermeable shell) in birds are strategies developed as life moved on to land. Changes from water-based reproduction to water-independent reproduction represent a common trend across the plants and animals, from fish, to amphibians, to reptiles, to birds and mammals, and from algae, to mosses, to ferns, to gymnosperms and angiosperms. This lies at the heart of significant differences in these groups. If our distant planet had oceans and land, we might expect to see similar differences occurring in life forms. Of course it is important to emphasise that the movement away from water-based reproduction was not some great direction, some destiny or calling. It was merely the spread of matter in response to energy, diffusing across the planet over time, and responding to the differing energetic contexts encountered. No one way is better than another, but, rather, it reflects the response to a given context.

Reproduction can also be important in dealing with stress, where organisms produce spores or seeds with thick walls that can allow the lineage to survive extreme conditions. Such spores could, theoretically, form propagules that could travel between planets as in Panspermia. This is important, as the potential to be able to spread to another planet is likely to demand conditions on the home planet that provide a niche for such a propagule to arise in the first place. The other origin of panspermic properties would, of course, come from a panspermic origin of life on the home planet itself. Written into the life forms would be the way to escape, since that is how their ancestors got there in the first place. However this circular argument has to end eventually, as the original ancestor must have arisen *de novo,* somewhere. Dispersal is likely to arise in heterogeneous landscapes, where resources are patchily distributed, both in space and time. The need to travel in order to find resources is a fundamental aspect of many reproductive events, particularly if the adult phase is non-motile. Finally, if two or more individuals are needed in order to produce the offspring, mate detection and selection may play a role, with issues such as sexual dimorphism and sexual selection coming in to focus.

Extraterrestrial species?

Underlying all of this is the thorny question of species. Under what circumstances would we expect species to exist on another planet? On our planet, species represent barriers to gene flow. They are defined on this basis, though as we have seen earlier, the species definition is a controversial and problematic one. If we stick with the reproductive definition, then how does this arise? Different species are reproductively isolated from one another due to structural, temporal, behavioural or biochemical barriers. Species are maintained by population interactions, stemming from a common gene pool that individual members contribute to and take from. Does a biosphere need species and are they an automatic outcome of the organizational processes acting on that biosphere? These are difficult questions. In this book, we would suggest that species are very much a side product of central processes, and their occurrence on another planet will be dependent on similar processes occurring. Energetically, species allow for relatively stable structure in the biosphere, and for specialization between organisms, in the same way as multicellularity has allowed specialization within organisms. Thus the drivers that led to multicellularity can be seen to be paralleled within speciation, acting at a higher level. Multicellular organisms find themselves partitioned, as species, within energetic niches, both in terms of succession, zonation and trophodynamics. This is where the species finds its place. Species can be seen as responses to energetic considerations at the level of organization where they are relevant. So just as cellular specialization occurs in individual organisms, so functional specialization at an ecosystem level can be seen to result in species.

Without species there would be, potentially, one huge gene pool, but limitations in terms of organismal specialization. Thus the outcomes of specialization, in terms of ecosystem function would be absent. Since the energetic niche and the pressures of energy acquisition within a limiting resource base are likely to be common across most planets, then speciation may well have occurred as a response to these things. However, just because specialization can be seen to be useful, this does not mean that these specializations have to be reproductively isolated.

Many organisms pass through different niches during their development, exhibiting very different specialization at different stages. Take, for example, a butterfly. As a larva, it is a foliovore (leaf eater), whereas as an adult it may not feed at all, or feed on nectar. Many birds are fed on insects as hatchlings, but in adulthood, they may be granivores (grain eaters). So on our other planet, organisms may change in their roles through time, or may be able to morph into different roles depending on what is needed, acting as a "polyspecies" with the ability to transform between different specializations depending on need. We have already noted that some photosynthetic plants can have a carnivorous habit.

Thus, there is no requirement for a reproductively isolated species concept. It may or may not happen. Certainly among the Bacteria and Archaea on Earth, the species concept is all but redundant given the proclivity of horizontal gene transfer. The benefits of one collective reproductive pool are multiple, and we could even envisage a situation where although morphologically distinct, individual organisms could share in some matrix of inheritance, benefiting from wider access. The specialized aspects of an organism could be inherited differently from more widely available material. Inherited "genomes" do not have to come in single units. Even we inherit our mitochondria independently of sexual reproduction. In the same way as multicellular organisms benefit from being in a collective, so a partitioned genome might bring similar benefits, even allowing multiple contributors at a parental level, each contributing different parts of the genetic material. At its most extreme, we could envisage a sort of "borg" collective, where organisms can sample genetic information from any other organism, adding this information to the collective. The Borg of *Star Trek* fame assimilated information from organisms across the Universe! In ways, eukaryotes have assimilated whole organisms in borg-like fashion, such as chloroplasts and mitochondria. Horizontal gene transfer operates in a similar way. Of course, assimilation can also be driven by the "assimilated" as well as the "assimilators". For example, DNA viruses implant parts of their genome into their host's DNA.

The context of species

If species do exist, they will be part of a food web, a succession and a zonation. Communities evolve within both temporal and spatial contexts. They find their place within these contexts. We would therefore expect our exobiosphere to be organized in various ways. As organisms interact with their environment, the feedback will most likely lead to changes in the environment, allowing other species to fill new niches. The flow of energy within a particular trophic level will impact on that level and those above and below it, leading to change in soil, sediment and water chemistry. The atmosphere will likely change over time as well. Changes will lead to new opportunities for life on our distant planet. Thus there will be dynamic events occurring. Depending on the age of the community, and the amount of disturbance on the planet, the community will be shaped in different ways. There may be mass extinction events, driven by the geology of the planet (huge volcanic events like the Deccan and Siberian Traps on Earth), impacts of bolides (like the Yucatan collision 65 million years ago that is linked to the extinction of the dinosaurs) and even dramatic changes in cosmic energy, such as gamma rays from an exploding neutron star (possibly implicated in the Ordovician mass extinction). All of these events will likely have dramatic significance in terms of how the exobiosphere has developed over time, altering the dominant life forms on the planet. It will also depend on what stage a planet is observed, as to what state the exobiosphere will be in. This is important, as direct comparison with our present Biosphere will be unlikely to be of use. If extraterrestrial life forms had visited Earth just after the Permian mass extinction, they would have come across a very different biosphere than that of today.

Some exogeophysical considerations

It is worth mentioning that our distant planet will no doubt have biomes, driven both by the curvature of the surface relative to the local star, and to circulatory currents. Winds have been observed on neighbouring planets within our own solar system. On Mars, polar regions are visible that change throughout the Martian year, representing seasonality. Our distant planet may also have one or more moons, and these will impact on any exobiosphere, both in terms of direct and indirect effects, possibly protecting the planet from bolides. Tectonic plate movements may also occur, impacting on biogeographical distributions. Mountain ranges may well form, influencing the climate around them, providing zonation along physical gradients, and possibly isolating groups of organisms from others.

Contingency revisited

This brings us back to Stephen Jay Gould's contingency theory. Earlier we argued that contingency, or lady luck, cannot be viewed as necessarily significant, since whatever has happened would always happen. However contingency theory finds a much more interesting role in comparing two or more planets. If these planets have similar starting points, then comparing life on them will indicate the strength of contingency. It is highly unlikely that any two planets will have identical histories in terms of geology and bolide impact. By carefully studying differences in the planets, we would not be re-running the film of life, but rather looking at two different films and seeing how constrained is the evolution of each biosphere. What roles do particular events play? Will the films lead to the same, or similar, outcomes? Does the interaction between energy and chemistry produce dramatically different biospheres? This would be one of the most interesting things to study, offering an insight into key questions about how biospheres evolve. The rules are the same. The raw material belongs to the same periodic table and so the chemistry is the same. The energetic voices are the same. So how different will the games of biology turn out? The energetic hypothesis presented in this book would indicate that the levels of organization and the ways that these operate will most probably be recognisable. The exobiosphere will have evolved under constrained opportunism, and the key constraints and opportunities will be energetic. Given that molecules, organisms, populations and communities all dance to tunes relevant to their level of organization, and given that the underlying processes of succession, zonation, trophodynamics and population ecology are energy-driven, then we should see similar patterns.

Differences will be contingent upon things like the presence or absence of water (and thus oxygen), the replicative molecules, the location and type of the nearest star, whether "life" is organic or inorganic in nature, and the frequency and types of mass extinction events. However the dance will not be led by these, but by the multifaceted interaction between physics and chemistry, with the universal laws of physics shaping all. Taking an energetic approach allows us to predict much more than is possible using a gene-centric approach, since we are not limited to the gene, and we are not limited to a single unit of selection, but rather a multilevel synthesis, where a single agent operates in different ways at each level.

Invasion from outer space?

Finally, what are the chances of extra-terrestrial life forms visiting our planet? To answer this we need to understand what might drive this. One word comes to mind, and that is "dispersal". Organisms disperse for one reason, and that is to find resources. The drive to disperse is an interesting one, and the drive not to disperse is also fascinating. Many species on oceanic islands evolve in such a way as not to disperse. This is thought to be because once they reach a distant island, further dispersal is likely to land their offspring in the water! The original dispersion was most likely aided by a freak wind current, and so the reverse trip is unlikely. There may also be factors related to a lack of predation. For example many insects and birds become flightless over generations on islands, possibly because the need for flight to escape predators is no longer a factor. In terms of extraterrestrial dispersal, there are two likely levels, one at the spore level and one at the advanced intelligence level. Problems in terms of time and conditions mean that the dispersers need protection. A dormant spore, highly protected against cosmic energy, could, theoretically, disperse. The advanced life forms would need to design a transport method that protected them from the damaging radiation, cold and aging processes that would occur, given that hospitable planets may be highly dispersed throughout the Universe.

In humans, the search for planets is driven by the underlying fear that our planet may become inhospitable, and so there may be a possibility of engineering a way to reach an alternative planet that would allow the continuation of the species. If there were intelligent beings on other planets, it is likely that they too would realize that planets do not last forever, and impending destruction may be imminent. Thus just like us, they may attempt to disperse deliberately. Of course, they would be capable of remotely sensing huge detail on our planet without coming near it, and so are unlikely to drop by for a look! The movie, *Signs*, has the ridiculous situation where visiting aliens are killed by water. If a species has the intelligence to cross the Universe and reach our planet, whose surface is 71% water, then it would be a bit of an oversight for them not to have spotted this "deadly" molecule before landing!

A planet does not have to be hospitable initially. Much research is being carried out in terms of habitat engineering, looking at ways to create conditions conducive to life, in a field known as *terraforming*. Terraforming is a mainstream scientific area of research, as well as a topic of fiction, such as Arthur C. Clarke's *The Sands of Mars*, and *Green Mars* by Kim Stanley Robinson.

With patchily distributed planets across the Universe, we can envisage the presence of biology as a disease occupying a host. Two possibilities exist for its presence. Either the disease has spread from another host, in the process of Panspermia, or the disease has evolved independently on each planet. Energetic constraints will act upon both scenarios equally, and this may mean that both end up in a similar outcome.

Of course the starting point could be very different. We can divide our planets into two categories: Earth-like and non Earth-like. Earth-like planets could well share a similar basic biosphere bauplan: water-based life. Non Earth-like planets could be very different, but in all cases, the laws of thermodynamics will fundamentally shape what can and cannot occur. There will be a biological game, played to the same rules, whatever its starting point.

And so we near the end of our journey, which began with the challenges offered by our Biosphere, struggled with the mechanism of evolution and emerged with a new way of understanding things. Having used this understanding to examine some of the major debates in evolutionary biology, we turn, finally, to a very different issue, that is impacting upon all of us at present: climate change. What does our theory propose in terms of both the causes and solutions to this crisis? As we shall see in the next section, this book presents a clear and simple way ahead, that ultimately emerges from the energetic theory.

Section VII

Applying the Energetic Theory of Evolution to the Greatest Challenge Facing Humankind

What hope is there for the human race? Headline after headline paint an increasingly gloomy picture of a polluted world, over-heating and experiencing extremely high levels of species extinction, as humankind continues to alter the environment in such a way as to seriously damage the Biosphere. We are the practitioners of terraforming on our own planet. Governments now target a reduction in carbon emissions as the key strategy to reduce the onslaught.

We look at the causes of climate change and define the key issue that lies at the heart of the transformation that our planet is experiencing. Energetic perturbation, driven by our need to obtain sufficient energy in order to sustain our ever-increasing population, is the core problem. We then identify the single solution to our woes, and it isn't carbon emission reduction.

Chapter Twenty Three
Climate Change and our Place in the World

One of the most radical implications of this book lies at the heart of the challenges facing the human race today: how to confront the problems arising from our impact upon the Biosphere. While turning these pages, the human race has continued its march towards survival and expansion, inexorably converting the planet into a different world, transforming the atmosphere and hydrosphere, and dramatically impacting upon the Biosphere, of which we are all a part. As we have seen in the previous pages, it is energy that structures the living planet, and it is energy that accounts for change within it. It is also energy that lies at the centre of the huge, multifaceted industrial, technological, agricultural and medical machine that wrecks havoc upon this planet, a machine that acts as a life support system for our sub-species.

If I was to ask you what the greatest impact of the human race has been upon our planet, what would your answer be? Carbon dioxide increase? Sea level rise? Habitat destruction? Pollution? Extinction of rare species? Certainly these are all consequences of the recent activities of *Homo sapiens sapiens*. A deeper question would ask if there was any link between these problems, or if they are all separate issues. This book argues that there is one single cause, energy.

All of these major threats to the health of the Biosphere stem from our need to acquire resources in order to maintain the population expansion. Each of the six and a half billion humans is a resourcer, needing energy to survive. We need energy from food. We need energy to keep warm, or cool. We need energy to earn money, which has become a kind of energy token, to be exchanged for food and other resources inextricably linked with our survival. In this respect, power and authority stem from ownership of such energy tokens. This is why the subjects of economics and biology share so much in common. We need energy to fly around the world and to transport resources. We need energy to establish territories for breeding and to provide for our offspring over their increasingly lengthy and costly period of parental care. But where does all of this energy come from? In the end, most of it comes from the Sun. The fossil fuels represent energy from Christmas past, entrapping energy from the Sun hundreds of years ago, while today's fields of corn, maize, rice and wheat represent the conversion of the Sun's radiation into chemicals (sugars) which allow the energy to pass through the foodchain. As we shall see in this chapter, it is our attempt at increasing the energy flow necessary to support our hugely inflated population that has led to all of the problems facing the Biosphere. But how can we increase the flow of energy into the Biosphere?

Firstly, we need to understand the different ways in which the energy arriving on the surface of our planet can change. Four different types of event alter the supply of energy from the Sun. Let's look at each of these in turn.

1. Changes in the Sun

The Sun is not an unchanging object, but is aging through time. It has gradually "warmed up" over its history, increasing in terms of the radiation released. Eventually it will expand to consume the Earth. Obviously, man can have no effect on this aspect of the variation in energy available to him. On a shorter time scale, huge storms occur on the Sun's surface, producing cooler regions, called sunspots. Careful indirect observation of the Sun reveals these darker areas. Never look directly at the Sun, especially not through binoculars or a telescope, as you will likely be instantly blinded. Instead, take a piece of card and make a small hole with a large sewing needle. Use this to project an image of the Sun onto a wall, or some white card. By altering the distance between the pinhole card and the wall, you can vary the size of the image. You can now look for sunspots!

Over time, the number of sunspots changes. In fact, every 11 years, this reaches a maximum, in what is known as the Schwabe cycle, after the German astronomer, Samuel Heinrich Schwabe (1789–1875). Interestingly, Schwabe made the discovery while searching for something completely different. He believed that there was a small planet between the Sun and Mercury, called Vulcan, and looked for its silhouette against the Sun. He never found it (it doesn't actually exist, we now know) but instead noted that sunspots followed a cycle of intensity. This cycle turns out not to be constant either, and every 80 years, it goes from being 8 years at its shortest, to 12 years at its longest. This is known as the Gleissberg cycle, after Wolfgang Gleissberg (1903-1986), another German astronomer.

However the change in solar radiation due to these perturbations turns out to be a storm in a teacup, amounting to a maximum decline of 0.14%, not enough to explain global warming or cooling. Larger forces are in action. This brings us to the second set of events that change the amount of energy reaching the Earth.

2. Changes in the distance between the Earth and the Sun

In 1840, a Swiss geologist, Louis Agassiz, wrote a book entitled *Etudes sur les Glaciers*, which revealed that large parts of Northern Europe had once been covered in glaciers. He deduced this from looking at their giant footprints. Glaciers leave behind them huge amounts of squashed rubble. Like huge bulldozers, they move across the landscape, and their trail of destruction gives testament to their presence, even many thousands of years after they disappear. It was soon recognized that, in fact, glaciation events have happened many times in the history of the planet. But how did these events happen? Sunspot cycles cannot account for such dramatic changes in the Earth's climate. There had to be a greater periodic disturbance in the energy reaching the Earth. Focus has come to bear on another important set of events that control the distance between the Earth and the Sun. The closer we are to the Sun, the more solar energy we receive, and the further we are from it, the less energy reaches the planet surface. It's like the spokes on a bicycle wheel. The closer to the centre of the wheel, the closer the spokes are. Thus if you imagine the Earth as a tomato, the closer it is placed towards the centre of the wheel, the more spokes will pass through it.

There are three ways in which the distance between the Earth and the Sun changes over time. Firstly, the Earth doesn't always follow the same orbit around the Sun. The orbit is not circular, but more like an oval. If you take an elastic band, and stretch it between your thumb and first finger, then imagine the Earth following the path of the band, you get close to the orbit. However, over a period of about 100 000 years, the orbit becomes more or less stretched. The result is that the distance between the Earth and the Sun changes, and when it is furthest away from the Sun (i.e. the band is most stretched), the radiation reaching the Earth is 30% less in January than in July, leading to exaggerated seasonal differences. At present, there is only a 6% difference in radiation between the closest and furtherest points in the orbit, as we are close to a circular path.

As we have already noted, the Earth is tilted at around 23.5 degrees, and this leads to seasonality. In January, the Northern Hemisphere is tilted away from the Sun, whereas in July, it is tilted towards the Sun. The opposite is true of the southern Hemisphere. The impact can be quite extreme. Take Moscow for example. In January, the average temperature is -10.5 degrees centigrade, while in July, it is 23.4 degrees centigrade. Moscow hasn't moved, but the Earth to which it is attached has! However the angle of tilt is not constant. In fact, it varies between 22.1 and 24.5 degrees. These changes occur in a cycle that takes 40000 years. The more tilted the planet, the more extreme are the seasons, with colder winters and warmer summers.

The final change that occurs to the Earth over time involves a wobble, often compared to a spinning top which, as it slows, starts to move. The axis of the Earth at the moment points towards Polaris, the North star. This star can be used to identify north if you get lost (as long as it is not cloudy!). However, the axis hasn't always pointed in this direction. In fact, every 26000 years, it traces out a circle in the sky. Amazingly, this was first discovered 2000 years ago, by Hipparchus (190-120BC) the Ancient Greek astronomer.

So our planet is dynamic in terms of its relationship to the Sun. Milutin Milanković (1879-1958), the famous Serbian geophysicist, had puzzled as to why, over geological time, there had been periods of ice ages and others when the planet was ice-free. He started work as a civil engineer, specializing in building reinforced concrete structures across the Austrian-Hungarian Empire. Appointed to a chair in Applied Mathematics in 1909 in Belgrade, he turned his attention to ice ages and, finally, in 1941, published his *opus grandis*, *Canon of Insolation of the Earth and its Application to the Problem of the Ice Ages*. He put the three great cycles (orbit, tilting and wobble) together, and found that when they coincided at their most extreme, they would lead to significantly colder winters, and, more importantly, significantly cooler summers that would allow ice from the previous winter to remain. Over time, this leads to a build up of ice, year upon year, leading to an ice age. As the planet becomes covered in ice, another event takes place, called the *Albedo effect*. Simply, ice reflects more energy than soil or rock, because it is white. This further reduces the amount of radiation impacting on the surface, acting like a giant mirror.

Milanković predicted when ice ages would occur from this pattern of cycles, but evidence to support his theory didn't emerge for another thirty years. The problem with an ice age is that it tends to wipe out evidence of the ice age before it, just as a bulldozer destroys the track marks of an earlier vehicle. However, deep in the ocean, in the sediments that slowly accrue over time, a record builds up that is not destroyed, and it was this that showed that Milanković had come very close in his predictions.

3. The atmosphere acts as a sunscreen

The third way in which the amount of energy reaching the planet can be altered occurs in the skies above us. The atmosphere stands between the incoming radiation and us. It has three effects: general blocking, selective blocking and insulation.

A. General blocking

If the atmosphere is filled with dust, either from volcanic activity or as a result of a giant asteroid striking the Earth, then the Sun's radiation will be blocked and the planet will cool. Photosynthesis will also start to struggle, and that spells huge problems for the entire Biosphere. Blocking like this has been recorded in tree rings. The trunk of a tree marks such dramatic reduction in energy availability by having narrower annual growth rings than in normal years, because there was a reduction in sunlight and, therefore, a reduction in growth. A more extreme situation results in a complete breakdown of the food chain, and, often, significant atmospheric blocking of solar radiation has led to a mass extinction. Usually, it isn't the actual asteroid impact that creates the mass destruction in the Biosphere, but, rather, it is the dust that results from it. It's the atmosphere that does the killing!

B. Selective blocking

Selective blocking of particular wavelengths also can occur. Ozone absorbs only some of the radiation from the Sun, ultraviolet radiation (UV). The ozone layer is in the upper atmosphere, some 10 to 50 km above the surface. Charles Fabry and Henri Buisson, two French physicists, discovered it in 1913. The ozone story is actually quite complicated. UV leads to the synthesis of ozone in the first place, as well as its breakdown. The UV is converted to heat during this process. At lower levels in the atmosphere (the first 10 km above the surface), a small amount of ozone (about 2%) also exists, and here it acts to return heat energy to the surface.

Perturbation in the amount of ozone can have significant results. The normal cycle of breakdown and formation of ozone balances out, but man-made pollutants such as chlorine lead to greater breakdown, thus upsetting the balance. Recent holes in the ozone have been linked to increases in skin cancer, cataracts and weakened immune systems. In 1935, 1 in 1500 people suffered skin cancer in the United States of America. By 1991, this had risen to 1 in 150. In Queensland, Australia, 3 out of 4 people will experience some form of skin cancer. However, again, things are more complicated than many people realize. UV is essential for the formation of vitamin D. No organism can synthesise this essential vitamin without exposure to UV. A lack of vitamin D has been implicated in colon cancer, bone weakness and problems with intestine and kidney function. So UV isn't all bad, and actually plays an important role in the health of organisms. Finally, UV is a major cause of mutations, and without mutations, evolution would be very limited, since there would be a great reduction in new sequences of DNA.

C. Indirect effect

The atmosphere can also have an indirect impact on the amount of radiation received on the planet. Carbon dioxide, water, methane and other "greenhouse gases" act to absorb heat energy escaping from the surface of the Earth. The idea that the atmosphere has an impact on planetary warming was first noted by Jean Baptiste Joseph Fourier (1768 - 1830), in 1824, when he compared it to a glass hothouse or greenhouse. The word *greenhouse* is misleading, in that the process of warming is, strictly speaking, somewhat different than what occurs in a typical greenhouse. Greenhouses work by preventing warm air from escaping, due to some sort of barrier (usually glass or plastic). Warm air naturally rises, but this is prevented by the walls and roof of the greenhouse.

The *greenhouse effect* on our planet doesn't involve a barrier as such. The radiation that comes from the Sun, and hits our planet, will either be reflected back, or might be absorbed and released again. It really depends on the colour of the part of the surface that we are considering. A white surface, like the Arctic, will reflect most of the radiation back, whereas a dark surface, like a road, will absorb the radiation, heat up, and then release it as heat. This warms the air above the road surface, and this warm air then rises. This heat would normally leave the planet and be lost. Unlike a greenhouse, the gases in the atmosphere act like lots of tiny mirrors, rather than a barrier, absorbing the heat and then releasing it again. The release is a random process in terms of the direction, so the heat won't necessarily be sent back to Earth, but some of it will. Therefore the more greenhouse gas particles that are in the atmosphere, the more heat will be directed back, and the warmer the planet will get. This is what we refer to as *greenhouse warming*.

Carbon fixation and our fixation with carbon

Greenhouse gases have been important in the past as well as today. Without them, our planet would be considerably colder, and inhospitable to most life forms. High levels of carbon dioxide have been important in ending ice ages, particularly the great snowball Earth situations, when the planet threatened to become an ice ball forever. Low levels of the same gas have been involved in the onset of ice ages. More importantly still, carbon dioxide is essential for photosynthesis, also called carbon fixation, acting as the receiver of energy at the end of the process, where it is used to build sugars. It sits centre stage in the conversion of light energy to chemical energy. Carbon is also the central building block of many of our key molecules, such as proteins and nucleic acids, as well as of key cell structures, such as membranes.

However it has become the evil joker in today's world, blamed for all of our problems. Headline after headline screams for reduced carbon emissions. This is in spite of the fact that water vapour is responsible for most of the greenhouse effect (30-70%) whereas carbon dioxide is only responsible for 9-26% of the effect. Of greater concern is the fact that warmer air contains more water vapour than cooler air, and so although man's activities do not increase the amount of water vapour directly, increases in other greenhouse gases due to his activities will indirectly lead to higher levels of water vapour, thus exacerbating the problem.

Charles Keeling (1928 - 2005) was the most influential climate change scientist to have lived. He developed the first method of measuring carbon dioxide in the atmosphere, and, in 1957, began monitoring levels of this gas. Up until his work, it was thought that excess carbon dioxide would be absorbed by the oceans and would not remain in the atmosphere. Instead, Keeling recorded a steady increase in levels throughout the latter half of the twentieth century, going from 315 parts per million in 1957 to 380 parts per million today. Carbon dioxide was identified as a key problem and became the focus of world governments in terms of reducing its emissions. Things had come a long way from Walther Nernst (1864-1941), the German Nobel Laureate and chemist, who suggested setting fire to coal seams in order to warm the Earth!

4. Making the most of what you've got.

The final way that the amount of energy from the Sun can be altered lies on the surface of the planet itself. It doesn't matter how much energy hits this spinning, wobbling, orbiting third rock from the Sun. Unless it is converted into a form that the Biosphere can access, then life as we know it would not exist. Most energy enters the Biosphere through photosynthesis, where light is converted to chemical energy. This is not some form of supernatural alchemy, but merely a transition of energy from one form to another. In order to increase the entrance of energy into the Biosphere, you need to increase photosynthesis. It is the only way to do it.

Most of the impacts that humankind have had on our planet have stemmed from the use and abuse of this fourth set of ways to increase available energy from the Sun. In order to provide chemical energy, plants need three things: access to sunlight, access to nutrients (including carbon dioxide) and access to water. Our attempts to increase plant production have been targeted at increasing these three crucial components and have led to humans wrecking havoc upon the planet, as we shall see.

Creating access to sunlight for plants has led man down a path of habitat destruction and fragmentation, destroying major parts of biomes by clearing them and converting them into agroecosystems. The need for land to grow crops, graze animals or grow biofuels has irreparably damaged huge tracks of previously unspoiled primary habitat that has taken thousands of years to form in the first place. As fossil fuels are deemed to be insecure, both in terms of amounts available and political instability, a new market in green fuels from plants such as oil palms, sugar cane and soybean has developed. Deemed to be carbon neutral, in that the carbon dioxide released by them as fuels will be absorbed again by the next year's growth of the plants, they have been flagged as an environmentally friendly alternative to fossil fuels. The problem is that they take a large amount of land to grow. This has led to large parts of the orangutan's last refuge on Earth, in Borneo and Sumatra, being destroyed. The orangutans would have probably survived global warming, but not the removal of their habitat. The fuel may be green, but the loss of one of the most intelligent animals on our planet is a huge price to pay.

The destruction of habitat is a long term problem. Rainforests don't just grow back. Rare animal species that only live in these areas are lost forever. In the end, the areas cleared of natural habitats often prove useless for crop and animal husbandry after only a few years.

The problem with nutrients

So we continue to clear the planet in order to give our crops the area they need to access sunlight. But sunlight is not able to be converted to chemical energy without a number of key helping hands. These helpers are nutrients such as phosphate, nitrogen, potassium and carbon. The word "nutrient" conjures up thoughts of strange tasting drinks from health food shops in many peoples' minds. Yet nutrients are much more important in the whole scheme. Basically, they determine how much energy gets into the Biosphere. Two few nutrients and the system collapses from energy starvation, too many nutrients, and the system collapses from energy over-dose. Nutrients are central to any understanding of how our living planet works. Nutrient acquisition is the name of the game, and before any of the energy from the Sun can get involved with the biology of the Earth, plants need to get hold of these things. These substances make up the players who pass the energy parcel along the line, allowing energy to move to where it is needed. The only problem is that the key nutrients are hard to get hold of. In fact, one of the mysteries of how life began involves why the Biosphere ended up being so reliant on such rare elements.

Anti-social nitrogen

Take nitrogen as an example. 78% of the atmosphere is made up of nitrogen. So how can it be that it is in short supply for plants? Surely we are bathing in a sea of it? The reason is that the nitrogen in the air is just about impossible to use. Called dinitrogen, it consists of two nitrogen atoms tightly bound together. The bonds are so strong that it is very difficult to separate them, and so they won't join up with other kinds of atoms to make the chemicals needed. In this way nitrogen is quite antisocial! Only bacteria and lightening can separate it from itself naturally. Even when a plant gets hold of some nitrogen, and makes its amino acids and DNA, the nitrogen becomes stuck in these compounds after the death of the plant. Amino acids are usually too complicated to be taken up by plants themselves, and so this creates further problems.

Extremely social phosphorus

Phosphorus can be equally tricky to get hold of, but for the opposite reason of nitrogen. There is often a lot of it around in the soil, but it is attached to things like aluminium and calcium. It gets involved in deep chemical conversations with other substances and it becomes difficult to prize away. Yet phosphorus is centrally involved in DNA structure, membrane structure and the all important ATP (adenosine triphosphate). ATP is the major player in energy movement within an organism and therefore is central to life itself. No phosphorus, no show. Adenosine triphosphate has a tail of three phosphorus groups (hence the word *tri*phosphate), and the last one of these, when removed, releases energy, leading to the ATP being converted to ADP (adenosine diphosphate, the *di-* indicating 2 phosphorus groups in the tail). This ADP then absorbs energy by attaching a phosphorus group to itself, making ATP again. It's really simple but extremely important. The lengthening and shortening of the tail allows energy to be taken up and dropped off where appropriate. ATP will be involved somewhere in almost all the activities of our bodies, from growth to movement and from taking energy from our food to getting rid of toxins. It is also central to the process of photosynthesis, being made from the light energy, and then being used to provide the energy to construct sugars from carbon dioxide.

To solve the supply problems, nature has worked in creative ways. If an organism can come up with an answer to these problems, it will gain a huge benefit in terms of being able to survive. In general, photosynthetic organisms, such as plants, algae and cyanobacteria, are the major doorkeepers that control the entrance of energy into the Biosphere. They work at the frontline, doing the crucial first step, by converting light energy into chemical energy. The rest of the Biosphere relies on them. The games of biology can only be played if this chemical energy is available. These photosynthetic organisms also manage the movement of nutrients, such as nitrogen and phosphorus, into the foodchains. This makes sense, since the molecules that handle energy need these nutrients in order to work.

Having cleared the Earth to make room for food and biofuel crops, we next need to provide these plants with the necessary nutrients, so that the light energy hitting the plants actually gets made into sugar. Without the nutrients, the plant wouldn't grow. We have created a huge problem as a result of feeding our crops, a problem, this book would argue, that is the greatest of all. But to understand why this is the case, we need to take a closer look at the relationship between the Biosphere and nutrients.

Getting hold of nutrients, as we have seen, is a significant challenge. To overcome this challenge, nutrient uptake is facilitated in three ways: at the species level, at the community level and at the ecosystem level.

Nutrient uptake at the species level

Individual plant species approach the challenges of finding these elusive elements by either chemically manipulating their environment, or by making friends with someone who can help. Plant roots don't just take things from the soil. They also put things into it. These things are chemicals that alter the soil. Sometimes they acidify the soil around them. This is done because acids can free up some of the nutrients. For example, phosphorus becomes more available. By making the soil more acid, this disrupts the chemical conversations that phosphorus was having with its best friend, calcium. However too much acid can make phosphorus start to link up with aluminium and so it is a fine balance that must be achieved.

Plants also release other things that break up conversations by surrounding the close friends, distracting them and then grabbing the phosphorus. These chemicals are called chelating agents (from the Greek language, meaning claw).

Roots can release all sorts of other chemicals. Some of these kill the roots of other species, thus reducing competition, while others encourage bacteria to grow, often benefiting the plant, since these bacteria free up nutrients themselves. Plants release different chemicals depending on their requirements. If they are running low in phosphorus or nitrogen, they will release more of the appropriate chemical weapons needed for the specific challenge.

Collaboration at the community level

Another approach taken to get hold of these elusive nutrients is to collaborate. As the saying goes, "*Two heads are better than one*". Some plants build housing complexes on their roots, called nodules, where members of a completely separate domain, Bacteria, can live. These bacteria have a very special skill. They can convert dinitrogen, the tightly bonded nitrogen in the air, into a form that plants can use. This trick is called nitrogen fixation. The plant provides safe accommodation and a supply of sugar. The bacteria and the plant work together and the plant becomes independent of the soil in terms of not needing to search for nitrogen. This is a huge benefit, since it can now occupy places where plants would not normally be able to survive. There are many species of plants that do this, including all of the legumes. Clover is an example. Farmers, for centuries, have rotated what they grow in their fields, and every three years, they would plant the field with clover. During this year, the clover would gain nitrogen from the air, thanks to the bacteria living in the nodules. When the clover died, this nitrogen would be returned to the soil, and become available to the crop plants over the next two years.

Rice paddy fields have been managed in the same way using a different system. Farmers put floating ferns, called *Azolla*, into the water. The ferns contain little cavities filled with cyanobacteria, ancient organisms thought to have been some of the earliest originators of photosynthesis, and some of the earliest known to have existed on Earth. These bacteria not only photosynthesise, but can fix nitrogen. The fern offers protection and gains nitrogen. The bacteria need to spend less energy on making sugar, and can spend more on fixing nitrogen. Some of this nitrogen enters the surrounding water, and the rice can access it, therefore allowing it to grow faster and stronger.

Plants also make friends with fungi. The fungi grow thin, very long thread-like structures, called hyphae. These can penetrate into tiny spaces in the soil that the plants' roots cannot access, as they are too big. Fungi can access nitrogen and phosphorus. They grow into the plant roots and barter nutrients for sugar. Around 90% of all plants have this fungal friend, and together they are called mycorrhizas (*mycor*: fungus, *rhyza*: root). Some plants have both bacteria and fungi, forming a tripartite relationship. These three bedfellows work together to satisfy each other's needs.

Nutrition at the ecosystem level

The final level at which nutrition is managed is at the level of the ecosystem. We have already seen that limited nutrient availability leads to a great diversity of life, with lots of different strategies used to overcome the problems. Organisms are part of a greater level of organization, and at this level we see the ecosystem operating to hold on to nutrients.

Coral reefs

Coral reefs are well known as major sources of diversity. For example the Great Barrier Reef, off the East coast of Australia, has over 1500 species of fish, 360 species of corals, 200 species of birds and 125 species of sharks associated with it. Yet the great paradox is that this hugely diverse ecosystem lies on the edge of starvation, the great blue deserts that we know as the oceans. While water around large land masses is rich in nutrients, mostly from rivers that carry material from the land, the deep ocean is a very different place. Coral reefs are found on the edge of these oceans, in very low nutrient levels, and have a very tight budget, recycling everything that they can. The secret to success is not to lose precious resources. Each organism may lose material, but the ecosystem as a whole is very self-contained, with little leakage. Like the ultimate in green technology, everything gets re-used. Things die, are broken down and are re-distributed, but little is lost. This is an essential trick to play, as once lost, it is hard to find new nutrients. Indeed, reefs may well build up their nutrient bank over long periods of time.

Rainforests

Rainforests are similar to coral reefs in terms of nutrient management. Again, things are different from what they first appear. The soil of a rainforest is often less than 20 cm deep, and the rainforest rapidly recycles material through a whole host of organisms. The whole ecosystem is almost independent of the soil, which is used as a rapid transit zone. If you chop a rainforest down and drive it away in lorries to make furniture, the soil that remains will not provide the bounteous supply of nutrients for crops that it appears to promise. Surely all this productivity, the towering resplendent trees, the vast diversity of life all signifies the most wonderful soil imaginable for growing little crop plants? Not so. While you drive away the trees, you also drive away most of the nutrients of the ecosystem. More importantly, you break the chain. By this, I mean that because the whole system works on recycling, the soil of a rainforest is set up to rapidly break down and liberate nutrients for the plants, which then distribute it throughout the rest of the ecosystem. If you remove the plants, the soil continues to offer up its nutrients, and, after a heavy shower, these crucial elements will be washed away in the floodwater.

This occurs in temperate rainforests too. In a classic, long term experiment called the Hubbard Brook Ecosystem Study, located in the White Mountains of New Hampshire in the eastern United States of America, scientists compared what happened when a forest is cut down with what happens if it is not. They chopped down the trees in one area and looked at the runoff that came from the area by analysing water in the streams. They measured how much water entered the area by measuring rainfall, and how much left, by measuring stream flow, and then measured the difference between nutrient levels in the rainfall and the streams. The same measurements were made on an intact forest.

The differences were interesting. Firstly there was much more water leaving the deforested area compared to the forested area. This is because the trees absorbed water through their roots, and this water passed through the trunks and out of the leaves, into the atmosphere. No trees meant that this water instead went into the streams, and posed an erosion threat. The second discovery was that if the trees were removed there was a huge increase in the nutrients washed out of the system. The biology acted to keep nutrients in the ecosystem, but if you get rid of the biology, this entire nutrient store was lost. Here we see another ecosystem acting to maintain a tight cycling of nutrients.

The Swiss chronometers of the Biosphere and how to upset them

So our ecosystems are geared up to prevent nutrient loss and to operate best at low nutrient levels. One species works with other species to survive, and the whole thing functions like a Swiss watch, quietly ticking over, and allowing energy to flow through.

The problem comes when humans need to eat; almost seven billion of them. Nature acts too slowly for humans. The ticking Swiss watch, with its minute interacting cogs, generates enough power to turn the tiny little hour and minute hands around. However, there is not enough energy flowing through the system to satiate our requirements. When our population numbers were low, it worked. As hunter-gatherers, we plucked fruit, killed the odd animal and lived in a sustainable way. Today, vast metropoli spread across the planet, and the huge, collective human mouth gapes open, demanding food, like some enormous fledgling waiting for the parent bird to return to the nest. Food means energy and energy means increased photosynthesis in order to side-track more of the solar radiation into the game we call biology.

Fertilizing the planet

So we clear the land and give our chosen crops the space to grow. Next, we provide them with nutrients. In modern agriculture, there is no time for crop rotations, clover and floating ferns. Instead, we make fertilizers, pesticides and herbicides and douse our fields with them. It was Fritz Haber (1868-1934), a German chemist, who came up with a way to make nitrogen fertilizer in industrial quantities. Haber's life was surrounded in tragedy, with the suicide of his wife Clara, in 1915, being attributed to her disgust with Haber's involvement in the development of poison gases in the First World War, a war that also claimed the lives of their two sons. He was finally stripped of his professorship and forced into exile by the Nazi regime because of his Jewish roots. The story is brilliantly told by Vaclaw Smil, in his book, *Enriching the Earth* (2001).

By combining dinitrogen from the air with hydrogen, at temperatures of around 400 degrees centigrade, and under extreme pressure (200 times atmospheric pressure), ammonium could be formed. Carl Bosch (1874-1940), a German industrialist developed the large scale process based on Haber's work, and the process is now known as the Haber-Bosch process. This process costs a huge amount of energy to complete, because of the temperatures and pressures involved. It is amusing, in a way, that little bacteria can do the same thing without this whole industrial, heavily polluting process. It is like using a bulldozer to crack a nut, whereas the elegant biochemistry of single-celled organisms can do it quietly and cheaply using enzymes.

Plants need nitrogen. While carbon dioxide, sulphur and lead emissions can all be reduced by alternative technology (non-fossil fuels for sulphur and carbon dioxide and a switch to unleaded petrol for lead), there is no substitute for nitrogen. No nitrogen, no plant, no food, no energy. Indeed, it has been estimated that without the Haber-Bosch process 40% of the world's human population would not exist! So mankind has poured nitrogen on the agricultural landscape. We now make as much nitrogen fertilizer industrially as the entire Biosphere fixes naturally. More importantly, about half of the nitrogen that we pour onto our crops does not get taken up by them, and, instead, leaks out into our waterways.

Ecosystem collapse

This is where the problem comes. As we have seen, nutrients like nitrogen are in short supply in many natural ecosystems. That is why we need to add them to our fields in the first place. However the addition of nutrients is catastrophic for natural habitats. Nutrients don't recognize fences, and so move in water bodies and dust storms. They transform habitats, dramatically upsetting the natural balance. One of the biggest effects is a collapse in diversity. One or two species tend to dominate, outcompeting the others. It is akin to what happens with the removal of a predator. Just as we might assume that the predator always suppresses diversity by eating it, and thus its removal should lead to increased diversity, so we might likewise conclude that since nutrients are limiting in the Biosphere, adding them to an ecosystem is a good thing. In both cases we would be wrong. The removal of predators and the addition of nutrients both destabilize the balance of nature at the ecosystem level, and greatly reduce diversity. This is because energy is the architect of the ecosystem.

The collapse is largely related to a loss in specialist species, whose expensive methods of survival in poor conditions become meaningless in a nutrient-rich soup. Now outcompeted by energy-hungry, fast-growing species, they are unable to survive. The problem with fertilizers is that they are mobile by nature, and so quickly spread to the streams, rivers, lakes and oceans. They unleash anarchy within natural systems. Toxic cyanobacteria bloom, poisoning wildlife. Huge amounts of algae grow, die and rot, sucking oxygen out of the water in the process and leading to catastrophic fish death. In coral reefs, so geared up for low levels of nutrients, fertilizers that have made their way into the oceans have devastating effects. Mutiny breaks out as the little algae that live inside the coral animals begin to multiply out of control, and kill their animal partner. Meanwhile larger algae start to proliferate in the water, and these provide food for the deadly predators of corals, such as the crown of thorns starfish. The large algae also lead to dramatic drops in oxygen. Many reefs are now in decline because of agricultural practices. Unlike natural terrestrial ecosystems, unnatural agroecosystems are leaky. The energy balance is completely shifted, and since energy acts as the agent of organization, the repercussions are inevitably serious.

Man's attempts to bring more solar energy into the Biosphere in order to feed himself have been successful in terms of allowing the numbers of humans on the planet to rise dramatically. However the repercussions have been huge. Natural ecosystems have been blown apart by nutrient over-dose and habitat destruction. In addition, ozone damage has led to increasing UV reaching the surface of the planet, which is also extremely damaging to corals.

All of the perturbations we have caused to the Biosphere are energy-based: the burning of fossil fuels in an attempt to get hold of energy from the past, leading to an increase in heat energy on the surface due to the greenhouse effect; the destruction of ozone leading to a drop in the barrier that prevents particular wavelengths of energy from reaching the planet; the production of fertilizers, allowing a huge increase in energy flow, not just through fields of corn, but through fragile, low-energy, natural ecosystems.

Repercussions of nutrient pollution

Determining the impact of man-made changes on our planet in the longer term poses an interesting challenge. All we can really do is to look at what has happened in times past. We know that carbon dioxide levels, sea levels and temperature have been much higher and lower than today on many occasions. The planet has been ice-free and almost covered in ice for long periods in the Earth's oft times dramatic 4.5 billion year history. The Biosphere has come through these times, and its present appearance has been shaped by these changes. At the beginning of each ice age, for example, carbon dioxide levels and temperature have dropped, whereas they rise at the end of the ice age. John Raven, the renowned palaeobiologist from Dundee in Scotland, has shown that it is not the rise, *per se*, that is significant today, but rather the rate of change. The climate is currently changing at around ten times the rate that it did at the end of the last ice age. The question naturally arises as to whether or not the biology can keep pace with the speed of change.

Whatever happens, carbon dioxide and temperature change are not unique characteristics of the present. What is unique is the increase in nutrients flowing through the major ecosystems, and the facilitation of a greater energy flux that results from this. This is potentially extremely serious, both for the short and long term stability of the Biosphere. During mass extinctions, temperatures have tumbled dramatically following the impact of an asteroid (the cooling often referred to as an impact winter), but no process comes close to the rate and magnitude of nutrient increase over the last 100 years. In the short term, we have already seen that species diversity collapses. In the longer term, we will see a transformed Biosphere, where most of the planet becomes an extension of the agroecosystem that we are creating, a planet enslaved and converted into a fully synthetic support system for the human race. As a result, the Biosphere will become bloated on an energy-rich diet.

The next mass extinction on an energy-addicted planet

Another thing that we definitely know is that there will be another mass extinction event sometime in the future, be it a bollide or a huge volcanic event. Whatever its nature, the agent of change will always be energy. Each mass extinction is marked by a significant drop in energy flow through the Biosphere, mostly due to interruption in energy acquisition from the Sun. If humankind continues on the planet up until the next cataclysmic event, the impact will likely be very different from previous times. A Biosphere addicted to high energy flux will be much less likely to cope with an energy drop than one that operates at much lower energy levels, as our natural ecosystems have previously always done. Thus, as a result, it is likely that greater extinction levels will occur, with species that could have coped with the temporary drop in available energy having already been forced into extinction due to being outcompeted by species with high energy lifestyles. Our actions are leading to the disappearance of the species and ecosystems that would likely survive such energetic cataclysms, and these actions are, potentially, greatly damaging the ability of the Biosphere to bounce back. It is an irony that, having evolved in a low available energy world due to the scarcity of essential nutrients needed to handle this energy, the resultant character of our Biosphere is sadly extremely susceptible, in both the short and longer terms, to dramatic increases in these nutrients.

The Voice of the Biosphere

So what is at the heart of man's destruction of the Biosphere? Imagine the following scene. You and two friends have been hiking in one of the few remaining natural alpine meadows, and, at the end of a long, but wonderful day, filled with beautiful vistas and delicate wildflowers, you reach an old cabin where you know you can stay for the night. The owner is a mysterious figure, who has no name but is known as the Voice of the Biosphere. You talk with her late into the night as she answers questions on every aspect of the Cosmos, from the origin of life through to her compatriots on other planets across the Universe. Finally, as dawn approaches, she turns to you and your friends, and offers you an amazing opportunity. Each of you can choose to change one thing in order to help improve the world. She gives you ten minutes to reflect on this.

Your first friend immediately stands up and says that he doesn't need ten seconds, let alone ten minutes. It has got to be carbon dioxide. Surely if the carbon dioxide levels could be returned to, say, the levels they were at before the industrial revolution, then all would be well. Global warming would be eradicated! The ice sheets would no longer melt away and the sea levels would stop rising. Invading species would be halted.

The Voice of the Biosphere grants the wish. She groans and looks out of a window at the back of the cabin. You become aware of the sound of marching feet, hundreds of them. Looking out through the window, you recognize the familiar scene of a funeral procession, but unlike any that you have seen before. As far as the eye can see, following the twisting, narrow path across distant hills and mountains, are countless coffins, some large and some tiny, all accompanied by a myriad of mourning creatures of every shape and size. You ask who all the mourners are behind one particularly small coffin. The Voice explains that in the coffin is a species of bee. The mourners are plants that rely on it for pollination. Without it, they are now doomed.

The undertaker outside the cabin leads another funeral service for a small species of wood mouse that has just gone extinct because the forest it lived in had been converted into land for the production of crops. The undertaker's Biosphere burial business is still fully booked up for the foreseeable future. Nuclear fuel, wind and wave power churn out the energy needed to replace what was gained by fossil fuels. But the chaos continues. Your friend looks shocked and disappointed. The Voice sees his confusion and reaches out to him, touching his shoulder. She asks him to sit down. She explains that carbon dioxide perturbation is a temporary phenomenon. The era of fossil fuel exploitation is a mere blink in the geological eye. Carbon dioxide levels have been much higher in the past. The reality is that humans will have to survive without fossil fuels in the future, and not by choice. There won't be any left! So, the Voice finishes, your wish will come true anyway, but it won't make any difference. It's not carbon that's the problem. As far as most of the Biosphere is concerned, carbon is the food of plants, and is the store of energy. The Biosphere has been through many periods when there was no ice on Earth, and when sea levels were much higher than today.

Your second friend thinks deeper and asks that nothing else should go extinct. You look at your first friend and both of you wish you'd thought of that one. No more extinctions – got to be a winner. No more funerals for lost species, and no more mourning. You all turn to the Voice. She gives your friend a sympathetic look. You can't prevent extinction! In fact, extinction is part of an evolving energetic context. Just like plastic surgery, preventing extinction may look good on the surface, but beneath the skin tucks and implants lies an aging body. Energy drives change and the Biosphere changes as part of a greater whole. You cannot stand still on a moving elevator. You are part of the elevator. The Biosphere is an extension of the energetic Universe, and since the Universe continuously changes, driven by the laws of thermodynamics, then so shall the Biosphere. The Biosphere is not a closed system, but relies on the flow of energy through it and on the agent of organization working at every level differently. So if we stop all extinctions, then where would we be? Speciation occurs most often following extinction. It is extinction that represents the punctuation of the equilibrium, the freeing up of energetic space. No extinction, no speciation.

Increasing speciation without extinction would mean a hugely competitive world, where there wouldn't be enough niches to go around. So do you stop speciation as well as extinction? In other words do you freeze everything as it is? If the dinosaurs had not gone extinct, would reptiles have continued to dominate, preventing mammals and birds from radiating? So your friend could have their wish, but would they really want to? This raises the very difficult question faced by all conservation biologists: if we don't save everything, then what should we save? In other words, since we are far short of understanding everything, then how can we possibly decide what should live and what should die? If we save the rare, cute, fluffy creature, that creature may have little potential for future evolution. This may be why it is rare in the first place. It may be the last in a long line, suited to a different world of the past, but no longer possessing the wherewithal to cope in changing conditions. Energy drives change, and so it is impossible to avoid change. In the real world, you either cope or die. There will be changes in energy caused by changes in the Sun, and changes in the distance between the Sun and our planet. The ever-changing Biosphere is, in part, responding to greater changes than merely those in the short term. Species will come and go, and this is part of the nature of how energy expresses itself.

The room falls silent again. Everyone looks towards you. What would your wish be?

…………………………………………..

Where do we go from here?

In the end there is only one way to reduce our impact on the planet, and that is to reduce the increasing amounts of energy flowing through our ecosystems. The driver for this huge energy flow is, simply, the huge population of humans. Even if we led a completely environmentally friendly life, we still need to eat. You can stop using planes, ditch the car, power your house with a windmill, recycle everything, stop using aluminium, turn off the air-conditioning and stop heating your office. You still need to eat. And you are not alone. There are billions of people like you. The only way to arrest the devastating damage caused by the life support system surrounding us, particularly relating to the most serious problems of habitat destruction and nutrient enrichment, is to grow less crops. The only way in which this will work is if our population is reduced. If energy availability is reduced, then there will be a collapse of the carrying capacity. It's like supporting your house on the backs of five large elephants. At first it seems great, and decade after decade, the house stands strong. However eventually, if you don't feed them, the elephants will weaken, and finally, die, collapsing to the ground. The foundation upon which your house was supported has gone.

The gene as a solution?

The placement of deoxyribonucleic acid as central to the whole scheme of things, as celebrated in the Central Dogma and the central bell tower in Cold Spring Harbor, has led to a genetic world view dominating our understanding of the Biosphere. The impact of this approach stretches from medicine to feeding the world, from animal husbandry to conservation biology and from the basis of understanding the history of life on Earth, both in terms of its diversity and its origin, to the possibility of a new eugenics, based on genetic engineering rather than extermination. The brave new world is one where the dominant belief system among scientists sets out to evangelise and convert, in a broad mission akin to a crusade. Yet the bottom line of this approach is that if it does work in opposition to the energetic framework, then it will fail. The thesis of this book points to a completely different approach.

Take agriculture as an example. The argument is often made that, simply, the only answer to the problems of a hungry world is the production of genetically modified crops. This ignores the concomitant problems associated with artificially raising the carrying capacity – it is an unsustainable approach, and the further we drive this capacity upwards by irresponsible, energy-expensive input, which is the only way to do it, the greater the crash will inevitably be.

Medical approaches do the same, delaying death, and thus increasing the population by increasing the numbers of individuals reaching reproductive age, as well as altering the life history (the length of each stage in a life cycle) by prolonging life after reproduction.

Even more irresponsibly, it has been suggested that we should pour iron into the oceans, in order to increase primary productivity, and capture the evil carbon dioxide, dragging it, kicking and screaming, to the sea floor. We have already noted that nutrients (and iron is an important and limiting nutrient, hence the need to add it!) have widespread effects, not just on individual species, but on ecosystems as a whole, and that these impacts are normally negative rather than positive. It is absurd, then, to even think of iron addition as a reasonable solution to our problems, and typifies the reductionist, disconnected thinking of many scientists in our world today.

Agriculture is energetically expensive, but then we would easily predict this, as anything that raises the carrying capacity and prolongs life will be thus. However the greater problem is that agricultural practices are also facilitating the flow of energy throughout our Biosphere, by unlocking the flood gates and saturating it with the nutrients that allow a much greater flux of energy through ecosystems.

Restructuring our world

In the end, our solutions are energetically costly, and this is as clear an indicator as we need in terms of what rules the Biosphere. The only way to restructure our world is to do it with energy. So what of the future, in terms of *Homo sapiens sapiens*? Today, as you read these words, our subspecies sits on an elevated carrying capacity, sustained by massive energy turnover. Fossil fuels are running out and green energy, such as wind and wave power, does not look likely to satiate the energy requirements of seven billion people, especially when many of the larger countries are beginning to embrace more energy-expensive lifestyles than in the past. Does a sustainable future lie in nuclear fuel?

James Lovelock, the father of Gaian theory, interviewed by Mike Wade in *The Times* on 28th March, 2008, thinks so, under a headline "*Nuclear option is our only hope*". If our hope is the long term survival of the Biosphere, including ourselves, then this is questionable. Our energy theory would suggest a very different solution.

The fossil fuels are dwindling, and the release of their energy, originally captured around 200 million years ago from the Sun, is coming to an end. The issue is not where the energy comes from, but rather, where it goes to and what we need it for. The key point that I wish to make in this chapter is that it doesn't matter how "green" our energy is, the problem is the energy itself. Wherever the energy comes from, it must eventually go somewhere. High energy waste, both biological and industrial, will still be the outcome, no matter where we source our energy from, and it is this energy, that can neither be created nor destroyed, which constitutes ecosystem pollution. Examples include pollution from excess, energy-expensive fertilizers, disrupting aquatic and terrestrial communities and transforming them into high energy ecosystems.

Our present-day obsession with reducing carbon emissions has distracted us from the real problem, excessive energy use. Carbon dioxide is merely a waste product of the true underlying problem, and the solution is most certainly not to find an alternative waste product, but to focus on the cause. Playing with shadows is a futile game. Habitat fragmentation is caused by increasing populations, which are sustained by energy. Plastics and silicon-related pollutants will also continue to be generated, as will herbicides and pesticides. Fresh, drinkable water supplies are diminishing, again due to energy-fuelled pollution and population levels. These issues point to a non-sustainable situation that will be exacerbated by a switch to nuclear energy. Nuclear fuel offers no more hope for the Biosphere or mankind than fossil fuel. Aldo Leopold, the American founder of wildlife ecology, in his classic book, *A Sand County Almanac*, stated that the actions of humans are embedded into an ecological network that should not be ignored, and so if our approach damages the Biosphere, it will inevitably be very bad for us.

If we really want to make any kind of recompense for our actions, then we need to reduce the energy flowing through our activities. Whether our motivation is to save ourselves or to save the Biosphere, the solution is the same, and it is all about energy. This is a significant departure from Gaian theory, in that we view the planet as being under one agent, rather than focussing on the interactions between the living and physical worlds. It is not so much a self-regulating system, but rather a directed system, with energy and the laws of thermodynamics being sufficient to account for what we see, and what we see being merely a representation, or shadow, of that energetic reality.

What can you do to help?

In this chapter we have seen that the problems faced by the human race, and by all the other members of the Biosphere, stem from the elevated population of humans, and the manipulation of our planet to satiate the needs of this population. Is there anything we can do as individuals? The sheer size of the problem can seem overwhelming. However the only way the human race can achieve anything is if each member works towards that change. First, we need to have a will to act. The changes required are not comfortable ones, and the great tide of humanity yearns for comfort. Let's consider some of the things that you could do to make a difference.

1. Eat less meat

This might seem like a strange step in the direction of improving things. Animals eat plants, and in the process, use the energy of the plants to grow. However it is an inefficient process. Food chains are like pyramids. The higher you go, the thinner they get. This is because energy is lost at each level. 100 kg of plants don't produce 100 kg of animals. You need many more plants to do this. Thus a cow needs a great area of plants, with nutrients being poured on them, to grow. By eating less meat, we will reduce the area of plants needed for grazing. We are omnivores by design.

2. Family planning

As we have said earlier, the reduction in population size will make the greatest difference. If each family limited itself to two children, we could move towards a stabilized population. The only way to significantly reduce the population would be to limit family size to a single child. This may require a different family structure, where people lived in more extended family units (potentially better in terms of energy efficiency more generally) and children were brought up in groups of three or four, each child being the only offspring of one set of parents. Thus the child would enjoy the experience of siblings but within the single offspring model.

3. Responsible agriculture

While each of us is unlikely to be able to impact on how agriculture works directly, we can influence it through the ways we behave and in the ways we appeal to the policy makers in our nations. We can encourage our governments to re-examine how farming works in order to reduce the leakage of nutrients into the environment, and support policies that promote this. So what kinds of changes will help?

a) Large scale hydroponics

Plants can be grown in nutrient solutions. Here the plant is placed in aerated water containing the essential nutrients, in enclosed areas. This means that the nutrient solutions do not leak out into the environment. Of course there is added cost to this, and large scale operation needed to provide enough food for the world is a difficult thing to envisage. However it could be seen as part of the solution, particularly in areas where rare, nutrient-sensitive ecosystems still exist.

b) Agroforestry

Intensive agriculture is necessary to provide enough food for our already inflated population. Although reverting to a simpler hunter-gatherer approach, or a traditional agriculture approach, such as the small shamba in East Africa, would be less intrusive to the Biosphere as a whole, there are far too many of us to be sustained by these methods. As we noted earlier, it is estimated that 40% of the human population is dependent on intensive agriculture for its survival. So we need to look at how this industrial approach can be improved. The key to this relates to the fate of fertilizers. Firstly, more targeted application may reduce waste. A slow release system that doesn't lead to significant oversupply would help here. The use of agroforestry (literally combining trees with crops), with trees that free up phosphate or fix nitrogen naturally, may allow a reduced use of industrial fertilizers. Here, tree species such as *Grevillea robusta* are planted in rows between rows of crops. The system works because soil often contains phosphorus in forms that plants can't reach. These trees free up this phosphorus by releasing high levels of citrate into the soil, and so make it accessible to the crop plants. In addition, the trees grow quickly and provide firewood and construction timber, thus reducing deforestation and providing a much greater sustainability. They also reduce soil erosion, by having a large root system that holds soil together year to year. Agroforestry is mostly championed for use in the economically poorer parts of the world, as it reduces the dependence on expensive fertilizers, but we should consider its application throughout the planet's agroecosystems.

c) Sealed fields

Agroecosystems need to be sealed in, to prevent them contaminating other ecosystems. One way to do this is to develop borders around fields that contain species of plants that specialize in sucking up large amounts of nutrients, thus acting as vacuum cleaners, hovering up excess nutrients. Nitrophilous plants require large amounts of nitrogen, and have extremely efficient ways to take it from the soil. Such plants include *Urtica dioica*, the common nettle, *Sambucus nigra*, the elderberry, and *Heracleum sphondylium*, the cow parsnip. Planting a border of these and other similar species at the edges of agricultural fields would allow excess nutrients to be taken up. The resulting foliage could then be recycled as green manure, which is also a good slow-release method of fertilization. Nettles also absorb phosphorus very efficiently. This approach has the great benefit of being extremely economically feasible. Such vegetative barriers would also benefit wildlife, acting as beetle banks. A more expensive approach would be to collect drainage water from fields, by building physical barriers at the edges, then separating nutrients and other chemicals from the water, before it is returned to the waterways. All of these approaches take a will to do them. However we have seen the end of leaded petrol and lead pipes in houses over the last fifty years, and a reduction in sulphur dioxide levels in the atmosphere, so things can happen if we are determined to make them happen.

d) Reducing food waste

Some 6.7 million tonnes of food is wasted each year in the United Kingdom alone, most of which could have been eaten. This amounts to a staggering 10 billion pounds stirling. In the United States, it has been estimated that almost half the food produced ends up as waste. This means that our excessive exploitation of the planet, with the concomitant pollution of fragile ecosystems, is even worse than it needs to be. So a complete re-appraisal of how we use food is needed. Simple things like buying less, cooking and freezing food before it goes beyond its *'sell by'* date and planning menus before shopping would all make a big difference. Also, a willingness to eat "ugly" fruit and vegetables would prevent food manufacturers from dumping all but the perfectly round apple or perfectly conical carrot. Such a change in our domestic behaviour will have a huge impact.

No single approach will solve the problems, but appropriate combinations of those suggested above will have a significant impact on our planet. Different nations will require different emphasis, yet we can dramatically change the way we feed the world to reduce environmental damage. It is time for a new agriculture.

A final point to note relates to the relationship between energy flowing through the Biosphere and evolution and diversity. At low energy levels, such as during mass extinctions, the number of species declines rapidly, followed by intense speciation. Only organisms that can survive this energy crisis can go on to form the building blocks of the recovery. And the resultant ecosystems bare record to this time, by being extremely energy-efficient. At intermediate levels of energy flow, equilibrium is established. At high levels of energy flow, species diversity declines and remains low. The latter situation is what has resulted from recent human impacts. We can see clearly that alteration in the amount of energy flowing through the Biosphere has significant repercussions for how the Biosphere is shaped. Energy is both the agent and substance, whose quantity may be altered by us, but the result of such change comes from a source beyond us. The shadows of rising sea levels, increasing temperatures and carbon dioxide levels hide a deeper truth. The key impacts upon the Biosphere are energetic in nature and our attempt to manipulate the energetic framework within which we exist will have repercussions far beyond what we might imagine.

And so we near the end of our journey, which began with the challenges offered by our Biosphere, struggled with the mechanism of evolution and emerged with a new way of understanding things. Having used this understanding to address the critical issue of climate change, and the real challenge that it presents, we now turn to the final section, in which we will draw together our thoughts at the end of the journey. You have been extremely patient and made it. Well done! However, although our journey of exploration is nearly at an end, the challenges presented in this book mark a new beginning in terms of our response to this new theory of evolution. We can now set out on a fresh journey, to discover what lies outside the cave.

Section VIII

Light at the End of the Tunnel

This section brings together the key ideas presented in this book. The journey we have taken began by considering some of the major inconsistencies that exist within current evolutionary theory. We recognized that there was a vacuum of understanding. We then examined the Biosphere in terms of how it is organized, in search of clues as to what lies behind its structure and evolution. We have discovered a new way with which to understand how life on Earth has evolved, functions and is structured. This approach is very different from that of Neo-Darwinism, and the conclusions, likewise, represent a very different outcome, that there is no unit of selection, but rather, a single agent of organization: energy. Energy makes different demands, depending upon what it is acting upon. Each level responds in its own way, dependent on its structure. The Biosphere is a product of energy flowing upwards, downwards and throughout each level.

We examined why, starting with the same raw materials, we have ended up at such a different destination from neo-Darwinian thinking. We considered the implications of our theory in terms of the great debates of evolutionary biology, and finally, turned our attention to the greatest challenge facing us today. In every case, our theory presents a clearer, fuller explanation than the alternatives available.

The Universe, in its physical, visible form, is acting out a drama that is scripted by energy. The rules of physics have taken on physical form, but if we want to understand these shadows, we must look beyond them.

Chapter Twenty Four

Life Beyond the Cave

We have come to the end of our journey. It has, I hope you will agree, been an interesting one. We have defined what isn't life. We have realized that everything may have originated from spontaneous generation, and that not all cells have come from cells. We reflected on the fact that Mesmer and Abraham Lincoln both played the glass harp. Problems with the concepts of species and populations, along with difficulties with the Central Dogma, came to light. Horizontal gene transfer was encountered, as was the problematic lack of relationship between the rate of mutation and the rate of evolution through time. In combination with this, we realized that in terms of resource acquisition and altruism, it was more straightforward to consider that a hungry animal will actually be more interested in feeding, and the interactions that will promote this, than in whether the individual offering him some lunch is a relative or not. We touched on the uncanny similarity between science and religion, recognizing the high priests, denominations, articles and practice of faith and evangelical fundamentalism within the scientific community. Finally, we assessed the risks of ray guns and alien invasions.

At a more serious level, this book presents a new way in which we can understand how life on Earth has evolved, functions and is structured. The approach taken is very different from that of neo-Darwinism, and the conclusion, likewise, represents a very different explanation. So how come, given that we started with the same raw material as everyone else, we have ended up at such a different destination?

In the end, it is all to do with historical baggage, as is so often the case. Once you set up a framework, you are limited by it. Modern evolutionary theory traces its roots back to a time before a monastic experiment in Brno, to fancy pigeons and pigs. It also relies on taxonomy and the tree of life as a starting point. The taxonomic interpretation of the Biosphere, while interesting, ignores many of the other levels of its organization. This book's approach is completely different, using information from every level, from biome to biochemistry, in order to better understand the entirety of the situation, and thus it stands a much better chance of explaining how and why it all exists in the way that it does. Artificial selection, and concern about population density, drove Darwin to his theory as much as, if not more than, his observations on (and off) the *Beagle*. Once natural selection had taken centre stage, an equally natural question had to be raised. What was the unit of selection? There were many putative levels of selection that were candidates for being the unit of selection. The necessity of identifying one unit became an obsession, partly driven by the need for a single unit to aid mathematical modelling. In searching for a single unit, there was a requirement to support the Darwinian concept of individual selection within populations, which underpinned *The Origin of Species*. Selection above this level was a threat to the entire cathedral, and when Wynne Edwards suggested group selection, the response was swift and combative.

Soon the gene was presented as the one and only unit of selection, and the repercussion of the proposed characteristics of the gene, such as selfishness, were deemed to automatically pass up to more advanced levels of organization, such as the organism. These levels were looked on as mere products, outcomes or machines. The individual came to be seen as the vehicle in which the genes rode, dispensable, but still a useful point of reference. Altruism also came to be viewed as genetically driven. The entire gene-centric argument made sense within itself, and produced a workable hypothesis of how the Biosphere evolved. The original concepts of competition, survival of the fittest and natural selection could all be accommodated within the new genetic structure. The world beyond the gene was really just an extended phenotype.

Yet neo-Darwinism is, in its essence, a derivation, an emperor's suit of new clothes, shadows on the cave wall. In its most modern expression, it takes the gene and imbues it with properties or characteristics, insisting that these characters are not present in the atoms that make up the gene, but are, rather, emergent properties. Yet it also argues that this is not the case for levels above the gene, and that these levels cannot be the units of selection. So there is one rule when it suits, but another rule when something works against the dogma. In this book, we have, instead, looked at the reality of the Biosphere in all of its richness, and then, from this fundamental starting point, have identified a different set of drivers that explain how it all works. Thus we have focused on the levels of organization, rather than dwelling on the putative unit of selection. By directly looking at how the Biosphere is structured, we can actually deal with what is there rather than using an abstract concept such as the selfish gene.

We went on to identify *units* of organization upon which an *agent* of organization could work, rather than a unit of selection upon which an agent of selection could work. By examining how each level operates, we recognized that there were different types of organization at each level. However, these different types of organization can be seen to be different facets of the one agent, energy. Importantly, energy acts in a different way at each level of organization, and so there is not one single unit of organization. Every level is a unit, contributing, in its own unique way, to the total, and representing a portal through which the agent of organization can work, in a form that is inimitable to that level. Having identified the agent, it became straightforward to understand other aspects such as evolution and altruism within this context.

Energy makes different demands, depending upon what it is acting upon. Each level responds in its own way, dependent upon its structure. This establishes an important point, that a reductionist approach is a strategy of doubtful value. The Biosphere is a product of energy flowing upwards, downwards and throughout each level. While organisms make up communities, communities are not organisms, and neither are organisms communities. There are completely different energetic issues for each of these. Communities are shaped by temporal aspects such as succession and by spatial aspects, such as zonation and biome character. Individual species fit into communities, both in terms of the trophodynamic position that they occupy, and in terms of the biome and successional stage in which they occur. Any property of the community, such as the presence of a top predator, can have a significant impact upon species lower down the food chain, often allowing otherwise weak competitors to survive. This has nothing to do with the genes in the weak competitors, nor, obviously, with the competitive abilities, or otherwise, of these weak species. Rather, it is a community level influence, generated by, and through, that level of organization.

One of the great tragedies of the neo-Darwinian dogma is that it has severely held back research into community level aspects of both ecology and evolution. Its dogmatic refusal to consider important, multilevel interactions, and its failure to recognize that the Biosphere is a highly integrated entity, with its organization, evolution and function being dependent on inputs at every level, has been extremely frustrating. This is a great pity, as it has restrained progress in properly understanding how our planet works, and recognizing our place within it. Even more damaging, it has prevented us from addressing the significant problems that we are facing at present, in terms of overpopulation and climate change, instead presenting genetic modification of crops as a way to feed the world, only exacerbating the underlying issues. By accepting the gene as the key unit of selection, modern science has viewed its manipulation as the panacea for all things.

Escaping the fancy pigeons and the cult of the bases

Instead of being tied down by the baggage of fancy pigeons and the cult of the bases, we have gone back to real science and have had a fresh look, emerging with a very different explanation. We realized that competition is often not the main driver of evolution (as George Williams conceded). Most animals, for example, die before they reproduce, and often their death is predation-related. Plant seeds have no influence on where they land. The likelihood is that death will often not be related to genetic fitness, and so it is not a case of survival of the fittest, but, rather, survival of the surviving. Imagine two bird eggs sitting in a nest. Each has a very different genetic make up, representing the extremes of the parents' genetic makeup, one being extremely fit, with a great combination of genes, while the other is genetically weak. Yet on the outside, both eggs look identical. A red squirrel arrives and eats one of the eggs. Each egg has the same chance of being eaten, in spite of the great differences in the genes. The

Atlantic cod (*Gadus morhua*) lays many millions of eggs, but only one in every million will grow to adulthood. The lottery of life is exactly that, with the chances of winning down to luck rather than genetic superiority. The great dream of ever improving lineages, tested at regular intervals on a level playing field, and providing brave and strong victors, selected for by their genetic and reproductive fitness, is only that. Survival is often nothing to do with the genes. A few survivors will, of course, continue their given lineage into the next generation, but in no way is there any guarantee that they will be the fittest of the original cohort. A giant filter feeding whale, consuming a huge shoal of krill, will not be a selective force upon that shoal. Survival will be random. It is this randomness that is thought to be a key benefit of being in a large group. If there was not the possibility of a random element to predation, then there would be no benefit to being in a group, in terms of reducing the likelihood of being eaten due to numerical dilution of the risk (a tenet of the selfish herd hypothesis!), given the cost of reduced resources available to each member of a large group.

Having established the energetic theory relating to the development, function and organization of the Biosphere as a viable explanation, we used the same approach to investigate five key areas of debate: the tempo of evolution, speciation, exobiology, multicellularity and altruism. In each case, we examined the fundamental origins of each of these, rather than trying to fit them into a pre-existent theory. This provided us with a fresh understanding in each case, again, not derived, but from first principles.

One of the great questions relating to life on Earth asks "*Is there a destination*?" In other words, is evolution going somewhere in particular, or is it merely a random walk? Neo-Darwinism suggests that selfish motivation within a competitive environment should lead to the dominance of fit solutions, with selfish genes spreading. Yet we see population structure and species, as reproductive units, both creating barriers to this. Also, trophodynamic interactions can preserve the weak, rather than the strong. The competitive exclusion principle rarely holds. The world is a very different place than it was 3 billion years ago. Is there any drive towards a summit, an ultimate destination, the resting place for a Biosphere that has thrashed and struggled through time? Determinate organisms certainly grow to an end point, and then stop growing. Many communities pass through a number of stages before reaching a climax such as an oak forest, which remains stable. We have seen that after mass extinctions, speciation events follow niche liberation within the context of a temporal succession. So will speciation eventually come to a halt at any point? Will evolution finally cease?

Well, in a way, the equilibrium in punctuated equilibrium represents a stasis, or an end point. Of course, speciation continues during these long equilibrium periods, but at a much slower rate, and mostly in locally disturbed or isolated habitats, such as oceanic islands. This is negligible in comparison with post-extinction periods. Thus we can see our Biosphere as a snow globe (the little plastic spheres with a cottage scene and lots of plastic snow flakes). Each time it gets shaken up, the flakes fall in a different way and they settle in energetic niches. This represents an evolutionary climax, and will persist until significantly disturbed again. Local disturbance and opportunity (such as a new island like Surtsey, off the coast of Iceland) will create a small number of niches between the big events. As energetic niches fill, so stability is approached. It is normally energetic disturbance that shakes the Biosphere into creative turmoil, and energetic processes that re-establish stability. The cottage in our snow globe never changes. The plastic snow flakes find different ways of relating to this fixed landscape each time.

What other drives might exist? One of the more radical suggestions is that since the second law of thermodynamics demands increasing entropy, it may also promote processes that generate entropy. Along this line of thinking, more energetically expensive lifestyles, such as warm-bloodedness, will become increasingly likely to evolve. Even the history of humankind represents the actions of an ever more entropy-generating sub-species. It is an interesting idea, but would appear, at best, to be subordinate to the disturbance-climax cycle that we have explored.

Our energetic approach also creates a new context for each of us. We are no longer tied down by our genes, be they good or bad, male or female, fit or unfit. Energy has no gender or race or creed. The shadow of Eugenics is nowhere to be seen. Instead, each of us can celebrate our existence, and that of the wonderful world of which we are a part, participating in the universal dance, an expression of energy, flowing through us. During the brief histories of our lives, we experience what it is to be part of the great, cosmic gala ball. Everything is equal under the Sun.

Finally we also see the challenges facing our world in a clearer way, understanding that since everything is orchestrated by energy, then our lust for energy will have significant repercussions for the Biosphere. We disturb the orchestra at great cost to ourselves and our fellow revellers.

The Biosphere, in the end, is a representation of energy, from proteins through to biomes. What we see are the shadows, the dances of chemistry and biology, choreographed by physics. The agent of energy flows through every level of organization, and offers the best explanation as to why the vast array of shadows dance and flicker on the cave wall in the way that they do. The ultimate source of these shapes lies in a reality that is invisible, but tangible in its myriad representations in the physical world.

So, like Plato, we have emerged from the cave, and stand before the great star from whence much of our energy comes, yet understanding that even our Sun plays out its existence beneath a far greater authority. As our local star appears to set beneath the Earth's horizon, on a clear, winter night in Scotland, the myriad other stars and planets that co-habit our Universe, and that now sparkle and flicker above us, will testify to the same truth. This Universe, in its physical, visible form, is acting out a drama that is scripted by energy, and that is, through every level of organization, expressing the ultimate reality that lies behind all. This is the true meaning of the Biosphere, and all the other biospheres out there. The rules of physics have taken physical form, but if we want to understand these forms, we must look beyond them.

Shadows on the Cave Wall

Bibliography

This bibliography includes all the major sources of information used in this book, alongside a number of more general texts that the reader can use to explore, more deeply, some of the historical developments. There are a huge number of websites also available. These are not listed here, as web sites often become non-functional over time. The publisher's website, www.ardmachapress.com has a section devoted to this book where you can participate in discussion, ask questions and find a whole host of additional information.

Section I.

Clausius, R. 1865. *The Mechanical Theory of Heat – with its Applications to the Steam Engine and to Physical Properties of Bodies.* John van Voorst, 1 Paternoster Row, London, UK.
Collinson, M. 1983. *Fossil plants of the London Clay*. The Palaeontological Association, London, UK.
Cytowic, R.E. 2002. *Synesthesia: A Union of the Senses.* Second Edition. MIT Press, Boston, MA, USA.
Cytowic, R.E. 2003. The Man Who Tasted Shapes. *MIT Press, Boston, MA, USA.*
Eyles, N. and Miall, A. 2007. *Canada Rocks: The Geologic Journey*. Fitzhenry and Whiteside, Markham, Ontario, Canada.
Fowler, J. 1997. *Hinduism: Beliefs & Practices*. Sussex Academic Press, Eastbourne, UK.
Hill, R.S. 1994. *History of the Australian Vegetation: Cretaceous to Recent.* Cambridge University Press, Cambridge, UK.
Levi-Setti, R. 1993. *Trilobites*. University of Chicago Press, Chicago, IL, USA.
Plato 1992. *The Republic* [translated by Grube, G.M.A. and Reeve, C.D.C.]. Second Edition. Hackett Publishing Company, Indianapolis, IN, USA.
Popper, K.R. 1963. *Conjectures and Refutations*. Basic Books, New York, USA.
Popper, K.R. 1968. *The Logic of Scientific Discovery*. Basic Books, New York, USA.
Popper, K.R. 1979. *Objective Knowledge: An Evolutionary Approach.* Clarendon Press, Oxford, UK.
Prasad, M.N. 2006. *Chandogya Upanishad: Translation and Commentary.* DK Print World, New Dehli, India.
Raven, J.A. and Sprent, J.I. 1989. Phototrophy, diazotrophy and palaeoatmospheres: biological catalysis and the H. C, N and O cycles. *Journal of the Geological Society* 146: 161-170.
Rodriguez-Pereyra, G. 2002. *Resemblance Nominalism: A Solution to the Problem of Universals.* Clarendon Press, Oxford, UK.
Smil, V. 2003. *The Earth's Biosphere: Evolution, Dynamics, and Change*. The MIT Press, Cambridge, MA, USA.
Stanford, C.B. 1998. *Chimpanzee and Red Colobus: the Ecology of Predator and Prey.* Harvard University Press, Cambridge, MA, USA.
Whittaker, R.J. and Fernández-Palacios, J.M. 2007. *Island Biogeography: Ecology, Evolution and Conservation.* Second Edition. Oxford University Press, Oxford, UK.
Wilson, J.T. 1965. A new class of faults and their bearing on continental drift. *Nature* 207: 343-347.Wilson, J. T. (Ed.). 1976. *Continents Adrift and Continents Aground.* W. H. Freeman and Co., San Francisco, USA.Woodworth, L. and McGonacal, D. 2005. *Antarctica: The Blue Continent.* Frances Lincoln Publishers, London, UK.

Section II

Aristotle 1997. *De Generatione Animalium* [translated by de Moerbeka, G.]. Drossaart-Lulofs, H.J. (Ed.). Brill Academic Publishing, Leiden, Netherlands.

Buranelli, V. 1975. *The Wizard from Vienna: Franz Anton Mesmer.* Coward, McCann & Geoghegan, New York, USA.

Bergson, H. 1999. *L'Evolution Creatrice.* French & European Publications, New York, USA.

Cairns-Smith, A. G. 1985. *Seven Clues to the Origin of Life.* Cambridge University Press, Cambridge, UK.

Cairns-Smith, A. G. 1993. *Genetic Takeover and the Mineral Origins of Life.* Cambridge University Press, Cambridge, UK.

Cobb, M. 2000. Reading and writing the book of nature: Jan Swammerdam (1637-1680). *Endeavour* 24: 122-129.

Crick, F. H. C., and Orgel, L. E. 1973. Directed panspermia. *Icarus* 19: 341-346.

Crick, F. H. C. 1981. *Life Itself: its Origin and Nature.* Simon and Schuster, New York, USA.

Davies, P. 1999. *The Fifth Miracle: The Search for the Origin and Meaning of Life.* Touchstone, New York, USA.

Dodson, E.O. 1984. *The Phenomenon of Man Revisited: A Biological Viewpoint on Teilhard De Chardin.* Columbia University Press, New York, USA.

Dyer, B.D. 1994. Tracing the History of Eukaryotic Cells: the Enigmatic Smile. Columbia University Press, New York, USA.

Gilbert, W. 1986. The RNA World. *Nature* 319: 618.Harris, H. 2002. Things Come to Life: Spontaneous Generation Revisited. Oxford University Press, Oxford, UK.

Hoyle, F. and Wickramasinghe, C. 1984. Evolution from Space: A Theory of Cosmic Creationism. Simon & Schuster, London, UK.

Huxley, T.H.H. 1868. On some organisms living at great depths in the north Atlantic Ocean. Quarterly Journal of Microscopical Science 8:203-212.

Joyce, G.F., Visser G.M., Van Boeckel C.A.A., Van Boom J.H., Orgel. L.E. & Van Westrenen, J. 1984. Chiral selection in poly(C)-directed synthesis of oligo(G) *Nature* 310: 602 – 604.

Kingsley, P. 1995. *Ancient Philosophy, Mystery, and Magic: Empedocles and Pythagorean Tradition.* Clarendon Press, Oxford, UK.

Lamarck, J.B. 2004. *Lamarck's Open Mind: The Lectures.* High Sierra Books, Oregon, USA.

Lewes, G.H. 2004. *Problems of Life and Mind.* Kessinger Publishing, Whitefish, USA. Lucretius 1995. *On the Nature of Things: De Rerum Natura* [Translated by Esolen, A.M.]. The Johns Hopkins University Press, Baltimore, USA.

Melhado, E. M. 1981. *Jacob Berzelius: the Emergence of His Chemical System.* University of Wisconsin Press, Madison, USA.

Miller, S. L. 1953. Production of amino acids under possible primitive Earth conditions. *Science* 117: 528-529.

Miller, S L. and Urey, H.C. 1959. Organic compound synthesis on the primitive Earth. *Science* 130: 245-251.

Nadler S. (Ed.) 2000. The Cambridge Companion to Malebranche. Cambridge University Press, Cambridge, UK.

Nelson, K.E. Levy, M. and Miller, S.L. 2000. Peptide nucleic acids rather than RNA may have been the first genetic molecule. *Proceedings of the National Academy of Science USA* 97: 3868–71.

Oparin, A.I. 1953. *The Origin of Life* [Trans. Margulis S.]. Dover Publications, New York, USA.

Orgel, L.E. 2000. A simpler nucleic acid. *Science* 290 (5495): 1306–7.

Oró, J. 1961. Mechanism of synthesis of adenine from hydrogen cyanide under possible primitive Earth conditions. *Nature* 191:1193-1194.

Parker, C. and Riches, C.R. 1993. *Parasitic Weeds of the World. Biology and Control.* CAB international. Wallingford, UK.

Pliny the Elder 1991. *Natural History.* Penguin, London.

Rasmussen, H.N. 1995. *Terrestrial orchids. From seed to mycotrophic plant.* Cambridge University Press, Cambridge, UK.

Roach, M. 2005. *Spook: Science Tackles the Afterlife.* W.W. Norton, New York, USA.

Schummerr, J. 2003. The notion of nature in chemistry. *Studies in History, Philosophy and Science* 34:705-736.

Seuss, E. 1875. *Die Entstehung Der Alpen* [*The Origin of the Alps*]. W. Braunmuller, Vienna, Austria.

Teilhard de Chardin, P. 1975. *The Phenomenon of Man.* Harper Perennial, New York, USA.

Tritton, K. 2001. Earth, Life and the Universe: Exploring Our Cosmic Ancestry. Curved Air Publications Limited, Bury St Edmunds, UK.
Vernadskii, V.I. 1986. *The Biosphere.* Synergetic Press, Santa Fe, NM, USA.Woese, C.R. 1967. *The Genetic Code: the Molecular Basis for Genetic Expression.* Harper & Row, New York, USA.
Wood, M. 2000. *Vitalism: the History of Herbalism, Homeopathy, and Flower Essences.* North Atlantic Books, Berkeley, CA, USA.
Woods, H. 2007. Augustine and Evolution: A Study in the Saint's de Genesi Ad Litteram and de Trinitate. Kessinger Publishing, Whitefish, USA.
Wyckoff, J. 1975. Franz Anton Mesmer: Between God and Devil. Prentice-Hall, Upper Saddle River, NJ, USA.
Yam, P. 2003. *The Pathological Protein: Mad Cow, Chronic Wasting, and Other Deadly Prion Diseases.* Copernicus Books, New York, USA.

Section III

Christner, B.C., Morris, C.E., Foreman, C.M., Cai, R.M. and Sands, D.C. 2008. Ubiquity of biological ice nucleators in snowfall. *Science* 319**:** 1214-1214.
Clements, F.E. 1916. *Plant Succession: an Analysis of the Development of Vegetation.* Carnegie Institute of Washington Publication 242.
Copeland, H. F. 1938. The kingdoms of organisms. *Quarterly Review of Biology* 13: 383-420.
Coyne, J.A. and Orr, H.A. 2004. *Speciation.* Sinauer Associates, Sunderland, MA, USA.
Dagan, T. and Martin, W. 2006. The tree of one percent. *Genome Biology* 7: 118.
Darwin, C.R. 1859. *On the Origin of Species by Means of Natural Selection or the Preservation of Favoured Races in the Struggle for Life* . John Murray, London, UK.
Darwin, C. R.1868. *The variation of animals and plants under domestication.* John Murray, London.
Darwin, C.R. 1871. *The Descent of Man and Selection in Relation to Sex.* John Murray, London, UK.
Gleason, H.A. 1926. The individualistic concept of the plant association. *Bulletin of the Torrey Botanical Club* 62: 1-20.
Gowaty, P.A. (Ed.) 1997. *Feminism and Evolutionary Biology: Boundaries, Intersections and Frontiers.* Springer, New York, USA.
Haeckel, E. H. P.A. 1866. *Generelle Morphologie der Organismen.* G. Reimer, Berlin, Germany.
Haeckel, E.H.P.A. 1905. *The Wonders of Life: a Popular Study of Biological Philosophy* [Translated by Joseph McCabe]. Harper & Brothers, New York, USA.
Harvati, K. and Harrison, T. 2006. *Neanderthals Revisited.* Springer, Dordrecht, Germany.
Harvati, K., Gunz, P. and Grigorescu, D. 2007. Cioclovina (Romania): morphological affinities of an early modern European. *Journal of Human Evolution* 53: 732-746.
Hutton, J. 1788. Theory of the Earth; or an investigation of the laws observable in the composition, dissolution, and restoration of land upon the globe. *Transactions of the Royal Society of Edinburgh* 1: 209-304.
Lorenz, K. 1966. *On Aggression.* Methuen, London, UK.
Ochiai, K., Yamanaka, T., Kimura, K. and Sawada, O. 1959. Inheritance of drug resistance (and its tranfer) between *Shigella* strains and Between Shigella and *E.coli* strains. *Hihon Iji Shimpor* 1861: 34 [in Japanese].
Poulton, E.B. 1904. What is a species? *Proceedings of the Entomological Society of London*: lxxvii-cxvi.
Sagan, D. and Margulis, L. 1999. *Slanted Truths: Essays on Gaia, Symbiosis and Evolution.* Copernicus, New York, USA.
Seehausen, O., Vanalphen, J.J.M. and Witte, F. 1997. Cichlid fish diversity threatened by eutrophication that curbs sexual selection. *Science* 277: 1808-1811.
Syvanen, M. 1985. Cross-species gene transfer: implications for a new theory of evolution. *Journal of Theoretical Biology* 112: 333-343.
Traub H.P. 1975. Proposals for upper ranks of living things *Taxon* 24: 293-295.
Woese, C. and Fox, G. 1977. Phylogenetic structure of the prokaryotic domain: the primary kingdoms. *Proceedings of the National Academy of Science USA* 74: 5088–90.
Woese, C., Kandler, O. and Wheelis, M. 1990. Towards a natural system of organisms: proposal for the domains Archaea, Bacteria, and Eucarya. *Proceedings of the National Academy of Science USA* 87: 4576–9.
Whittaker, R.H. 1969. New concepts of kingdoms or organisms. Evolutionary relations are better represented by new classifications than by the traditional two kingdoms. *Science* 163: 150–60.

Section IV

Avery, O.T., MacLeod, C.M. and McCarty, M. 1944. Studies on the chemical nature of the substance inducing transformation of pneumococcal types. Induction of transformation by a desoxyribonucleic acid fraction isolated from Pneumococcus type III. *Journal of Experimental Medicine* 79: 137–158.
Cano, R. J. and Borucki, M.K. 1995. Revival and identification of bacterial spores in 25- to 40-million-year-old Dominican amber. *Science* 268: 1060-1064.
Carlini, A. and Novikov, I.D. 1996. Time machines and the principle of self-consistency as a consequence of the principle of stationary action (II): the cauchy problem for a self-interacting relativistic particle. *International Journal of Modern Physics D* 5: 445-479. Carroll, L. 1899. *Through The Looking-Glass.* M.F. Mansfield and A. Wessels, New York, USA.
Caswell, H. 1978. Predator-mediated co-existence: a non-equilibrium model. *American Naturalist* 112: 127-154.
Chauvet, J-M. 1998. *Dawn of Art: The Chauvet Cave. The Oldest Known Paintings in the World.* Harry N. Abrams, Inc., New York, USA.
Conway Morris, S. 1998. *The Crucible of Creation. The Burgess Shale and the Rise of Animals.* Oxford University Press, Oxford, UK.
Courtillot, V. 1999. *Evolutionary Catastrophes: the Science of Mass Extinction* [translated by McClinton, J.]. Cambridge University Press, Cambridge, UK.
Dawkins, C.R. 1976. *The Selfish Gene.* Oxford University Press, Oxford, UK.
Dawkins, C.R. 1982. *The Extended Phenotype.* Oxford University Press, Oxford, UK.
Dawkins, C.R. 2006. *The God Delusion.* Bantam Books, New York, UK.
Darwin, E. 1791. *The Botanic Garden, a Poem. In Two Parts. Part II. The Loves of the Plant.* J. Johnson, London, UK.
Dollo, L. 1993. Les lois de l'évolution. Bulletin de la Société Belge de Geologie de Paléontologie et d'Hydrologie 7: 164-166.
Donne, J. 1999. *Devotions upon emergent occasions and death's duel.* Vintage, Toronto, Canada.
Eldridge, N. and Gould, S.J. 1972. Punctuated equilibria: an alternative to phyletic gradualism. In: *Models in Paleobiology (*Schopf, T.J.M, Ed.). Freeman Cooper, San Francisco, USA. Pp. 82-115.
Falkowski, P.G., Katz, M.E., Milligan, A.J., Fennel, K., Cramer, B.S., Aubry, M.P., Berner, R.A., Novacek, M.J. and Zapol, W.M. 2005. The Rise of oxygen over the past 205 million years and the evolution of large placental mammals. *Science* 309: 2202 – 2204.
Fara, P. 2003. *Sex, Botany and Empire: The Story of Carl Linnaeus and Joseph Banks.* Icon Books Ltd., Cambridge, UK.
Gaspar, E. 1887. *El Anacronópete.* Daniel Cortezo y C[a], Barcelona Arte y Letras, Barcelona, Spain.
Griffith, F. 1928. The significance of pneumococcal types. *Journal of Hygiene* 27:113-159.
Gould, S.J. and Lewontin, R.C. 1979. The spandrels of San Marco and the panglossian paradigm: a critique of the adaptationist programme. *Proceedings of the Royal Society of London, Series B* 205: 581-598.
Gould, S.J. 1989. *Wonderful Life: the Burgess Shale and the Nature of History.* Penguin, London, UK.
Grant, B.R. and Grant, P.R. 1992. Hybridization of bird species. *Science* 256: 193-197.
Hallam, A. and Wignall, P.B. 1997. *Mass Extinctions and Their Aftermath.* Oxford University Press, Oxford, UK.
Hamilton, W.D. 1964. The genetical evolution of social behaviour I and II. *Journal of Theoretical Biology* 7: 1-52.
Hartmann, W.K. 1991. *The History of Earth.* Wadsworth Publishing Co., New York, USA.
Henig, R.M. 2000. *Monk in the Garden: The Lost and Found Genius of Gregor Mendel, the Father of Genetics.* Houghton Mifflin Company, Boston, MA, USA.
Hoyle, F. and Wickramasinghe, N.C. 1978. *Lifecloud.* J.M. Dent & Sons Limited, London.
Kaplan, J. and Pigliucci, M. 2000. The fall and rise of Dr Pangloss: adaptationism and the *Spandrels* paper 20 years on. *Trends in Ecology and Evolution* 15: 66-70.
Keller, E.F. and Lloyd, E.A. 1992. *Keywords in Evolutionary Biology.* Harvard University Press, Cambridge, MA, USA.
Kropotkin, P.A. 1998. *Mutual Aid: A Factor of Evolution.* Freedom Press, London, UK.
Larson, J.L. 1971. Reason and Experience: the Representation of Natural Order in the Work of Carl von Linné. University of California Press, Berkeley, USA.

Lewontin, R.C. 1974. *Genetic Basis of Evolutionary Change.* Columbia University Press, New York, USA.Maddox, B. 2002 *Rosalind Franklin: Dark Lady of DNA.* Harper Collins, London, UK.
Malthus, T. 1798. *An Essay on the Principle of Population.* Printed for J. Johnson, in St. Paul's Church-yard, London, UK.Mann, C. 1991. Lynn Margulis: science's unruly Earth mother. *Science* 252: 378-381.
Maynard Smith, J. 1988. *Did Darwin Get it Right?: Essays on Games, Sex and Evolution.* Chapman & Hall, London, UK.
Miescher, F. 1871. Ueber die chemische zusammensetzung der eiterzellen [On the chemical composition of pus cells]. *Medicinisch-Chemische Untersuchungen* 4: 441–460.
Paley, W. 1802. *Natural Theology, or Evidences of the Existence and Attributes of the Diety Collected from the Appearance of Nature.* R. Faulder, London, UK.
Peter, L.J. and Hull, R. 1969. *The Peter Principle: why things always go wrong.* William Morrow & Company, Inc., New York, USA
Pittendrigh, C. 1958. Adaptation, natural selection and behaviour. In: *Behaviour and Evolution.* (Roe, A. and Simpson, G.G., Eds.). Yale University Press, New Haven, USA. Pp. 390-416.
Popper, K.R. 1979. *Objective Knowledge: an Evolutionary Approach.* Revised Edition. Clarendon Press, Oxford, UK.
Raup, D. 1991. *Extinction: Bad Genes or Bad Luck?* W.W. Norton and Company, New York, USA.
Seuss, Dr, and Geisel, T.S. 1955. *On Beyond Zebra!* Random House Books for Young Readers, London, UK.
Spencer, H. 1864. *Principles of Biology.* 2 vols. Williams and Norgate, London, UK.
Tangley, L. 1997. One species or two (or three)? *Science* 275: 1418.
van Valen, L.M. 1973. A new evolutionary law. *Evolutionary Theory* 1: 1-30.
Walcott, C.D. 1910. Abrupt appearance of the Cambrian fauna on the North American continent. Cambrian geology and palaeontology II. *Smithsonian Miscellaneous Collections* 57: 1-16.
Walcott, C.D. 1911. A geologist's paradise. *National Geographic Magazine* 22: 509-521.
Ward, P., Labandeira, C.C., Laurin, M. and Berner, R. 2006. Romer's gap: a low oxygen interval constraining the timing of arthropod and tetrapod terrestrialization. *Proceedings of the National Academy of Sciences, U.S.A.* 103: 16818-16822.
Watson, J.D. and Berry, A. 2003. *DNA: The Secret of Life.* Knopf, New York, USA.
Williams, G.C. 1966. *Adaptation and Natural Selection.* Princeton University Press, Princeton, NJ, USA.
Wynne-Edwards, V.C. 1962. *Animal Dispersion in Relation to Social Behavior.* Oliver & Boyd, London, UK.
Wynne-Edwards, V.C. 1986. *Evolution Through Group Selection.* Blackwell Scientific, Oxford, UK.
Zimmer, C. 2002. Darwin's avian muses continue to evolve. *Science* 296: 633-635.
Zufall, R.A. and Rausher, M.D. 2004. Genetic changes associated with floral adaptation restrict future evolutionary potential. *Nature* 428: 847-850.

Section V

Axelrod, R. and Hamilton, W.D. 1981. The evolution of co-operation. *Science* 211: 1390-1396.
Billings, E. 1872. Fossils in Huronian rocks. *Canadian Naturalist and Quarterly Journal of Science* 6: 478.
Ghannoum, M.A. and O'Toole, G.A. 2004. *Microbial biofilms.* ASM Press, Washington DC, USA.
Hoffman, P.F. and Schrag, D.P. 2000. Snowball Earth. *Scientific American* 282: 68-75.
Odum, E.P. and Odum, H.T. 1959. *Fundamentals of Ecology.* Saunders, Philadelphia, USA.
Odum, E.P. 1969. The strategy of ecosystem development. *Science* 164: 262-270.
Paine, R. T. 1966. Food web complexity and species diversity. *American Naturalist* 100: 65-75.
Skene, K.R. 2003. The evolution of physiology and development in the cluster root: teaching an old dog new tricks? *Plant and Soil* 248: 21-30.
Stanford, C.B. 1998. *Chimpanzee and Red Colobus: the Ecology of Predator and Prey.* Harvard University Press, Cambridge, MA, USA.
Thompson, D'arcy W. 1917. *On Growth and Form.* Cambridge University Press, Cambridge, UK.
Trivers, R. L. 1971. The evolution of reciprocal altruism. *Quarterly Review of Biology* 46: 35-57.
Turing, A.M. 1952. *The Chemical Basis of Morphogenesis.* Philosophical Transactions of the Royal Society London B 237: 37-72.
Webster, G. and Goodwin, B.C. 1996. *Form and Transformation.* Cambridge University Press, Cambridge, UK.
Wolpert, L. 1971. Positional information and pattern formation. *Current Topics in Developmental Biology* 6: 183-224.

Section VI

Anstett, M.C., Hossaert-McKey, M., and Kjellberg, F. 1997. Figs and fig pollinators: evolutionary conflicts in a coevolved mutualism. *Trends in Ecology and Evolution* 12: 94-99.

Arrhenius, S. 1907. *Worlds in the Making*. Harper & Bros., London, UK.

Axelrod, R. 1984. *The Evolution of Cooperation.* Basic Books, New York, NY, USA.

Cavalier-Smith, T. 2006. Cell evolution and earth history: stasis and revolution. *Philosophical Transactions of the Royal Society of London B.* 361: 969-1006.

Clarke, A.C. 1951. *The Sands of Mars*. Sidgwick and Jackson, London, UK.

Espinosa-Urgel, M. 2009. Multicellularity, neoplasias and Biofilms. *Research in Microbiology* 160: 85-86.

Hamilton, W.D. 1964. The genetical evolution of social behaviour I and II. — *Journal of Theoretical Biology* 7: 1-16 and 17-52.

Hutton, J. 1788. Theory of the Earth; or an investigation of the laws observable in the composition, dissolution, and restoration of land upon the globe. *Transactions of the Royal Society of Edinburgh* 1: 209-304.

Keister, A.R., Lande, R., and Schemske, D.W. 1984. Models of coevolution and speciation in plants and their pollinators. *The American Naturalist* 124: 220-243.Lovelock, J.E. 1965. A physical basis for life detection experiments. *Nature* 207: 568–570.

Maurer, A. 1984. Ockham's Razor and Chatton's Anti-Razor. *Medieval Studies* 46: 463–475.

Maynard Smith, J. 1978. *The Evolution of Sex*. Cambridge University Press, Cambridge, UK.McCully, M.E. 1987. Selected aspects of the structure and development of field-grown roots with special reference to maize. In: *Root Development and Function* (Gregory, P.J., Lake, J.V. and Rose D.A., Eds) Cambridge University Press, Cambridge, UK. Pp. 53-70.

Meyer, M.R., Backman, D.E., Weinberger, A.J. and Wyatt, M.C. 2007. Evolution of circumstellar disks around normal stars: placing our solar system in context. In: *Protostars and Planets V* (Reipurth, B., Jewitt, D. and Keil, K., Eds.). University of Arizona Press, Tucson, USA. Pp. 573-588.

Meyer, M.R., Carpenter, J.M., Mamajek, E.E., Hillenbrand, L.A., Hollenbach, D., Moro-Martin, A., Kim, J.S., Silverstone, M.D., Najita, J., Hines, D.C., Pascucci, I., Stauffer, J.R., Bouwman, J. and Backman, D.E. 2008. Evolution of mid - infrared excess around Sun - like stars: constraints on models of terrestrial planet formation. *The Astrophysical Journal Letters* 673: L181–L184.

Mills, L.S., Soule, M.E. and Doak, D.F. 1993. The keystone-species concept in ecology and conservation. *BioScience* 43: 219–224.

Nickerson, R. 1987. *The Friendly Whales: A Whalewatcher's Guide to the Gray Whales of Baja California.* Chronicle Books, San Fransisco, USA.

Paine, R.T. 1966. Food web complexity and species diversity. *The American Naturalist* 100: 65–75.

Rice, D.W. and Wolman, A.A. 1971. The life history and ecology of the Gray whale (*Eschrichtius robustus*). American Society of Mammalogists, Special Publication No. 3.

Ridley, M. 1995. *The Red Queen: Sex and the Evolution of Human Nature.* Penguin Books, New York, NY, USA.

Robinson, K.S. 1994. *Green Mars*. Bantam Books, New York, NY, USA.

Roca, A.L., Georgiadis, N. and O'Brien, S.J. 2004. Cytonuclear genomic dissociation in African elephant species *Nature Genetics* 37: 96 – 100.

Seyfarth, R.M. and Cheney, D.L. 1984. Grooming, alliances and reciprocal altruism in vervet monkeys. *Nature* 308: 541-543.

Shapiro, J.A. 1998. Thinking about bacterial populations as multicellular organisms. *Annual Review of Microbiology* 52: 81-104.

Slack, A. 2000. *Carnivorous Plants.* The MIT Press, Cambridge, MA, USA.

Stanford, C.B. 1998. *Chimpanzee and Red Colobus: The Ecology of Predator and Prey.* Harvard University Press, Cambridge, MA, USA.

Thomas, H. 1994. Resource rejection in higher plants. In: *Resource Capture by Crops* (Monteith, J.L., Scott, R.K. and Unsworth, M.H., Eds.) Nottingham University Press, Nottingham. Pp. 375-385.

Trivers, R.L. 1971. The evolution of reciprocal altruism. *Quarterly Review of Biology* 46: 35-57.

Williams, G.C. 1975. *Sex and Evolution.* Princeton University Press, Princeton, NJ, USA.

Section VII

Agassiz, L. 1840. *Études sur les Glaciers.* O. Petitpierre, Neuchatel, Switzerland.

Bormann, F.H. and Likens, G.E. 1994. *Pattern and Process in a Forested Ecosystem: Disturbance, Development, and the Steady State Based on the Hubbard Brook Ecosystem Study.* Springer, New York, USA.

Fabry, C. and Buisson, H. 1913. L'absorption de l'ultraviolet par l'ozone et la limite du spectre solaire. *Journale de Physique Paris* 3: 196–206.

Fourier, J. 1824. Remarques générales sur les températures du globe terrestre et des espaces planétaires. *Annales de Chemie et de Physique* 27: 136-67. Translation by Ebeneser Burgess,E: 1837. General remarks on the temperature of the Earth and outer space, *American Journal of Science* 32: 1-20.

Gleissberg, W. 1958. The eighty-year sunspot cycle. *Journal of the British Astronomical Association* 68: 148-152.

Hetherington, N.S. 2006. *Planetary Motions: A Historical Perspective.* Greenwood Publishing Group, Westport, CT, USA.

Keeling, C.D. 1997. Climate change and carbon dioxide: an introduction. *Proceedings of the National Academy of Sciences USA* 94: 8273-8274.

Leopold, A. (1949). *Sand County Almanac, and Sketches Here and There.* Oxford University Press, New York, USA.

Milankovitch, M. 1998. *Canon of Insolation and the Ice-Age Problem.* Zavod za udžbenike i nastavna sredstva, Belgrad.

Schwabe, S.H. 1843. Solar observations during 1843. *Astronomische Nachrichten* 20: 234–235.

Smil, V. 2001. *Enriching the Earth.* The MIT Press, Cambridge, MA, USA.

INDEX

A

B

C

D

E

F

G

H

I

J

K

L

M

N

O

P

Q

R

S

T

U

V

W

Z

Further copies of this book are available, *exclusively*, from Ard Macha Press.

Go to:

<u>www.ardmachapress.com</u>

to order one of the few remaining First Edition, First Issue copies, signed by the author.

Also at this web site:

- **keep up to date with the author's blog**
- **register for news of future products**
- **contact the author**
- **join the debate and tell us what you think**